The Scholastic Art & Writing Awards presents

THE BEST TEEN WRITING OF 2012

Foreword by
EDWIDGE DANTICAT
American Book Award Recipient
and 2012 Scholastic Awards Judge

For information or permission, contact:
Alliance for Young Artists & Writers
557 Broadway
New York, NY 10012
www.artandwriting.org

Copy Editor: Ingrid Accardi
Designer: Michael Vinereanu
Cover art by: Gaetano Icangelo

Dedication

The Best Teen Writing of 2012 is dedicated to the President's Committee on the Arts and the Humanities (PCAH) and the Institute of Museum and Library Services (IMLS). In 2011, the Alliance, PCAH and IMLS launched the National Student Poets Program (NSPP), the country's highest honor for youth poets presenting original work, with the shared vision that talented young poets whose work exhibits exceptional creativity, dedication to craft and promise should be recognized annually for a year of service as national poetry ambassadors. National Student Poets, chosen from among the national medalists in the Scholastic Art & Writing Awards, receive college scholarships and opportunities to present their work nationwide.

PCAH is an advisory committee to the White House. Its focus includes: arts and humanities education, cultural exchange and community revitalization. IMLS is an independent federal grant-making agency dedicated to creating strong libraries and museums. PCAH and IMLS have been leaders in developing the National Student Poets Program and expanding the reach of the Scholastic Writing Awards. The Alliance thanks Susan Hildreth and Marsha Semmel at IMLS and Rachel Goslins, Olivia Morgan and Kimber Craine at PCAH for their collaborative spirit.

About *The Best Teen Writing of 2012*

The works featured in *The Best Teen Writing of 2012* are selected from this year's Scholastic Art & Writing Awards, a national program presented by the Alliance for Young Artists & Writers, which recognizes talented teenagers in the visual and literary arts. The Awards were founded in 1923 to celebrate the accomplishments of creative students and to extend to them opportunities for recognition, exhibition, publication and scholarships.

In 2012, more than 200,000 artworks and manuscripts were submitted in 28 categories to regional affiliates across the country. Professionals reviewed the works for excellence in three core criteria: technical skill, originality and the emergence of a personal vision or voice.

More than 1,600 students received National Awards and joined the ranks of such luminaries as Richard Avedon, Truman Capote, Bernard Malamud, Carolyn Forché, Sylvia Plath, Joyce Carol Oates, Robert Redford and Andy Warhol, who all won Scholastic Awards when they were teenagers.

This year, 473 teens were recognized as the best young writers in the country. The works selected for this publication represent the diversity of the National Award winners, including age and grade, gender, genre, geography and subject matter. They also present a spectrum of the insight and creative intellect that inform many award-winning pieces.

Selected works are excerpted here. A complete listing of National Award winners and online galleries of winning works of art and writing can be found on our website at www.artandwriting.org. There, you will also find information about how to enter the 2013 Scholastic Art & Writing Awards, a list of our scholarship partners, and ways that you can partner with the Alliance to support young artists and writers in your community.

2012 National Writing Jurors

We are grateful to this year's panel of jurors for their commitment to finding compelling young voices.

Writing Portfolio
Jess Browner
Edwidge Danticat
Lauren Keane
John Leland
Davy Rothbart
Patricia Smith

Dramatic Script
Scott Alan Evans
Gregory Mosher
Caridad Svich

Flash Fiction
Aimee Bender
Edith Freni
Rene Saldana

Humor
Kathryn Erskine
Gersh Kuntzman
DC Pierson

Journalism and Persuasive Writing
Thom Duffy
Phyllis Kaufman
Kevin Olivas
Margy Rochlin
David Shenk
Stephen Sherrill

Personal Essay/ Memoir
Moira Bailey
Enrique Floris-Galbis
David Sedaris

Poetry
David Hernandez
Christopher Luna
Zach Savich
Laura Sillerman
Samantha Thornhill
Grant White

Science Fiction/ Fantasy
Courtney Eldridge
Gerald Richards
Julia Whicker

Short Story
Carla Jablonski
Jacob Lewis
Carson Moss
Luc Sante
Catharine Stimpson
Alec Strum

American Voices
Tanya Baker
Andrea Barnet

Thomas Sayers Ellis
Tom Feigelson
Marian Fontana
Alfred Gingold
Joseph Legaspi
Manuel Munoz
Jon Skovron

Best in Grade
Rebecca Bondor
Regie Cabico
Eireann Corrigan
David Treuer
Ned Vizzini
Chuck Wentzel

Creativity & Citizenship
Sarah Darer Littman
Tomas Mournian
Trent Reedy

New York Life Award
Esther Allen
Ekiwah Adler
   Belendez
Courtney Eldridge

Contents

Editor's Introduction xiii
  —Haris Durrani

Foreword xv
  —Edwidge Danticat

Portfolio Gold Medals xix

Drunken Rooster Days 1
Stairs to Nanjing 3
  —Yan Zhang

The Citizenship Test 5
Delivery Failure 6
  —Haeyeon Cho

Little River 9
  —Leah Lierz

Mother May I (Go on Maternity Leave)? 17
  —Emma Goldberg

Girl 20
Pink 22
  —Rosa Wolf

The Conversation 23
My Toes 26
  —Lashanda Anakwah

Doorknobs 27
  —Diane Ward

Gold, Silver, American Voices and Creative Concept Awards 35

Poetry 37

They Are the Patriots.. 37
  —Haley Lee

Camp Delta, Guantánamo Bay 39
   —Darby Cressy

Caught Like Smoke 40
   —Zoe Cheng

When Earth Shook Cairo 44
   —Nicole Sadek

Detroit 46
   —Abraham Younes

Annenberg 48
   —Kelly Yeo

The Destruction Room 49
   —Dylan Combs

Fear 50
   —Mariah Rippy

Brave Little Soldier 51
   —Christina Voss

Icarus in the Digital Age 54
   —Amy Chen

1937 55
   —Jenna Realmuto

The Last Will and Testament of
Some Woman Who Died (Name Unknown) 56
   —Mary Taylor

Women 60
   —Michelle Farina

Ode to Liberty 61
   —Sojourner Ahebee

Take Me to Hullabaloo 63
   —Lauren Feiner

Equilibrio 65
   —Karen Zheng

Mixed Roots..67
——Caroline Kelly

Chinatown Date-Night...69
——Benjamin Sobel

Still Winter Comes..70
——Ashley Huang

Unleashed Steel..71
——Joyce Freitag

Personal Essay/Memoir...73

Miss Hiroshima-Nagasaki Says Her Piece 73
——Christine Hirata

America's Favorite Cookie..77
——Kamry Goodwin

Mustangs and Thunderbirds 83
——Jessica Lalonde

I Need to Practice My Farsi;
Man Bayad Farsi Ro Bishtar Tamrin Konam...............86
——Erika Jobson

Ghosts of Another Land...89
——Emily Green

10:23 Tuesday 95
——Morgan McManus

Blueberry Whispers..103
——Johanna Bear

Final Apology 106
——Claudia Fang

Bing 111
——Kristina Hu

Fourteen Months on the Home Front........................118
——Michaela Coplen

Poverty and Confliction 121
  —Brianne Sands

Flight.. 124
  —Isabella Giovannini

For the Birds 129
  —Francesca Longo

Russia.. 132
  —Diana Mellow

Osha Roots 134
  —Rhiana Rivas

Science Fiction/Fantasy 137
Excerpts From an Experiment With Shakespeare 137
  —Taylor Geu

St. Jude's Center for Ticking Time Bombs 143
  —Emma Hastings

The Room... 151
  —Carter Jimenez Jenkins

Dramatic Script 160
Four Angry Horsemen... 160
  —Alexander Valdes

Journalism 179
Use It or Lose It 179
  —Nicole Narea

Gimme Shelter 181
  —Alexa Horwitz

Persuasive Writing 188
Let's Cancel CSI 188
  —Julia Marino

The Limits of the Scientific Method 193
  —Eric Tweel

Fun-Sized, Pocket Pal and
    Other Euphemisms for the Better Height 197
    —Shruthi Deivasigamani

The World Is Not Flat... 200
    —Joel Wilner

Flash Fiction 204
I Am Noor 204
    —Katherine Fang

My Cuba...208
    —Marcela Grillo

Post-Op 211
    —Caroline Hamilton

Conjoined.. 213
    —Nathan Cummings

The Only Way... 217
    —Jane Wester

Puna.. 219
    —Elizabeth Gobbo

Witch's Lullaby...221
    —Jacqueline Knight

Mr. Ten Fifty 223
    —Grant Stoner

Humor... 226
The Global Origins, Evolution, Proliferation,
    Influence and Future of the Geek Empire...........................226
    —Rishi Mirchandani

Testing Theories of Love
    Using the Scientific Method 230
    —Jordan Myers

In That Case, I'll Stick to Politics...238
    —Szofia Komaromy-Hiller

Short Story 242

The Gone So Sooners 242
—Lylla Younes

A Ticket to Quivira 246
—Janaki Chadha

Sonata in the Key of Bea; a Eulogy...250
—Marlee Cox

Riding on Glass Wings 259
—Cary Williams

Green 267
—Emily Frech

Papi...275
—Audrey Bransfield

The Footage of Yangon 283
—Yi-Ling Liu

A Teacher's Guide to
The Best Teen Writing of 2012 288
Acknowledgements 291
Regional Affiliate Organizations.............................291

Editor's Introduction

Haris Durrani, 2011 Portfolio Gold Medalist

I've always stood by the maxim "Writing is more than words." It's not words themselves but their power that relates the human condition to a universe of ideas. Words can do so by submerging a reader in an experience or provoking an audience to question assumptions and consider new perspectives. Writing is about ideas as much as language; literature makes us think. The works in *The Best Teen Writing of 2012* exemplify these tenets and surpass them. Strong and audacious, these writers have something to say.

When I first dove into the mass of nationally award-winning poems, short stories, personal essays and more—more than 500 pieces in total—I expected sharp and moving prose but was delighted to also find a surplus of works about identity, philosophy and social change. They ponder youth and old age, heartaches and love, birth and passing. They humanize persecuted or forgotten groups by telling their stories, submerging readers in a culture or the feelings of the oppressed. They push for social justice by provoking readers, opening them to new, interesting worldviews.

During this age of economic, political and social strife in the U.S. and abroad, and as the number of ethnic minorities in America increases, it's vital that writers do more than write well. Using the power of words, they must address the problems of our time and their effect on the human condition. In April 2012, Aditya Chakrabortty of *The Guardian* noted the recent void of politically, socially active writers and asked, "Why are English and American novels today so gutless?" But the pages before you reveal the work of a generation of young writers who are concerned about today's problems, whether addressing immigration, identity, civil rights, the "99 Percent," the Arab Spring, war, life and death, or science and technology. It is a true testament to America—a nation of immigrants, audacity and ideas—that it has produced this critical, creative generation which, consciously or not, understands that writing is more than words.

For me, selecting the top works was tricky. At times I felt as though I were reading my way through the "slush pile," a phrase from the days when editors would arrive at work and allegedly wade through mounds of newly arrived submissions obstructing the path to their office door. But this 500-plus stash is no slush pile; it's a treasure trove. Chakrabortty may have labeled most of today's writers "gutless," but I can't say the same for tomorrow's.

I have so many people to thank: Lisa Feder-Feitel, my first personal acquaintance with the Alliance when she called two years ago about my first national award. An aura of optimism and generosity follows her everywhere. Alex Tapnio, who has moved on from the Alliance but whose advice will be remembered. Kat Hendrix for her understanding and graciousness, willing to help in any way possible. Michael Vinereanu for his support as a fellow student, someone with whom to share the pains of final exam season. A huge thank you to the amazing Alliance staff—Courtney, Carol, Dominic, Jeannette, John, Jonathan, Keren, Katie, Mariana, Monica, Rebecca, Scott, Virginia and more—for guiding me through the editing process day by day. Each of them made the Alliance a fun, friendly place to work. Most of all, I want to thank my friend and mentor Michael Fulton, who deserves more praise than I can give. He has tolerated so many of my drafts for more than half a decade, and his counsel on writing and life never misses a beat. I owe him more than I can repay. He is my Dumbledore, Yoda and Leonard McCoy wrapped in one. I would like to especially thank my parents for their affection and encouragement: Mom, my (possibly crazy) Latina Sarah Connor, prepping me to fight the Terminators of justice. Dad, the coolest Desi father in the world, a fusion of a Pakistani Rodney Dangerfield and a well-kept Tony Stark. I wouldn't be where I am today without them.

To the young writers in this book, keep writing. You have produced not only a collection of incredible work but also a tool of empowerment for a generation coming of age during an era of economic, political and social flux. You demonstrate a true concern for the social conscience and a desire to confront serious issues. With the power of words, you make your readers think, rethink and think again, contributing your voice to the world around you. If literature, as Chakrabortty suggests, is society's key to a better future, then our future is safely in your hands. All you need to do is keep pen to paper.

—Haris A. Durrani

Foreword: Lost and Found

Edwidge Danticat, 2012 Scholastic Awards Judge

Nearly two decades ago, when I was in my 20s, a newspaper reporter asked me to send him, via messenger, some family photographs for an article he was writing about my first novel, *Breath, Eyes, Memory*. Foolishly, I sent him an album filled with photographs of myself, my parents, my brothers, uncles, aunts and cousins at all different stages of our lives.

When days passed and the album wasn't returned, I anxiously called the reporter, who told me that he'd put it in the mail. I never saw that album again. The two pictures that were printed with the article—one of me at 6 and another of me at 11—were for years the only visible proof that I'd ever had a childhood. Later some of the lost pictures would resurface in other family members' albums. However, the one picture I miss most is one I posed for on my third birthday. I am standing on a wicker chair in a photo studio in downtown Port-au-Prince, and I'm wearing a sleeveless dress with cut-out butterflies all over the front. My lips are curled and my face is contorted and I am crying.

I have no memory of that day, but my mother, who'd sewn the dress for the occasion, would later tell me that she'd woken up at five in the morning to scrub me spotless and comb my short thick hair into three ribbon-bound plaits, which became undone just as the studio photographer was poised to shoot. My mother had hurriedly redone my plaits, and in her rush had braided them so tight that my head ached, which is why I was crying.

That picture, like most of the pictures taken of me before age 12, was taken with absent parents in mind. That photo session was the last for which my mother would be present before leaving Haiti to join my father in New York while I stayed with Aunt Denise and my Uncle Joseph in Haiti for eight years.

I didn't know there was another copy of that photograph until my father handed me a yellowed and cracked version as I sat at his bedside a week before he died. He'd carried the picture with him for 33 years.

"Don't lose it," he'd said, and I had promised him I wouldn't. However, in the confusion following his death, I did.

I continue to mourn that picture to this day. In many ways it embodies all the sadness I felt both being separated from my parents and leaving my homeland, a place that I have since continued—between visits—to imagine and reinvent for myself in my writing, which began, just as it did for many of the wonderful young writers here, in my teens.

Our family had faced many agonizing losses, and more lay ahead, by the time my father handed me that picture. But seeing it had momentarily consoled me for at least a few of those losses. When I lost the picture again, this time in a manner so reckless that I couldn't even remember when or where, I had to wonder whether I wasn't purposely trying to erase that little girl, the one whose head, and possibly whose heart, was frozen in time, visibly breaking. However, one thing I have not lost, perhaps because of the vigilance of others, are my preteen and teenage words of joy and grief, of certain and uncertain opinions. And for that I am extremely grateful.

Just about the time I was losing my pictures to that journalist, all those many years ago, I was asked by the Alliance to write some advice to young artists, a letter that was influenced by the loss of my life's memories. You can read it here—*http://bit.ly/edwidgedanticat*— as a snapshot of the celebration and wonder that is creating, writing, painting, with your whole heart when you are a teen. This letter, advice from a writer nearly out of her teens herself, still rings true for me today, and I still follow this advice from my much younger writing self.

Hope you enjoy this *Best Teen Writing of 2012* with your whole heart.

—Edwidge Danticat

Edwidge Danticat was born in Haiti and moved to the United States when she was 12. She is the author of 10 books. Her most recent work is Create Dangerously, *a collection of essays.*

Portfolio Gold Medals

Graduating high school seniors may submit a portfolio of three to eight works for review by authors, educators and literary professionals. Winners of the General Writing Portfolio Gold Medals each receive a $10,000 scholarship.

Drunken Rooster Days

Yan Zhang, 17
Millard West High School, Omaha, NE, **Fred Robertson,** Teacher

When my father was little, he lived in a village named after his family. Everyone in the village was either a Zhang or had married one, and circumstances had been this way for 600 years. His father, my grandfather, was the village doctor. He owned a little shop and a little plot of land, and his clothing always smelled of the pungent, spicy herbs he used to treat ailments ranging from morning sickness to broken bones.

My father, despite his status as the doctor's son, ran barefoot, harvested sweet potatoes and collected goat dung for kindling just like the other village children. However, perhaps because of his status, my father was a leader among the village children. To this day, my father still has a gleam of pride when he says his shouts would call a dozen other children to play. He was never without friends.

Those were the golden days, my father says. Before trash clogged the pond in which they used to swim, before construction and highways, before tax returns and overtime and corporate meetings.

But dad, I would counter, wasn't it a communist country? Yes, my father would earnestly agree, the restaurant service (not really restaurants, of course, more like roadside stands) was horrible! The workers didn't have any reason to work because they'd get paid no matter what. Oh! And the school, he would add, one year we didn't have a school building and we had to build desks out of the mud in the teacher's front yard. And there was no pavement, only dirt.

I could not understand what he meant by 'golden days.'

Zhang village was also extraordinarily dirty because people spit and threw food directly on the ground, and dogs and chickens ran free between the houses. Not cats, though—if cats were allowed to run free, they would eat rats and die of arsenic poisoning. My father owned a cat that was tied to the doorpost by a string around its neck. He fed it chewed pieces of steamed bread.

My father's family also kept chickens in a small yard. A flock of some hens and a rooster, all too expensive to eat. Thus they only lost their eggs, not their lives. However, a hen would sometimes die of disease or be eaten by a skunk and leave its chicks behind, which would not survive without their mother's protection. For this problem, all the villagers knew of a simple solution.

They let a rooster drink its fill of beer and then swung it around in circles until it became dizzy and unconscious. Then they placed it inside a coop with the orphaned baby chicks under its wing. When the drunken rooster awoke, it would act just like a hen. It would hustle the baby chicks in line behind it, settle into the coop with its warm body over them at night, and fiercely protect them against skunks and hawks. My father swears this is true.

And this was the yard where we did it, my father now tells me, as we stand in the yard of his old home. The roof is caving in, and the rooms seem ridiculously small and the ceilings are low. The floor is of the same earth as the yard. Of course, he adds, it wasn't always fun and games. We'd have to kill roosters sometimes, when they became too old. Sometimes the rooster could still walk after decapitation, and all the children would gather to watch it stagger and drip blood around the yard. Look, he says suddenly, they've finally paved the road.

As my father says this, he ducks inside the sagging doorway and hits his head on a musty beam now too low for his height. Golden sunlight pours through the narrow window and makes dusty particles from the floor dance in the air. My father's eyes fill with tears.

Now I understood.

Stairs to Nanjing

Yan Zhang, 17
Millard West High School, Omaha, NE, **Fred Robertson,** Teacher

As I walk down the long stairs
  Spiral and uneven
    I see at first a blue haze
      Sleepily weave itself over the city

And then
  My penetration deepening
    The crowns of many silver cars
      Of indeterminable brands
        Weaving and just barely
          Inching past the lights
Nudging pedestrians—
        —go faster, walk quicker
          Too many places to go
          In this city of mazes

Closer now
  Out of a window
    The top of a woman's head
      On it a single strand of white
        Her feet peeking out from polyester dress
        Clad in happy plastic sandals
        Carrying a weaved basket
        Sprouting with beans

Two floors up from the bottom
  I have seen exactly 32 weaved screen doors
    All tattered and
      Besieged by flies
        But each somehow significant
        With a meaning I do not know

Ground floor
    A red rooster, plump and dusty
        Weaving between my feet
            As I step into the street

Yan Zhang is from Omaha, Nebraska. Before attending Harvard University, she will spend a gap year in Ohio to work at City Year, mentoring low-income youth in schools with low graduation rates.

The Citizenship Test

Haeyeon Cho, 18
Milton Academy, Milton, MA, **Jessie Baker,** Teacher

He says he let go of the word.
It shook away from the coils
of his cuttlefish tongue, left behind
a Greek prefix and slithered
into the creaks of textile foot pedals.

I tell him he might fail the test.
I passed mine because my mother taught me
how to shed when she held scissors in hand,
kissed the top of my head and cut
every black hair onto the floor.

But he smiles with his cranberry eyes
(he will pass the test), offers me
licorice and I tell him to keep it.
He might want it after we cough up
all the words we can only mouth,
nothing fragrant left to taste.

Delivery Failure

Haeyeon Cho, 18
Milton Academy, Milton, MA, **Lisa Baker,** Teacher

When she came home that evening, he was cutting open a giant box with an X–ACTO knife.

"What's that?" she asked, slipping out of her heels. She walked to the kitchen for apple cider.

"Something I ordered," he said. The blade tore up both edges and the box farted open, letting out a small burp of cardboard fume.

"Online?" She reached for a glass from the cupboard. The pulpy brown shone through with ugly clarity.

"Yeah. The box is really big, though." He shuffled through the Styrofoam pellets. "I can't even see it." He dipped his upper body into the cube.

She poured the rest of the cider into the sink and sat down on the couch behind him. "Maybe it didn't arrive. It sometimes does that. They forget and ship an empty box."

"That's fucked up," he said. His louse-like head was flushed when he pulled himself out and sat on his heels. "But you might be right. I'll go get the receipt. I think I printed it." He went into the bedroom and shut the door behind him.

The living room was dim. She closed her eyes and rolled her head back. She could hear her husband fishing through piles of paper. She tried to remember the 43 people who had visited her desk that day at what she was told was a charity/welfare program. But she could not picture any of their faces, since it was not her job to tell people what to do. "You only have to hear them," she was told on the first day, "just watch them throw themselves and their problems into one deep hole. Then you come to me. I seal up that hole. We move onto the next." The boss with the fat tie pointed at the graph. "See how the slope is always positive? Profit is positive. This is how this nonprofit works." He swiveled around in his chair to face her. "For starters, try not offering them candy."

But no matter how hard she tried, she always left a part of herself in the mound of helpless strangers. It was the same feeling she had whenever she came home and found her husband drunk on the couch like the housewife she had once feared becoming. Ever since he lost his job two years ago, he had stopped having her eye mask ready in the freezer, stopped paying for dinner, stopped making fun of his her boss, and worst of all, never said a word about it. But years back, when the two found out that they could never make a family, she had not said a word, either, and now she could do nothing but let him bury her up to her chin every day.

She opened her eyes. "Any luck?" she called out.

"No," he yelled back.

She sighed and knelt down on the floor. She stuck both arms into the box. A moment later her hands found at the bottom an edge of a plastic bag. "I think I've got it," she said. She called out his name and he burst through the door.

The light from the bedroom showed them what it was. With her thumb and forefinger, she held an airtight, packaged baby.

"Thank God, there it is!" he shouted.

Her hair stood up.

"It came!"

The thing was the color and size of a peach. It had a little nose.

"So they didn't lie."

The plastic wrinkled tight around the baby like wet bed sheets. He took it from her fingers and ripped open the top. Immediately, the bag sucked up the air and the baby expanded to twice its size. It turned pinker.

"Oh, my god." She collapsed. "What the hell is that?"

"It's my baby." He took out the baby by its wrist and cradled it in the fold of his elbow. "Isn't it perfect?"

"Is it real?"

"Maybe. Unless it has a button somewhere."

Its face softened.

"Holy shit. Holy shit." Numb, she felt the black floors for the couch. "Why?"

"You didn't want one, you couldn't have one." He shrugged. "I mean, I think I deserve this. That day when we found out that we could never have a family, you didn't say a word. And in case you didn't know, this is what a family looks like: a husband, a wife, a child.

Wait, hold on." He flipped the baby over and smacked its bottom. He flipped it back and saw its face wrinkle toward its center. It started wailing without sound. "Shit," he said. "Malfunction."

He stood in front of her, complaining with the baby under his swollen chest and the bedroom light splashing on the back of his head like Virgin Mary's crown.

She felt her shirt separate from her skin. She stood up. "Give it to me," she said, her voice shaking.

"No."

She could not see his face with the light behind him. "I just want to see it," she said, extending both arms.

He hesitated. "Well, as long as you give it back." He handed it to her.

It was not light. She felt the pebbles of its spine on her palm.

"Okay, I want it back now," he said, bringing his arms forward. "I bought it. Not with your money, either."

Its eyelashes fluttered. She felt the heat of the baby crawl up her arm.

"Listen to me," he said quietly, pushing her right shoulder. She fell back on the couch. "Let go," he said, forcefully breaking her cradle.

She stared at the baby's soft face. He yelled but she could not hear him over her crying. He yelled again and she folded at the waist with the baby in her lap. He tugged her forward by her ears, hit her hard, and his voice choked up, but she kept bending forward and forward until they both heard a soft crunch.

Haeyeon Cho is from Milton, Massachusetts. Because her first language is Korean, she began writing English to improve her language skills. Her work deals with social issues such as fertility, gender roles and poverty. She will attend Yale University this fall.

Little River

Leah Lierz, 17
Governor's School for the Arts and Humanities, Greenville, SC,
George Singleton, Mamie Morgan and Scott Gould, Teachers

Josh Stroble was the one who came into Computer Applications class late that afternoon and told everyone what Tucker Johnson had done. He glided through the door and, over the noise of the rowdy class, made the announcement. Despite the swift silence that spread over the room, you could feel our collective giddiness. Sure, we were all sorry that Officer Jimmy, the school resource officer, had to get hurt in the process, but it gave the usual monotony of Little River High School a much needed break.

* * *

"I assure you," said Ms. Truesdale, the school principal, when asked about the incident, "Tucker Johnson will not be returning to school here at Little River. We have a zero tolerance policy for students who behave in such a violent manner." She rubbed her purple jaw at the point where it swelled, changing the subject to the increase in standardized testing scores seen over the course of her administration.

* * *

Some kid piped up, "Maybe he was in a gang!" But nobody really entertained that idea. Fights were rare at Little River, nevermind *gang* fights. In fact, any kid who wanted to be part of a gang pretty much had to commute the 45 minutes to Ridgeway High every day after school. Which some did. But, at the end of the day, they left that business in Ridgeway.

* * *

That night, Little River High ended up on the news. And it wasn't because we had the highest number of students in the state to skip class in order to attend Free Pancake Day at IHOP. No, not this time. It was because of Tucker Johnson.

The reporter kept referring to Tucker as "the 16-year-old student" since the Ridgeway County Sheriff's Department wasn't giving out his name. Probably because of his age and probably because, at that moment, he was being hauled off to the Department of Juvenile Justice in the state capital.

They gave the name of the "female companion," though. Jessica Griffin. Seventeen and charged with assault, battery and disturbing the schools. The news made it clear that she wasn't a student in the county.

* * *

In biology, Kayla, like everyone else, was talking about Tucker Johnson. "You have to know him, right? You know, the kid with the red truck? That Asian dude from *Star Trek* stenciled on the back of the cab?" Josh, his desk a couple rows back, perked up.

"George Takei," I said.

"Yeah, yeah. Right."

"That's not true, Kayla," Josh said loudly. Kayla glanced over her shoulder and shot him an irritated look. "Everyone knows that Tucker drove his mom's minivan."

"Whoa, whoa. I don't know what your deal is with me lately, but you need to back off," he said defensively. She looked down at her paper and began to copy the drawing of the Krebs cycle that was on the board. "By the way, how is it that you're such good friends with Tucker when I've never even seen you talk to him?"

* * *

Tucker smashed the pudgy man against the wall, then, quickly, before the man composed himself, slammed his head against Ms. Truesdale's desk. Ms. Truesdale watched in shock and scurried to block the exit in Officer Jimmy's place. Unfortunately for her, the path from her desk to the door, the one that avoided the struggle between Tucker and Officer Jimmy, included Jessica Griffin. The girl's eyes, caked with eyeliner and mascara, watched the principal impatiently—defiantly—as if to dare her to try to get to the door.

* * *

"You've probably never seen me talk to him because you don't even know what he looks like," Kayla said through clenched teeth. She didn't look up from her paper. "Granted, you probably can't see anything around that ginormous ego of yours, but still."

She dug deeper into the paper with her pencil. "But you still haven't told me anything about your supposed friendship with Tucker."

The tip of Kayla's pencil broke. She let out a frustrated groan and leaned back in her chair. With a sigh, she threw her pencil down on her desk.

"Fine, he's in FFA with me. He won first prize for Poultry when we went to state." She pulled another pencil out of her purse. Josh laughed loudly. Kayla looked at him, obviously peeved. "What?" she asked.

"Impossible. I know for a fact that Tucker is a wrestler. He doesn't have time to raise chickens or whatever. Besides, even if he did, he wouldn't be caught dead in the FFA."

* * *

Kathy Truesdale rubbed her jaw. It hurt pretty bad, but she didn't mind. It was the sight of the damn thing that she despised. How was she supposed to run a school when the entire student body thinks a teenage girl got the best of her? That *they* could get the best of her. I mean, she wasn't known as "the Buzzsaw" for nothing.

She stood in front of the mirror as she brushed her teeth, trying her hardest not to look at the purple splotch. Spitting into the sink, she held her hand to her face. She traced the wrinkles of her face in a slow, deliberate motion and, finally, drew circles around the purple mark with her fingertips.

She crawled into the left side of her empty queen bed and cried.

* * *

The game had been over for a while. The only people left were the players and a few straggling parents and girlfriends. The field lights had already been turned off, so it was rather dark. Hoots and hollers could be heard coming from the parking lot as students leaned out the window, waiting in the post-game traffic to get out of the lot.

Josh and the other players were ecstatic. They had just won their first game all season. In the field-house locker room, they yelled and screamed and laughed, pounding their fists against the structure.

"Dude, what was that in the third quarter? You were blocking like crazy," Josh said to Mungo, the biggest guy on the team.

"I know, right? I just felt it, like..." Mungo said before ramming his shoulder into the wall as a way of recreating his blocks. The surface of the wall crumbled a bit. Everyone yelled out in approval. Mungo hit the wall once more and, again, pieces of it fell to the floor.

After that, things got out of hand quickly. Several members of the team began pounding on the walls. Some of the more uncertain players tried to say something, but they were just too timid. Soon, anyone who wasn't participating in the field-house massacre had left. The players had started on the inside, but when they finished changing out of their uniforms, they came out and began to pelt the building from the outside with bricks that rested in a pile several yards away.

"What are you doing?" an unfamiliar voice behind them asked. Some of the players glanced over their shoulders to see who was talking, but most of them just kept throwing bricks. "What the hell are you doing? Are you morons?" Tucker rephrased his question.

"Whatever. You know as well as I do that these old locker rooms are in need of a major renovation," Josh said, laughing and picking up some more bricks out of the pile. Tucker didn't say anything. He just walked over to Josh, grabbed the bricks out of his hands, and chucked them to the ground.

"Hey, back off, man," Josh said, shoving him. Tucker, clenching his fist, looked as if he was about to do something. But instead, he shook his head and relaxed his hand.

"Whatever. I don't know what makes you guys think this is a good idea," he said, looking at the rest of the football players, who continued to hurl bricks. "Yeah, real geniuses." Tucker shook his head in disbelief. "I wonder what's going to happen when you're done. But I know you haven't thought that far in advance." He turned his back and walked toward the parking lot, not glancing back at the players for even a second.

Josh shook his head and laughed. "Can you believe that guy?" he said.

* * *

Tucker went to punch Officer Jimmy, but the man was more prepared this time. He tased the boy, who fell to the ground with a thump and a cry. Jessica stopped looking for her keys.

* * *

"I don't know who the girlfriend is," said Josh as he finished up his story. "By the sound of her, she probably goes to Ridgeway or something." The other kids laughed at this.

He looked around. The teacher still wasn't back yet from whatever she was doing—probably raiding the vending machines in the teacher's lounge again. Josh looked at the girl sitting at the computer a few feet from him. "Hey, Kayla, do you know who Tucker Johnson's girlfriend is? I mean, since you take cosmetology over at Ridgeway and all." Kayla didn't glance up from her computer screen, just kept arbitrarily shuffling red and black cards over the digital green.

"Who's Tucker Johnson?"

* * *

"Mr. Johnson, you cannot simply leave school just because you feel like it," Ms. Truesdale said. Her voice was firm and composed as she sat straight up in her faux-leather chair.

"Plenty of kids I know leave without their parent's permission," Tucker said, leaning against the wall opposite the principal.

"Those kids are, most likely, already 18. Adults. In any case, this is our policy. We have it so that the students here are safe." Tucker snorted back a laugh.

"Bull. You just don't like not having total control over everything we do," Tucker said as he lifted his shoulders from the wall. "Every day you wake up with nothing. No kids. No husband. No hope of either. Your only comfort is that between 8:30 and 3:30, you get to wield control over 400 kids," he said getting angrier. Just then, his pants pocket began to buzz. In one swift movement, he pulled out a cell phone, checked what must have been a text message and slid it back into his pocket. "And you love that," he said, completing his sentence.

* * *

Officer Jimmy walked out of McCormick Memorial Hospital later that afternoon. A concussion, the doctor told him. Honestly, he probably could've figured that out himself, but he still nodded and said thanks. On the curb outside of the hospital, he checked his phone. There were missed calls from both his mother and the sheriff's department. He didn't feel like returning either call.

* * *

Tucker never came back. Neither did Officer Jimmy for that matter. The most widely accepted hypothesis was that they were locked away somewhere, battling as gladiators for the amusement of the school board. One afternoon, though, Josh got up the nerve to ask Ms. Truesdale what happened to the two of them. He walked up to her side as she patrolled the hallways with her walkie-talkie.

"Hello, Ms. Truesdale, ma'am. Hey, I was just wondering, I mean, do you know what happened to Officer Rollins and that kid, um,

Tucker Johnson?" He slid his hands into his pockets and tried not to look her in the eye. She sighed.

"Not that it's any of your concern, Mr. Stroble, but Officer Rollins has been transferred to a different school." She didn't say anything about Tucker.

* * *

"Mr. Johnson—" Ms. Truesdale said finally.

"No, I'm not finished." Tucker took a step closer. "You like to keep us contained in this tiny world you've created for yourself." Ms. Truesdale picked up the walkie-talkie on her desk. "You don't tolerate senior pranks, no matter how harmless." He took another step closer.

"Officer Rollins. If you could come to Ms. Truesdale's office as soon as possible. Thank you," she said into the walkie-talkie. As she spoke, a small girl with dyed hair and chubby arms stepped into the office. Nobody acknowledged her. Tucker was too busy shouting.

"Once someone graduates or transfers schools, they are not allowed to come back to visit. Period. Also, no one's allowed to leave school for their lunch period anymore. Come on, the Wendy's is right next door!" Officer Jimmy Rollins stepped into the room, his eyes on Tucker as the boy continued to yell.

"Mr. Johnson, it's all in the best interest of the school and its students," Ms. Truesdale said, her fingers still gripping the walkie-talkie tightly.

* * *

"Tucker didn't want to go to school here anymore. Actually, he decided to leave right then and there, but Ms. Truesdale and Officer Jimmy wouldn't let him," Josh told the kids surrounding him. Grinning knowingly, he said, "So, of course, Tucker did exactly what Tucker would do." Everyone else chuckled a bit at this. "He started fighting Officer Jimmy, getting an advantage over him, and slamming his head against Ms. Truesdale's desk."

"No!" someone gasped a little too dramatically.

"Yeah," Josh said, nodding. "Ms. Truesdale just watched in horror while all of this went on." He paused and asked someone for a piece of gum. A freshman handed him a pack she kept in her purse. Josh gave her a grin and a wink as thanks, pulled out a piece, stuffed it into his mouth, and threw it back to her.

"I guess the ol' Buzzsaw is all talk when it comes to real action," he said finally. All the kids nodded and laughed. "When she finally got the nerve to break it up, Tucker's girlfriend punched her square in the jaw. A thing of pure beauty."

* * *

Officer Jimmy walked out of the hospital, bandages covering his head. He wouldn't be able to go back to work for a while, if ever again, because of his injuries. He held his broken ribs as he stumbled toward his wife's car. She tried to help him, but he told her he could do it himself. Officer Jimmy was nothing if not a man of pride.

* * *

Kayla smiled at Josh in biology. They spoke about Tucker Johnson and laughed, not paying attention to the lesson on the Krebs cycle. "Did you know him?" Kayla asked Josh.

"Nah, did you?"

"Nope. It seems like nobody did, really," Kayla said.

"Weird." Josh laced his fingers together. They sat there quietly for a moment. He broke the silence when, chuckling softly to himself, he said, "Guess nobody's going to get the chance now." She laughed too.

* * *

Tucker punched Officer Jimmy in the stomach, swiftly grabbing the Taser hooked to the man's belt. "Jessica, find your goddamn keys already!" Tucker yelled. He gave a few more good blows to Officer Jimmy's torso before he finally tased him.

Jessica still hadn't found her keys by the time Officer Jimmy got off the ground. She watched as he threw Tucker against the car and handcuffed him. Officer Jimmy didn't have another pair of cuffs for Jessica, but without both Tucker and her keys, she wasn't really going anywhere.

* * *

I knew Tucker Johnson.

He used to live next door to my grandma when we were kids. When I was 6, he dislocated my arm while we were playing ring-around-the-rosy. When I was 8, his dog ran away and I helped look for him. We found the dog on someone else's property a couple of miles away, in the woods. He had already died, but not of any unnatural causes. When we got back to my grandma's house, I couldn't think of anything to say, so I just made Tucker a root-beer float and gave him my favorite sweatshirt to wear. Whenever I used to have a bad day, those two things always cheered me up.

Back then, even though we were so close, we never hung out at school together. I kept with the girls, and he kept with the guys, so nobody really knew we were friends.

When I was in fifth grade, my grandma died. I pretty much stopped hanging out with Tucker after that. It just wasn't the same, you know, not having him next door every weekend. It's not that I was mad at him for anything, and I don't think he was mad at me for anything, but we just stopped being friends without really thinking about it.

I don't know if what they said about Tucker that day was true. I spent those first few days trying to understand why he did what he did. Trying to remember a part of Tucker that indicated that this might happen someday. But really, I stopped knowing Tucker a long time ago, and apparently, he did the same with not only me, but also the rest of the student body. I don't know why he did it. I can't pretend that I do. Sometimes I think it's because of the way people, like Josh, treated him. How they didn't even know who he was. But mostly I like to think, maybe, he knew it would make people talk and that's what he wanted. Maybe he just wanted to be remembered.

Leah Lierz is from Greenville, South Carolina. While 90 percent of her fiction is generated by imagination, she says it's that 10 percent of reality that often inspires her work. She will attend Honors College at the University of South Carolina.

Mother May I (Go on Maternity Leave)?

Emma Goldberg, 17
Writopia Lab, New York, NY, **Rebecca Wallace-Segall,** Teacher

Pop quiz: What do the United States, Papua New Guinea, Liberia and Swaziland have in common? Answer: They are the only four members of the United Nations that do not legally require employers to guarantee paid maternity leave.

I am a high school student in New York City, and I first discovered this issue last year when my teacher took leave to give birth to her daughter, then returned to school four weeks later. I was shocked. The U.S. Department of Health and Human Services cites the average childbirth recovery time at six to eight weeks. Returning to work after four weeks seemed to me difficult, if not dangerous. I inquired into the issue and learned that under federal law—the 1993 Family and Medical Leave Act—employers with more than 100 employees are required to grant 12 weeks of unpaid leave to all workers who have been employed for a minimum of 1,250 hours over a one-year period. The legislative requirements do not mandate compensation for new mothers.

Without paid leave, women like my teacher often find they cannot afford to take the full 12 weeks. Many worry, too, that the absence will hurt their careers. "What's happening now is women are afraid to take their maternity leave, they're afraid of not being in the office immediately after having a child, it seems," Carol Evans, executive director of Working Mother Media, told ABC News. "They should be doing the opposite of being afraid. They should be fighting this fear."

I spoke to school administrators, who told me they are deeply torn over the issue. "My heart aches when I look at our pregnant young women, facing for the first time the need to spend time with their baby and the desire to build a career outside the home," a school administrator told me.

Unfortunately, the administrators' choices are not easy. With a staff of 200, compensating family leave would put a strain on the budget and would mean leaching funds from other school programs. "It's a really tough balancing act," one administrator said. "Do we cut scholarships and programs for students so that we can pay for maternity and paternity leaves? So far the school has said no."

The same dilemma faces every institution and company, I learned; given all their competing demands and trade-offs, the most immediate priorities come first, and these usually don't include new mothers. Without federal legislation at their back, managers have a hard time justifying the cost of paid parental leave to their boards. The result is that most American workplaces do not provide it. According to a 2010 U.S. Department of Labor report, only 10 percent of private-sector employees have access to paid family leave, most of them in the highest-paid positions. And the number is actually declining—between 1988 and 2008, there was a drop of 11 percent in the number of companies offering it, according to a study by the Families and Work Institute.

The more I learned about it, the more it troubled me. Today's media declare that women are opting out of high-power careers. *The New York Times* recently published a profile of educated career women who gave up their work to become full-time mothers, declaring that "opting out" is the latest trend in mothering, a social revolution of sorts. But Catalyst research found that 57 percent of women in senior corporate posts do aspire to be CEOs. Well, if women aren't opting out of high-power positions, why aren't they pursuing those executive spots? Maybe because institutions convey the idea that women have to make choices—family or career, work or life.

The issues go beyond career advancement. Studies by the World Health Organization have shown that early return to work after childbirth has long-term negative effects on a woman's health. The European Union, meanwhile, has found that these impacts translate into lost productivity in the economy. All 27 E.U. countries now offer at least 14 weeks of paid maternity leave. A 1981 United Nations convention requiring paid maternity leave, without specifying the length, has been signed by 185 nations—but not by the United States.

In 2009, journalists Nicholas Kristof and Sheryl WuDunn wrote that women's rights are the cause of our generation. "In the 19th century, the paramount moral challenge was slavery. In the 20th century, it was totalitarianism. In this century, it is the brutality inflicted on so many women and girls around the globe," the pair wrote. Yet in the past year, the number of female CEOs of Fortune 500 companies has dropped from 15 to 12. Sexual harassment of high-school-aged girls is on the rise.

What's particularly alarming to me as a high school student is that my peers don't seem to notice this trend. I recently took a straw poll and asked a classroom of girls whether they see women as empowered and respected in today's world. Twenty girls responded with a resounding "Yes!" "We should still keep fighting for gender equality, but today women's rights are really being recognized," my classmate said. Tossing in a reference to the hit Beyoncé song, she added, "Today, girls run the world."

This is what my classmates believe. But within five years, many of us will be entering the workforce. Perhaps we will want to have children and we will contend with institutions that do not offer paid maternity leaves. We will have to choose—do we return to full-time jobs after only one month, still recovering from the turbulence of childbirth? Or do we give up on two more weeks of salary in order to give our bodies a semblance of a healthy recovery time? At that point, let's see if girls will still be singing along to Beyoncé's catchy tunes. Do girls really run the world if institutions and society at large don't value us enough to compensate our maternity leaves?

When I first approached my school administration and investigated the maternity leave policies, they told me, "Institutions have to make tough choices." Yes, the choices are tough. But let's make the right ones, so that my classmates and I won't be choosing between work and health five years down the line.

Emma Goldberg, a native New Yorker, feels her writing is a means of expressing her passion for advocacy, activism and social change. Emma will attend Yale University, where she plans to study political science, international relations and creative writing.

Girl

Rosa Wolf, 17
Boise Senior High School, Boise, ID, **Sharon Hanson and Jennifer McClain,** Teachers

I work at the bodega on the corner. You probably haven't noticed me unless you're the old Greek guy named George who always says "look at those lips" when I bag his cigarillos. My lips are thick and pink, and there's a little brown freckle on the left corner. I touch them when I'm nervous or when I don't know what to say.

I open on Saturdays and Sundays. The air inside the bodega gets real thick when I'm in it alone; the oranges piled by the windows are cold and sleepy, and the lemons look like smudges of oil pastel. When business is slow, I read novels behind the counter.

Mr. Alvaro owns the place. He has an orange tabby cat named Po Campo that likes to sleep with his belly on the cool glass above the ice cream. I think Po Campo and I understand each other because we both wonder sometimes if we're invisible.

Mama walks the 12 blocks from home and buys milk when she gets lonely. She's lonely a lot lately, with me working, Gabriel cruising around in black Tahoes with guys 10 years older than him, and Leila married off and living in Queens. Mama's waiting around for Leila to give her a *nieto,* and it shouldn't be long.

When she buys the milk, I take a long time to ring it up because I know that's what she wants. She leans on the counter with her dusty caramel elbows pointing at me and speaks Spanish like each word is burning her tongue. She asks me if I have a boyfriend, if I know how to wear eyeliner, if I've heard that Lucy Guerra went crazy last Monday and swallowed a whole bottle of sleeping pills. I usually just shake my head no.

Since the bodega down the street got robbed last spring, Mr. Alvaro is really nervous. When he's working, he keeps some of the money from the cash register in his left sock.

Little girls with big tits sometimes try to buy cigarettes and boxed wine from me. They say they're 21, or 19, or whatever, but they left their IDs at home. *"I can't sell it to you,"* I say. I pretend to be real sorry, like I give a shit, like I don't recognize them from school. They don't know me because I like to read poetry and write stories in my notebook. These girls purse their lips and shake their chests at me when they get mad.

Mr. Alvaro has two boys; he keeps their pictures taped to the glass in front of the rows of cigarettes. Sometimes I talk to the pictures when no one's in the store and I've finished all my books. I tell them I'm lonely and tired and my feet hurt; they always stare at me with the same blurry, silent smiles.

If the bodega ever gets robbed and some man holds a gun to my head, I know what I will do. I will pause with my hands cupped upward like petals and smile at him instead of reaching for the money. I will say something about life, to show I'm not afraid, maybe something that Milan Kundera has written.

Maybe I will say, "The brain appears to possess a special area that we might call poetic memory, and which records everything that charms or touches us, that makes our life beautiful."

Maybe I will laugh.

I don't know if the man will then kill me or just push me out of the way, but whatever happens, I imagine that there will be someone kneeling in the bread aisle with their hands in the air, and they will say, "Look at that girl. What a smart girl."

Pink

Rosa Wolf, 17
Boise Senior High School, Boise, ID, **Sharon Hanson and Jennifer McClain,** Teachers

I would like for you to ask me if I have any scars.
The answer would be
"Yes, just one,"
and I would lift the corner of my shirt
so you could see the pink
amoeba on my right hip;
shiny like soap bubbles, blushed like carnations.
Then, I would like for you to ask me
how it got there and the answer would be
"Moving too fast. *Almost* flying."
I would draw the scene for you
on the back of a grocery receipt:
the salty wind, the homeless man singing "Proud Mary" on the corner,
the asphalt rising up to meet me like a
dark handshake.
And then I would stand up and leave you
sitting in your chair,
and you would suddenly know exactly what you had lost.

    Rosa Wolf hails from Boise, Idaho, where she loves to read, write and longboard. Much of her work is inspired by her fascination with observing strangers. She plans to study creative writing and Spanish at the University of Arizona.

The Conversation

Lashanda Anakwah, 17
Girls Write Now, New York, NY, **Rachel Cohen,** Teacher

Girl, I'm really thinking about the lift. Ha ha, seriously, don't laugh. I'm serious! No, but seriously, I can't keep walking around like this. It's embarrassing. I mean, I've been thinking about it; I'm not being irrational. Everyone in my family has a butt. It's just me; I must have a genetic disorder or something along those lines. I just know it.

I've done my research—it's nothing too unnatural like I was worried about. Basically the surgeon sucks fat out of somewhere in the body and injects it back into the buttocks. It's my own fat, placed where it's supposed to be.

I mean, I'm African, it's my birthright. And if I was born without my butt, like some people are born without fingers, it's my duty to fix it. You don't understand. I feel like shit when I try on jeans and they just don't fit the way I want them to. I have the worst butt envy. I can never befriend a girl with a perfect bottom. I just can't. And it's like I never feel pretty because of it. I could wear the best outfit and do my hair real nice. I could feel like a million bucks, but if I catch just the tiniest glimpse of my butt, my whole day is ruined. Oh, I can't tell you how many good days have been ruined because of my inferior backside.

When I was in high school, I was running for treasurer. I already had everything planned out, how I was going to raise money, what I would use it for and guess what happened—lemme just tell you. Some pretty girl decided to run at the last minute. The butt on her too. I almost dropped out of the race but my friends wouldn't let me. Anyways, I lost. Don't get me wrong, I'm not getting the surgery just to look good, it's for my self-esteem too. It's just that I'm tired of not feeling equal to girls who are blessed with a backside.... When is the train getting here? It's been on 5 minutes for 10 minutes. Well, yeah, girl, what do you think? Wait—don't say anything, I know! I should be ashamed talking about how I'm so unfortunate, when there's people battling cancer and other terrible diseases and I feel like an asshole when I hear myself say this stuff out loud. I really do, but I've been feeling like this for a long time. And I mean a long time. It's time for me to quit thinking about it and do something—don't you think?

Yeah, it definitely is. There's just this feeling I can't shake, like I'm a failure or something. Ha ha, I know it's weird. What's up with this train, though? 'Cause it has to be more than just train traffic. It's around 9:50, almost 10:00, right? What was I saying? Oh, yeah, you know the stereotype about girls who get things done, they're fake and vain. I always bought into that and I know I'm not the only one. After the surgery, this probably won't be a problem, but if it were to come up, if someone had the audacity to ask if my butt was natural, I couldn't lie about it. You know what I mean? 'Cause that would mean I was ashamed of it, and if I get the lift, I don't want it to be something I'm ashamed of.

I don't know. I'm kind of disappointed that it's come to this. You know all that self-love crap they preach on TV? I was hoping to eventually love my body for what it is. I wish I could be the "Oh, well, whattaya gonna do" type of girl. I wish I could take my butt problem casually: "I've got a flat butt, oh well, whattaya gonna do. I just gotta live it with." Wouldn't that be great? Instead of cringing every time I catch my reflection in a store window. I just feel so inadequate at those moments. You know what I mean? Like my very existence is unimportant. I ask myself how I find the courage to live my life without the slightest bulge where my butt should be. How do I manage to go out in public? I should be ashamed. I actually tell myself all these things.

Sometimes I wonder if I didn't grow up in the Bronx, if I grew up on the other side of the world, would my lack of a hiney be such a problem? I started listening to rap in fifth grade, and all I've ever heard was guys appreciate girls with big butts. There's whole songs dedicated to that part of the body, and I've always known girls with nice rear ends have it easy. But this isn't about boys or attention. I want to get this surgery done for myself. I'm just not sure if I am, though. Do you think society's influencing me to get it done? Is it society's standards that I'm living up to or my own? I wish I knew.

When I think about it hard, everything gets all blurred. But a nice shapely butt is always a good thing. I deserve to have a nice butt!

Don't tell me to try lunges and squats, because I do them in my sleep and I'm still not getting the results I want. I was so excited when I heard a lot of people boasting about their new bottoms. You know Suzy, right? Yeah, well she was going on and on about how great her butt looks now. So just imagine how disappointed I am. You know how I feel about cosmetic surgery, I would do anything to avoid it and here was this surefire way to get the same results as a butt lift without the surgery. It just doesn't work. Well, it did make my butt more firm, but it didn't add any fat—obviously—to where I wanted it.

And then there's the whole issue of God. Oh, my gosh, I can't believe you let me go on like this. I've been talking for the past 20 minutes. And the train, uh... Why haven't you said anything? Girl, you are too polite! You don't mind? You sure? I don't wanna talk your ear off. My uncle used to say God created me perfectly for the guy I was destined to be with, and obviously that guy didn't care for big hineys. The little girl in me is still holding out hope, but that logic isn't working anymore. Do you see what I do? I've already decided to get the lift and now I'm analyzing the whole situation. I'm sabotaging myself, trying to prevent the surgery that needs to be done. It's like deep down for some reason my inner-self believes I can overcome my backside insecurity. If I could do that... If I could overcome hearing the voices in my head that bully me constantly about my butt, the world would be my oyster. Don't say it! Even though it's all I want to hear.

My Toes

Girls Write Now, New York, NY, **Rachel Cohen,** Teacher

They're not mine, the shriveled sausages at the end of my feet. They can't be mine—no one born and raised in America should have these toes. Those toes belong to someone who has known hardships beyond my comprehension. Possibly a slave who helped build the pyramids of Egypt, or picked cotton in the south. These toes have known more sun than raisins have. They have walked through the ash caused by an erupting volcano and witnessed the transformation from active to inactive. They have existed as long as the first breath, sin. Those things masquerading around attached to my feet, disguised as my toes, have walked the desert sands and run on hot coals. Those appendages have no place in heels or flats. They certainly do not belong on the red carpet or the front cover of *Seventeen* magazine. No amount of pedicures or nail polish can rid them of their past, and they're stuck on me.

Lashanda Anakwah is from the Bronx, New York. Her love of reading inspires her to emulate writers who make her laugh, smile and cry. She looks up to those who are trying to make it as writers. She will attend Ithaca College in the fall.

Doorknobs

Diane Ward, 17
Home School, Brandon, MS, **Karen Ward,** Teacher

1
[Ellipses]

Seawater splashed onto Koh's arm as he rowed the skiff over the skeletal reef. Below him, the bones of ancient Leviathans lay off the shore of the island. Bleached white by the sun, the skeletons of one generation overlapped the next in an immemorial dying ground.

Koh remembered his parents telling him the legends of how the Leviathans came here to die closer to their own realm, closer to the Spirit Door. Glancing over the side of the skiff, he saw the Spirit Door nested in the skeletons. Large as the island itself, it ran from sight into the deepest parts of the sea. Blue spidery veins spread over the door. And sometimes late in the night, if Koh looked out onto the ocean, he would see an azure glow.

But there was something missing.

A hole penetrated the door. Small, almost comically so—to be of such grave importance, yet be the size of a fist. The Leviathans had been locked out of the spirit world when a thief stole the doorknob, and the Leviathans had never stopped searching for their way back in.

Eels in deep shades of amethyst and jade glided near Koh, looking for extra pieces of bait. Schools of small fish hid in the pores of the reef, but Koh couldn't stop for them today. He rowed to the bobbing red bottle and hauled the trap up that drifted beneath it. Inside snapped three large crabs with muddy shells to hide in the sea grass. He dropped the trap and crabs into the boat in front of him. No point leaving the trap. It wouldn't survive the storm.

Though the reefs protected the island, farther out on the sea, the waves grew violent; a bruised horizon loomed with rolling clouds. Very rarely did the twin moons align on their ellipses. The astronomers and augurs on the mainland hypothesized that at the pinnacle of the moons' alignment, the earth would move nearly five centimeters. But of course they were still determining a way to test this calculation.

Although Koh didn't understand much about the heavens, he understood the cresting waves and too-full clouds clustered like flies over rotting fruit. His mother would rightfully worry if he weren't home soon, so he paddled quickly back to shore.

Once on the beach, Koh jumped off the skiff into waist-deep water and dragged the boat up into the jungle, tying it to the trunk of a vine. He hoisted the trap onto his back and pushed through the dense undergrowth of the jungle. The vegetation shook, buzzing with disturbed insects as the wind rose, signaling the coming storm. Koh ran home.

Koh quickly climbed the ladder to his house built in the trees and slung his mud boots off. With bare hands, he pried off the crab's shells by leveraging them against the floor. The shells snapped off in a single piece, smelling of all the sea. He scraped the insides onto the porch to be washed away by the rain, and dropped the crabs in a bowl of cold fresh water.

Inside, his mother was already cooking, and he set the bowl down on the counter. Normally his house glowed with an easy happiness, but not now. The alignment in the ellipses seemed to have imbalanced more than the tides and winds. He knew the emotions of the islanders were stretched very thin, near the point of snapping like an overtaxed fishing line. And his family was no different.

He walked quietly into the living room. His father sat by the window cleaning his harpoon, though he hadn't fished in weeks. The bruises were still visible from his fight with the dirigible's crew.

The mainland had sent the dirigible here to evacuate the islanders. Koh's father had said that they needed no evacuation, and that the Leviathans would protect them as they always had. But the dirigible's crew had pointed to the reefs, saying, "You'll be as dead as your gods if you try to stay."

The bridge of his father's nose was red and swollen from being hit with a brass knuckle. Even though his father hadn't told him of the fight, Koh knew that it had been over the evacuation. Their beliefs forbade them from leaving the island, but with the storm looming and the astronomers insistent that the island would be swallowed by the effect of the alignment, many of the islanders were evacuating.

Koh's family had refused.

The dirigible was hosting a tour tomorrow to convince the rest of the islanders to evacuate before finally setting sail to return to the mainland. Koh wanted to see the inside of the marvelous aircraft, even though he knew he was staying, but seeing the bruises on his father's face made the flying airship seem suddenly less glorious.

Koh sat by the window and watched the storm. It was raining so hard he could barely see outside. It was as if the entire island shook with the swaying of the trees and vines. He could imagine tonight would be another uneasy one, pregnant with silence. It was then that his father spoke.

"Do you want to see the dirigible?" his father asked.

Koh said nothing, his eyes widening. If he said "yes," he would sound like a traitor. It was a dangerous question to answer.

"You should go. We shouldn't try to offend them," his father said before Koh could reply, his expression softening.

"Just remember: don't even think about joining them. The island is set too close to the door. Things bleed over. You can't rejoin the rest of the world. It doesn't work like that."

Later Koh fell asleep to those words.

2
[The Leviathan]

Koh, a grand voice reverberated.

Currents undulated dark and depthless around him. An eel with a head like a crystal that had been shattered and small, aquiline round eyes swam by. Looking down, Koh saw only deep, resounding darkness. Looking up, he expected to see the buttery glow of the distant sun, but there was only more murk as the sea ran for fathoms in every direction.

Koh tried to swim and found he maybe wasn't in water after all. He couldn't push off of it, as if it were textureless. He only succeeded in pointing his head downward. Then he felt a stab of dizziness at the loss of direction; there was no difference between down or up. Panic stuck him like a cold needle.

Koh, listen to me, the voice echoed again, sending tremors through the water that shook Koh's entire body.

Out of the murk, it pressed forward, slowly making itself visible. A hulking thing with a shell seemingly carved from gray stone drifted before him. Engraved encryptions and spiraling patterns ran along it in blues and greens. Its eyes were large and intelligent and reminded Koh of brightly polished black stones. Looking into them was like looking directly into a very deep part of the ocean.

LISTEN TO ME, the Leviathan boomed.

Koh doubled over clenching his ears, even though the sound hadn't quite been heard.

The Leviathan seemed to settle.

I need you to help me. I need something from your island or I will not be able to protect it as I have before. The waves will devour it. If anyone leaves, they compromise the protection of the island. Do not think anyone who desires to abandon us will be protected.

Koh knew what the Leviathan would ask for before the Leviathan even named the price. They always asked a certain sum in response to their protection, and it was always the same. The Leviathan gave a low almost musical hum as it named its sum.

Doorknobs.

3

[The Dirigible]

The hull of the dirigible shone in the morning light like a smoldering star. The entire island was there to see the dirigible off, even his father. The loyal islanders stood beside his father. His father, who was still bruised from the skirmish, stood proud and unapologetic even though Koh could see the dirigible's crew—and even some of their islanders—looking at him as if he were a fool.

Koh felt his cheeks burn with angry embarrassment. He wanted to tell them his father was right. He had seen a Leviathan just last night. But he could imagine how they would chuckle at him, tell him to stop dreaming.

The dirigible moored over the beach, swaying dangerously in the rising winds. Shaped like the beaks of two great birds placed together at the wide end, it glimmered in the sun like a polished coin. A single exhaust pipe jutted from its sleek hull, spouting quickly dissipating steam into the darkening sky.

A line of the children from the island led up to the dirigible, ready for the tour. Koh looked toward his father and his father nodded at him; Koh knew his father was only letting him go because he knew how much it meant to him.

In the lift stood the captain, decked in a full gray suit despite the clinging, humid heat. His blond hair seemed to be nearly sun-bleached white, and a scar that looked like it had a poor stitching job that had never healed quite right peeked out from under his collar. The captain was in his early 40s, so far as Koh could tell. Even though the officer looked as if he should have been a stern person, he grinned broadly and made a sweeping motion with his arm to lead the group inside.

Koh sat crammed shoulder to shoulder with the other children in the lift. He grinned across at his friends, Tomo and Uye. He hadn't seen them since the storms. It was unsafe to go outside, and as much as he wanted to tell them everything, he knew he wouldn't see them till it was over. Slowly they were retracted into the large metal thing, not unlike insects going back to the hive, Koh thought.

Inside the dirigible, the walls were covered with various pieces of mechanical equipment gilded with copper. Lines of staff passed them as the officer explained the functions of each instrument.

Koh stopped to stare at a mechanic who wore heavy goggles that had a set of focusing lenses that seemed too dark to see through. A pair of brass knuckles hung off the mechanic's belt. They were large and heavy looking. The knuckles jutted out wickedly like shark's teeth ready to rip open skin. Koh shuddered looking at them. He remembered all too clearly the wound from a pair of knuckles on his father's face. And looking at the mechanic, he had no doubt that this was the same man.

The mechanic turned to face Koh and gave him a grin filled with teeth the color of bronze. Koh felt a chill travel up his spine as he looked into those heavy goggles. The captain who had been leading them stopped. He glanced back at Koh and then to the mechanic.

"That's Kinsky," the captain said. "He works on keeping the shell intact, repairs any leaks, as well as being generally handy."

* * *

As Koh stood again on the beach, he felt fat plops of rain starting to fall and wondered how many doorknobs he had seen in the dirigible. *Am I meant to collect all the doorknobs or just some doorknobs?* he wondered. And what would he do with them once he got them? His mother squeezed his shoulder and broke his line of thought.

He watched as the islanders who would be evacuating boarded the dirigible. Some of them whispered apologies to his father, but others simply pretended he was not visible. Finally full of islanders, the dirigible rose grandly like a great, sleek beetle and soared over the gusty water.

Koh saw something glow distantly in the reefs.

Seawater fell off of it in a great crashing sheet as the skeleton of a Leviathan rose up. It opened its maw wide, wide enough to swallow the moon. And swallowed the dirigible whole.

His mother grabbed his arm with a cry, and the entire beach erupted in panic. Koh felt his feet slip out from under him as his mother pulled him away.

Later Koh sat back in his house crying. He wanted to take the doorknobs he'd collected and throw them back into the sea to watch them sink. His mother told him that the dirigible had simply failed in the winds, and once it had tipped too close to the ocean a wave had lapped it up. His father went with some of the other fishermen to try to dive down to save any survivors.

He'd been gone for hours.

It was dark now, and they still hadn't even found the dirigible, even though it should have been in the reefs.

Only Koh had seen the skeleton swallow it.

4
[Black Fish]

Koh jerked on the bamboo knob using all of his strength to loosen the screws. The knob popped off with a satisfying snap! Grinning in triumph, Koh tossed it into his bag of knobs, before starting off to the next one. Even as he watched the bag fill, he wondered if it would be enough. He couldn't truthfully imagine the doorknob, the key to the spirit world, was really in this bag. Still, he had no choice. It would have to be tonight that he left.

Water, dark as liquid obsidian, crashed on the island's shore, licking up to the edge of the jungle. The sea reflected the sky swollen with clouds. Goosebumps rose on Koh's arms, and his fingers numbed in fear as he dragged the skiff.

As soon as he stepped into the water, he saw a figure rise out on the reef. Something crested on the waves like a rounded dorsal fin, and it moved steadily toward him. As the figure neared, he saw it wore a mechanic's uniform.

Kinsky.

Kinksy's flesh had been picked away by the fish, and blue veins covered his bone. Behind Kinsky, more of the dirigible's passengers surfaced. Kinsky opened his mouth to say something, but dark water gushed out, killing the words. He dropped a bag before Koh.

Koh screamed, jumping backwards, and fell against the vines. When he looked up, Kinsky was gone. Flopping on the beach instead was a black-scaled, eyeless fish as large as a shark. The fish gaped at him, drowning in the air till the waves carried it away.

Koh snatched the bag Kinsky dropped before the waves also claimed it, and he saw it was full of doorknobs from the dirigible. He tied the bag to himself to keep it from being torn away. He climbed into the skiff and ducked his head, folding himself over the bag to protect it. The sky flashed white with lightning. Thunder resonated deep within him and settled in his pounding heart.

Waves carried him out to the storm. Koh struggled to breathe, with the water constantly being thrown into the boat. The skiff would flip, or be thrown back against the beach. And suddenly Koh knew he was going to drown here. He caught only a glimpse of the towering waves before the sea engulfed him.

* * *

Doorknobs drifted in the water.

Behind each of them a new door appeared, each entirely different from the original door Koh had pried them from. Koh floated past them, as if he were being carried on a gust of wind.

He had to squint from a bright gleam from the sun. He saw the water covered in doors and doorknobs.

Koh gripped one of the doors and hoisted his chest up, laying on it as best he could. As he slowly drifted back toward the island, he watched the reef of skeletons move below him, spiraling and piecing themselves together and apart. Knitting themselves together, they rose from the water to form an exoskeletal dome over the island.

* * *

The jungle wasn't covered in the normal assortment of driftwood, seashells and debris left after a storm. It was covered in doorknobs. And not just the recent knobs, but old ones that no one recognized, ones covered in barnacles and thin bits of coral.

The villagers stood bewildered. Some of them had recognized their lost doorknobs and picked them up, but most were too preoccupied trying to see where the storm had blown. Storms couldn't just vanish. The alignment of the moons was unchangeable, and yet the storm was nowhere to be seen.

Koh smiled to himself when he climbed out of a door lying face down in the beach. His mother soon spotted him. She ran toward him and hugged him tight. Looking out, he could still see doorknobs reflecting the sun like stars in the sky floating on the calm sea's surface.

Later Koh would sail with his father to continue searching for the dirigible. When they dove, they would see large, eyeless fish that they'd never seen before the storm. It wasn't long before they were tested for eating, and people discovered that if they cut the fish open, they would find bits of things that had been with the people on the dirigible. In one fish they found a pair of large brass knuckles.

Diane Ward is from Brandon, Mississippi. She appreciates speculative fiction's ability to indulge the imagination and writes about topics that inspire her. Diane will study chemistry and creative writing at Millsaps College in Jackson, Mississippi.

Gold, Silver, American Voices and Creative Concept Awards

Students in grades 7–12 may submit works in 11 writing categories. This year more than 2,000 regional award-winning writing submissions were reviewed by the authors, educators and literary professionals who served as national jurors. Gold, Silver and American Voices medals were awarded to works that demonstrated originality, technical skill and emergence of a personal voice. Creative Concept Awards specifically recognized works that dealt with grieving and loss (The New York Life Award), and bullying (Creativity & Citizenship)

They Are the Patriots

Haley Lee, 14
BASIS Scottsdale, Scottsdale, AZ, **Hadley Ruggles,** Teacher

Soldiers chasing savage beauty tear down the horizon with precision.
This is a crusade against compassion, against the old regime and a
   fear of apology,
so raise your weapons.
Boom.
Missiles kiss the skyline and we are done
in a flair of gunpowder and smoked horror.
Children holding hands with skyscrapers
scrape their mothers' blood from the kitchen floor
and every night they wish for the bombs to stop falling so they can
   start living.
Feet muddy,
hearts stained.

They are the patriots.

Land mines triggered by our greed
melt skin from bone,
slitting scars in the Earth deep as the Grand Canyon.
So much for the sanctity of human life.
Our fingers are stained like roses from the wounds of another
   generation
and a bleeding flag keeps a thousand caskets warm.
There are families trapped inside temples set ablaze
that turn to ash with their heads tilted toward the heavens.

They are the believers.

Continents are shaking.
Every time we vote for war, can you hear the pulse of the innocent?
It is the anthem of the forgotten,
the cry of the victim.

It is the sound of a shovel pounding out midnight funerals
inside a city that weeps for its fallen.
But for every shot fired we are digging our own graves.
Hide behind the pursuit of Justice,
but the terror of a life severed short cannot fit into a seven-letter excuse.
Our hate spans oceans and we are using virtue as a reason to kill.
Who handed you the right to judge?

A triplet, fencer and musician, Haley Lee is from Scottsdale, Arizona. She wrote this piece after reflecting, in the post-9/11 era, on her family history during WWII—her mother's Polish and Austrian family in German concentration camps and her paternal family's displacement after the Japanese invasion of China.

Camp Delta, Guantánamo Bay

Darby Cressy, 17
New Orleans Center for Creative Arts, New Orleans, LA,
Andy Young, Teacher

Closed eyes
forget
the 8x8 salty stench.
I imagine
the Gulf.

Beads that collect
along the ridges
of my mouth
are dew drops the Zagros Mountains
struggle to gather.

I see those mountains
behind eyelids
that remind me I'm in Iran
on my prayer mat,
with bowed head I face
the Jameh Mosque.

I look past the armed guard
when he delivers my meal,
and see my son return from school,
running to hug me.

I look past the armed guard
and I'm home.

Darby Cressy is from Metairie, Louisiana. Her aunt, a civil engineer, is her role model. In college, she hopes to major in engineering or medicine and minor in writing.

Caught Like Smoke

Zoe Cheng, 14
Walnut Hills High School, Cincinnati, OH, **Kyle Scudder,** Teacher

Hijab: A head cover worn by Muslim women.

My hijab was beautiful.

My first one was pink, the color of
Mama's fingernails, a gorgeous silky perfection
laced with bits of stringy crimson.

I wove my fingers through the stretchy fabric,
Mama taught me how to wind it around my hair just right,
how to tuck away my flyaway curls so they wouldn't blow free
in the lackluster wind.

My billowing head of hair disappeared under my *hijab*,
and my cheeks, dripping with baby fat, lay swollen,
guarding my puckered lips that drooped with skin.

My mother had held my face in her soft palms,
fingering the supple textures of my smooth forehead,
the tiny hairs of my sparse eyebrows.
She kissed my cheek and said,

"Ah, Aedila, I am jealous of your skin,
it is soft, like baby's, see?"

And she would touch my fingers to the rivets hallowed out
in her cheeks and my eyes would stray to her own *hijab*,
modest and simple, like her dark eyes.

I donned my *hijab* at the time most girls
my age started getting boyfriends,
silky shiny hair slinking down the hallway,

lips curled around other lips like rose petals.

Sometimes it was hard to remember I was wearing
my *hijab,*
until I washed my hands in the girl's bathroom
or changed into my gym clothes.
I tried ignoring the spikey chitterchatter words
streaming around my head like silver smoke,
the stares that painted flushing red roses onto my cheekbones.

The other girls wore shirts that bore their bellies,
soft fat clinging to gaunt hip bones,
sometimes with a piercing at the navel.

They would mock me with their perfect pale skin,
blue eyes wide and innocent, makeup just so,

"Eye—dill—AH," they would say my name,
tongue curling around the soured consonants,
the overcooked syllables,
"How do you say that? It's Indian, right?"

And my baby-soft skin, the skin that my mother
envied, would flush with roses and red the color of blood.

I would feel the words I wanted to say
drop like heavy balls of lead into my stomach,
far away from my dry tongue
and my chattering teeth.

And the perfect pictures of perfection would walk down the hallway,
whispers and gossip and my name floating back over their skinny
  shoulders,
surrounding my ears like buzzing flies.

I used to cover my ears when they taunted me with stereotypes,
used to block the sound of their ruthless giggles,

turning my heart to stone.

My mother used to cradle me in her arms
when I cried, arms as strong as tree branches
carrying the weight of the wind in their nooks and crannies.

I let loose my troubles, let them roll off my tongue
like marbles, tears collecting in the corners of my eyes
until it became too hard to cage in what was already
too wild, too free.

My *hijab* was the most beautiful thing I had ever laid eyes upon,
the most gorgeous piece of fabric that billowed in the lackluster wind.
I wanted the girls at school to see my *hijab* like I did,
wanted to tear their robin's egg eyes from their sockets
so they would stop laughing, giggles following me down the hallways,
burning in my ears like fire, tears caught in my throat like a haze
  of smoke.

My mother let me cry to her, let me speak the words I could not
  hold inside.
I adorned my troubles with lies, glimmering stars that over-shone
the ugliness hidden inside of me, lying to myself
that things would get better, that one day the smoke would clear and
I would be waiting, hijab proudly wrapped around my head.

I painted my cheeks with rubies,
Let the gauze of my *hijab* soak in the diamond tears running down
  my cheeks,
glittering in the moonlight.

I wrote down every bad word they said to me, shredded the creamy
  white paper
to pieces.
I opened the window and let them fly through my fingers like butterflies,
beautiful creatures caught in a lackluster wind taking them far,
far away

from a world with lies caught between each star like smoke,
a netting separating me from everyone else.

I lit one candle for each tear that I shed, hiding myself inside the
   bouncing flames and
I watched the golden light thrown onto the walls.
I let them pull me back to safety, inhaled the musty, wood smell of
   their smoke, let the dancing gray ghosts surround me.

I watched the memories of yesterday and tomorrow
dancing in my heart,
slender girls laughing at me,
noses wrinkled with disgust at my *hijab* and what it stood for.

I let the tears run down my face until I could feel them splashing
   onto the
ruby-red carpet,
I let the flickering bulb of anger breathe flames into my head,
roiling in my crimson despair—
I hated myself.

I let the candles burn to the wick, and
lit some more.

I danced until
I couldn't breathe through the haze of smoke,
I cried until
all I could smell was fire,
I fed the flames of my candles
until all I could feel were the blood-red hues of their perfect laughing,
burning at my skin.

   Zoe Cheng is from Cincinnati, Ohio. Her dream is to "write anything and everything." As a minority she thought it would be interesting to write from the perspective of a young woman who is bullied for being Muslim.

When Earth Shook Cairo

Nicole Sadek, 13
Charleston County School of the Arts, North Charleston, SC, **Francis Hammes, Sean Scapellato and Rene Miles,** Teachers

Eyes are aligned in circles,
like mirrors of imitation.
The torches of crackling red reflect.
You can smell the rubble,
see the wreckage,
etching an image
in the white of an eye.
The black of the pupil,
becomes larger and crimson.
The crimson that boils,
bubbles popping with vigor
and seeping out a furious fume.
The brown band encircling the eye,
echoes back the scene:
the multitude of rebels,
with wooden sticks, flames.
These are the eyes of Cairo's witnesses.

Voices ignite in a downpour of sparks,
like thunder that batters the air.
It quivers,
shudders of screams,
as if it were an earthquake
in a single city.
You can hear the daggers.
They are shredding the air.
Lightning spits,
rides through the sky,
then the booms begin
seven seconds later.
These are the voices of Cairo's witnesses.

Years after, debris outlines the roads,
streets coated with images:
a slide show of rewinding colors,
red, black, gold,
with a painted eagle perching
in between.
This is the Egyptian flag,
embossed in concrete.

And I, I stand on it.

Born and raised in Cairo, Egypt, Nicole Sadek is from Mount Pleasant, South Carolina, where she is a dedicated level seven gymnast. Stories from family in Egypt and the news served as inspiration for this piece.

Detroit

Abraham Younes, 17
Bolton High School, Alexandria, LA, **Nancy Monroe,** Teacher

there's an old black man humming hymns on the steps
of the old black church with injured windows
whose body would swell on sunday mornings
before the storm came and the sermon ceased.

"and i used to love this place," he said,
one hand on his heart, the other his head
as he watched a withered world die around him,
lost in the welfare of poverty.

detroit.
the glint in the immigrant's eye
turned the small flame of a rheumy pupil.
it fights the world's concerned accusations
with an iron fist suspended in midair.

detroit.
motown turned nowhere-to-go-town,
the unkempt ghost town
at the rims of suburbia's consciousness,
where assembly lines leave for mexico
and graffiti is mother goose.

it's waiting there
for the traveler just passing through.
armed with a beckoning smile that says
come in, opportunity abounds, my friend!
a worried mother with diseased children
whose calloused hands scramble to dress the scars
and watch herself bloom in rebirth.
the other day, i walked away
in silence. from that old black man on michigan avenue

whose small mouth quivered in the loose quiet
of a stale november morning.

i walked away from him with just
one quick look back, and left because
there were other places
with cleaner streets and prettier faces.

it fell into the dustbin of memory,
a scrap of iron from an oldsmobile.

    *Abraham Younes is from Alexandria, Louisiana, and believes
"poetry is king" because of its ability to stir audiences' emotions. He
will attend Rice University to study anthropology and literature. He
wrote this poem after celebrating Thanksgiving with family in Detroit.*

Annenberg

Kelly Yeo, 15
Culver City High School, Culver City, CA, **Leona Mullen**, Teacher

Well, a woman must be pretty, and that's what I've been told
And all the bullshit that we buy is the stuff Big Beauty sold
And now I can't feel cute without a touch up of powder
I feel guilty for even thinking of indulging in clam chowder.

For runway models hold the reins of all our adoration
The porn stars hold the groins of one repressive nation
I'm done with the powder, the lipstick, the liner, I say
But I'm back at the mirror by the first light of next day.

This is curse, born of woman and nursed like babe at breast
For idealized Western beauty is simply one quiet futile quest
I'm done! I shout, I scream, I cry to quiet waiting voices
Who quietly guide me back to the old life choices.

I once wished to be a supermodel, to be vapid and filthy rich.
Unfortunately, my height proved to be one major glitch.
Now I get depressed for even entertaining such a notion
While my mother slathers on her anti-aging lotion.

Bound slave I am, I shall toil for the rest of my short life
With eye cream in hand and in the other, a knife.

Kelly Yeo is from Culver City, California. As in this work inspired by the Beauty CULTure exhibit at the Annenberg Space for Photography, her writing often tackles controversial issues such as the follies of Western civilization. She hopes to practice medicine while keeping up art on the side.

The Destruction Room

Dylan Combs, 17

Fine Arts Center, Greenville, SC, **Sarah Blackman,** Teacher

I work in the destruction room. It's not a tough job, all that I do is make sure people don't destroy themselves by jumping in. Other than that, I watch the world fall into the room, look at everything that falls through the door on the ceiling and make a 20-meter descent to the floor. People dropped all sorts of things. Bowls hit the floor and splattered into ceramic droplets. Furniture unbuilt itself, boards and screws busted apart, returned to individuality. Even babies and children were thrown into the room, cracking their heads open, consciousness and responsibility spilled onto the ground. Soon they began to throw their feelings into the room. Fear crumbled in the air before it hit the ground in an array of geometric shapes. False hope fell down in a ball, bounced up and down until it finally busted into a cloud of black smoke. When somebody dropped reason, cubes with lost solidity stuck onto the walls and floor and couldn't be scraped off or chiseled away.

Dylan Combs is from Greenville, South Carolina. Inspired by a dream, this poem addresses the idea that people are finding less use for emotion in the modern world. He is interested in the natural world and humanity's place in it, in addition to primate and human behavior.

Fear

Mariah Rippy, 17
John Glenn High School, Walkerton, IN, **Paul Hernandez,** Teacher

She seeks refuge in the caves of the heart,
the air she breathes, murky and rotten.
She eats fish skeletons
leaving behind their flesh.
Poison is her drink of choice,
and she slithers like a worm
digesting all that she lives in.
Prayers make her writhe
with discomfort,
but darkness lets her grow
until she is larger than our souls.

Mariah Rippy is from Walkerton, Indiana. She cites J.R.R. Tolkien, Edgar Allan Poe and Stephen King as major influences. This fall, she hopes to study animation and concept art.

Brave Little Soldier

Christina Voss, 15
Walton High School, Marietta, GA, **Tim Church,** Teacher

And so here I stand.

I, the brave little soldier

at the mouth of the labyrinth.

The slanted brick facets of its skin

shield the hollow twists of its entrails,

its cold, arcane, impossibly tangled core. Its glass lips smirk at me,
coercing me behind their esoteric stranglehold.
I,
   the
        brave

             soldier

hold up my chin and brandish my valor, and step

          into   chaos

I am pushed into a riot of limbs,

limbs that contort and shove in the aggravation of compacted cluster,

that trip

and step

and force.

It together is a beast within the labyrinth, a beast that

moves with many writhing parts

as one whole being,

slowly   and without   deliberate   urgency.

I search for familiar faces among its dozens of heads,
its dozens of strange identities which I will never know,
and when perhaps I snag the gaze of a fellow trooper,
they say nothing,

for the labyrinth   severs past connections.

I, the brave soldier, fight on.

My eyes begin to strain at
                    the
                                        blinding
dull.

The fluorescent lights above
hum   discordantly
filling the labyrinth of hallways with a monotonous,

shrieking   white   light.

The walls of the creature's innards are coated with a sickening
grey-white,
and dizzying   grey-white tiles
endlessly line its floors,
leading to   grey-white rooms

with thin carpets of   grey.

The horrid madness

drains the thoughts of
                    color

          in my mind.

But I, the brave soldier, march on.

*A starting goalie on her lacrosse team, track runner and black
belt, Christina Voss is from Marietta, Georgia. She has played per-
cussion in the Metropolitan Youth Symphony Orchestra of Atlanta
and in a local punk rock band. She hopes to pursue veterinary
science, music and art.*

Icarus in the Digital Age

Amy Chen, 15
Lake Oswego High School, Lake Oswego, OR, **Jami Wray,** Teacher

If the moon were in the place of the sun
In this day of
Artificial
　　　Light
　　　Air
　　　Everything
Would I or anybody out there
Notice?

"Don't look at the sun"
Our mothers
And fathers
Always spoke
But I, with my wax wings
I always stared.

Amy Chen is from Lake Oswego, Oregon. This poem, about the way society considers nature unnatural, was written when she wrote one poem per night for several weeks. She hopes to be a polymath, bringing a diversity of fields to her writing.

1937

Jenna Realmuto, 17
Fine Arts Center, Greenville, SC, **Sarah Blackman,** Teacher

I. Mother,
   January.
   She debuts in a colorless room,
   contrasting in a warm coat of red.
   She is silent
   as her mouth gapes, closes,
   Gapes.

II. Dad,
    February.
    Conceived, but not detected.
    The vessel in which he travels
    sucks down Lucky Strikes,
    puffing smoke like a steam engine.
    He squirms uneasily.

III. 1937,
     May.
     A good year for cartoons,
     but a bad one for gases and flying.
     On the day the Hindenburg explodes,
     Mother, in her stroller, and Dad, in his womb,
     pass each other in the street.

   Jenna Realmuto is from Greenville, South Carolina, where she waits tables 35 hours a week. She will attend Converse College's Honors program. She hopes to write and direct her own play or film and to keep writing, even if it means waiting tables for the next decade.

The Last Will and Testament of Some Woman Who Died (Name Unknown)

Mary Taylor, 17
Mississippi School for the Arts, Brookhaven, MS, **Jeanne Lebow,** Teacher

One
I leave all of my furniture to the house
and the house to the estate
and the estate to myself.
I wish to be buried there so I may own it always
while my children fight over the bank accounts that have
been emptied into the house. And I will be forgotten,
body broken beneath a home that crumbles from the outside in,
in on itself on top of me. And I will push at the bricks
from within the walls, send smoke up the chimney in June,
soil the carpets upstairs with fossil footprints and the hair
of a cat four times reincarnated.
And I will live in my room, bar the door, scratch at the
windows and scare the neighbor boy. Never daring to sleep
for fear of leaving my body behind.

Two
I leave all of my money to those opposed to my death,
to the state that would sell my remains to the highest bidder,
a bribe on behalf of those too careless, too far gone,
too dead and decomposed
to rest in peace.
Do with it what you will. I cannot leave it behind and cannot
let my children see what I have done
so I will leave them numbers of lock boxes I do not possess,
fake account numbers, accidents that can be the fault of the bank.
Anyone who deals with money has sinned at one time
or another so I will not feel guilty.

Three

I leave the dog, a white-haired Shi-Tzu, which the children
pronounced "Shit-zoo" and is actually just a sad, beige color, to
   the streets.
May he find nothing but scraps of metal and irony swift as a kick
   that throws
him from the stoop where he hides from the outside world to which
he has never been formally introduced. He bit me once while I was
   trying to
feed him scraps from the table; he never apologized. At the very least,
he'll be hit by a bus—or lightning.

Four

I leave the children (for they are mine to give away)
to their gods, whichever ones they may claim.
I have not kept up with them these past years, but it is time that
they learned to fear something. Now is as good a time as any
to introduce them to fate. May their children run away from home
when teenage hormones claim their minds and may young men in
devil's disguise thunder down the driveway on lawnmower,
crotches ablaze, eager to deflower Daddy's little girl.
I told you that you would understand someday.

Five

I leave my sanity and my health to the doctors who
didn't come, who said I was fine, that I could go home.
Tell me, young man, what can your diploma tell me of
my own heart that I do not understand? There is nothing wrong
with being healthy and happy, except that it is far too boring
to make any story worth rereading and remembering. So I went mad.
I wish you luck with picking apart the clues leading
up to this moment. Let me know if you find my motivation,
my initiative, because frankly it was a last-minute decision.

Six

I leave the world and its troubles to those who refuse
to vote. You who cannot make a decision, you who don't count,

who don't care. Tell me, what would you rather have us do?
How would you change the world if you could, slacker?
You would shrug, eh, and keep living. After all, who
needs politics when you can simply...*wait,*
who is that, there on the television. Is that our new
prince, our new pride, our new president? I did not vote for
him, therefore, I can complain.
I wish you luck when the earth crumbles beneath you,
and you fall into oblivion without blinking.

Seven

I leave my waste, my sewage, my wrinkled skin,
my scars, my dislocated fingers, my nail clippings,
my fever blisters and Psoriasis, my mucus and my arthritis,
my chapped lips, my bruised knuckles, my stomach ulcers,
my dandruff, my leg hair, my sunspots, my weak knees,
and the old mop to the butler who was too
afraid to enter the garden for fear of snakes.
You will find, my dear man, that life can be far
more rotten when one doesn't stop to smell the roses.

Eight

I leave the news to its makers, its breakers, its
imitators. You who try to make the world
a cruel place are the cause for its destruction as well
as its entertainment. I applaud you. But I dare you to
try and entertain the dead, the widows, the homeless,
the hurricane bells, the blood-spattered and mud-flooded streets,
the walking skeletons and hopeless diabetics, the tear-drained
warriors and decapitated soldiers, the names in numbers rolling
across the screen below your inappropriately cheerful faces; reading
off events, statistics as if they haven't just occurred. Even the sirens
screaming behind your field reporters show more sorrow, more remorse,
more emotion than your blank faces. Is it your job to separate
yourselves so completely from the world? Is that what it takes to
keep you from becoming a part of the tragedies you cover and taking
them home to feed to your families? I believe you will all get your own

ring in hell, helplessly watching your families, friends, dreams
and bounty being shredded before your eyes as you are finally made
to experience the grief of the world you created.

Nine
I leave my favorite fountain pen to the lawyer or judge
unlucky enough to be deemed responsible for this
unimportant old woman's will. Your efforts, your
time and your canceled lunch dates are worthy of some small
consolation. I am sorry if my death was an inconvenience.
No, I lie. I hope my death is quite an inconvenience, because then
I will have made some sort of impression, ignited some flicker
of emotion in a stranger even after my passing hour. That will
make me worth remembering, that will let me live a little while longer.

Ten
I've changed my mind. I've decided not to die. Death is far too stifling
and it's crowded here, I wouldn't recommend it. I apologize for
   wasting your time.
Perhaps we will meet again someday. For now I think I'll become
   a reporter.

*Mary Taylor hails from Water Valley, Mississippi. She will major in
biology and chemistry at Delta State University and hopes to become
a veterinarian, though she plans never to stop writing.*

Women

Michelle Farina, 17
Blake High School-Magnet, Tampa, FL, **Casey Curry,** Teacher

Women,
Have dawn in their eyes and
The horizon on each fingertip
From the moment they unveil their soul
Until they are dead

Our patriarchal society casts shadows
Into their persona, trying to dictate who they can be

Their fierce eyes can penetrate the thickest of molds
Shatter them to dust and stones
Sweeping away the remnants
And skipping the stones across their oceans of potential

A woman is half strength and half grace
Working in perfect harmony
One leg for balance and one to transcend gravity
Her untamed hair, a symbol of freedom
And body her weapon of language

Art is the ink which women sign their declaration
Never can it be taken
Only modified to express the next emotion
Or interpret the next revolution

Michelle Farina is from Apollo Beach, Florida, where she has recently discovered a passion for photography. Her dream is to work as a writer and photographer for National Geographic, *traveling the globe to document the world.*

Ode to Liberty

Sojourner Ahebee, 16
Interlochen Arts Academy, Interlochen, MI, **Anne-Marie Oomen,** Teacher

I.
I have a brother and he is brown
My mother tells her son that the world is his oyster
Lay claim to all around you, she begs
And he smiles and believes in dreams that can't be scaled down.
As he gets older, like now, like 10 years old
My brother, who is brown, tall like the Sahara Desert on stilts,
Handsome like the Grand Canyon in a rainstorm
Has only the weapons of a violin and a painter's brush
And a bedroom plastered with heroes to calm his fears of the things
foretold.

Maybe not his fortune, doesn't have to be
But the wails of a mother tied to the wails of another
Linking hundreds of death cries over lost sons,
Released in one year, cascading through one city
Ours
Can spook a little brown boy thinking about living.

II.
I had a friend and he made me wonder about the world
He had crawled through airless tunnels,
Crossed deserts that froze his night tears and rode in trucks with
no breath
To arrive here in Our city.
We'd playfully argue
About what makes the best tamales—cornhusk or banana leaves—
And as he cleaned my mother's car, I played Lila Downs for him
To purposely make him homesick.

We arrived at the carwash one Sunday after praising God and giving
thanks

Looking for Cesar,
Not just to clean our car,
But for him to teach us our colors and how to be polite in the
  language of his home.
He is dead, he coughed himself to death.
Too afraid to seek a helping hand to soothe the fire in his chest.

III.

I invited Alex, a Main Line girl,
To the central branch of the library,
To show off one of the treasures of my urban splendor
But her father said no
Too many homeless men encircling the square
But my mom said they were once young boys
Full of sass and young hope
Until some war ate their souls,
Made them need more than blood in their veins.

IV.

I have a stick; it's more like a wand
I use to tickle Liberty, to play with it
To woo it from its safe havens
And to beg for it to come where I am and spread some love.

Sojourner Ahebee was born and raised in Côte d'Ivoire, West Africa, until the first Ivorian civil war and her father's death. A self-described "activist poet," she published a poetry collection, Thirteen Ways to Look at Me. *This piece addresses the gun violence, homeless war veterans and immigrants of her home, Philadelphia.*

Take Me to Hullabaloo

Lauren Feiner, 16
Bronx High School of Science, Bronx, NY,
Grace Ledwidge, Teacher

Take me
to abracadabra
and hullaballoo.
Show me the way
to hide and seek,
and ring around the rosie.

Take me back
to dewy eyes
coated in wonder, and
fudge-sticky fingers
licked one at a time.

Take me
to stuffed-animal dreams
and mermaid souls.
To make-believe mornings
and naptime noons.

Bring me back
to macaroni frames
and princess pretending.
To when an hour
was a year.

Show me
where we stored
our hopes and desires.
In our
cardboard crayon
boxes? Or

our plastic
play dough cans?
Teach me
how to be
the silly sound
of giggles, and
the sweet taste
of June.

Take me
to abracadabra
and hullaballoo.

Lauren Feiner is from New York City, where she rows crew—a sport that, like writing, forces her to search inside herself for that extra bit of strength she didn't know she had. She hopes to pursue journalism and creative writing.

Equilibrio

Karen Zheng, 17
Stuyvesant High School, New York, NY, **Kerry Garfinkel, Jonathan Weil and Mark Henderson,** Teachers

I am from the gray heavens of Lima and the red dirt of Independencia
a part of a whole trying to fill holes—but what do I know?
apples lipsticked red from constant nourishment,
and mountains purple in majesty, and all their unwant
I am from forty minutes a day
in Spanish class flipping through *Exprésate*,
from the accent on that e worth a fourth of a point
on a test—is this how they measure how we do our best?
I am from the self-dubbed Drama Llamas (we go crazy for llamas),
from all the *Inca Kola, ceviche y causa* our soles buy and our tongues
roll over like r's,
from empty suitcases of substance and heart
when our sojourn is over but our colors don't part

I'm from fingers linked with those of orphans,
from Spanglish conversations and Prince Royce's *No lloraré,*
No lloraré, oh I won't, shed a tear
I'm from eyes lined thick to cover weariness and loneliness, eyes
swept clean
after Raúl points to them, slanted, and everyone laughs
(you're slanted)
I'm from the late-night whispers and tears Natalie and I share in our
Peruvian-Asian-American
sisterhood
(because that happened to me too)
I'm from children's shouts of *Mamá, Mamá!* and their panicked
chasing after our van
when we leave, godforsaken

I'm from the mothers of Independencia,

who bind cloth to their backs to carry their babies, feed all six of
them with 100 USD a month,
and curse their runaway partners as fervently as they worship God
I'm from the abandoned, crumbling houses kids' dirty, rough hands
wander in,
from the puddles on soccer fields they beat us on every time,
and the holes in the nets, and the holes in the clothes
I'm from great wishes—a doctor! a policeman! the president!—and
the gangs that surround them
I'm from a huge concrete wall in a place where a dozen homes can be
destroyed by ground shifting
from six times the quantity of twelve wheelbarrows of dirt, ninety
shovels of rocks,
and five bags of concrete mix, plus water plus manpower plus manpower plus manpower plus
strength

I am from handfuls of sand seeping past my hands,
from a warm fire in a cold desert night,
from endless needles of hope piercing the black sky,
from I wish I may's, and I wish I might's
I am from years of kneeling at the foot of my bed
to greet the same stars
I am from years of newspapers read on the subway
about the same wars
I am from crunching Central and Van Cortlandt Park gravel beneath
running shoes
and gushing New York City summer rain beneath dancing feet
But I will always be from footprints winding along, under red dirt
and above gray heavens

*Karen Zheng is from New York City, where she writes about
gender rights, Asian-American issues and freedom of expression.
Her work as editor and writer at her school newspaper and her travels
abroad have shaped her interest in international relations, history and
policy. She will attend Yale this fall.*

Mixed Roots

Caroline Kelly, 15
Wellesley Senior High School, Wellesley, MA, **Courtney Cook,** Teacher

I find the term "mixed race" to be funny.
When people think of mixed race
They see Tiger Woods, or maybe Rosario Dawson.
And then their eyes wander over to me,
And they say, "Oh,
You're like that too?"
Like it's scrapbooking or knitting,
And they say, "Oh,
Isn't that nice,"
When they are thinking,
"There should be a pill for that."
And I can see myself,
Wasting my life away
Standing in line for that pill,
Deciding whether or not I even want it.
I don't know what I would look like afterwards,
But I do know that it's easy to see colors not shapes,
Just like it's easy to watch my whiteness
Crawl to the surface of my skin
Like a Wonderbread wave.
Spanish for roots is *raices*,
And sometimes when I was little
Pulling up weeds in the yard
To throw in a plastic bucket,
A science teacher voice in my head would say,
"Class, look at the structure of the root.
It is ideal for its function to
Absorb water and nutrients for the plant's survival,"
And all I could think of was my grandmother.
She sang *balladas* in the car,
Bought *leche condensada* in bulk,
And laughed with her teeth.

She would order for everyone in the family
At formal restaurants, even her full-grown daughters,
And was known to duck out of Christmas parties
To watch her favorite soap operas when they were on.
Once, with no context whatsoever,
She calmly informed me, half-seriously,
That if I ever married Pitbull,
Cuban though he may be,
She would not come to my wedding.
Last August, God
Cashed in on a very old promise.
Even though she was sick, and sleeping, I imagine
A feisty, albeit respectful, argument
And finally a wise consent.
We went down to Miami to make sure
That *el Padre, el Hijo y el Espiritu Santo*
Took good care of her.
The priest mispronounced her name. It rained.
I cried for the woman, and I cried for my *raices,*
Feeling like a mixed-race weed.
But every time I think about that magic pill,
All I can think of is her gold crucifix,
Now worn by my mother,
How I listen to *balladas* in the morning,
And how every time, when I put
Those weeds in a bucket,
I would replant them in a corner
Of the window box, and water them.

Caroline Kelly lives in Wellesley, Massachusetts, and uses a multiplicity of art forms to draw emotions from particular audiences. "Mixed Roots" captures her feelings of grief after the passing of her Cuban grandmother.

Chinatown Date-Night

Benjamin Sobel, 17
Hunter College High School, New York, NY, **Kip Zegers,** Teacher

An angry clash
dissolves into wind-chilled kisses
on an abandoned Chinatown street.
Smells of formerly fresh fish surround,
hand finds hand, the perfect puzzle pieces
but the fingers don't quite match up.
They aren't the same.

Greasy dumplings and scallion pancakes,
foods he can't comprehend.
The foods of her childhood,
only the Americanized versions.
No words are spoken as they eat,
simply enjoying the food,
and each other's company.

Sitting in the small park
together in a place he doesn't exactly belong,
but she brought him here.

These are Chinatown nights,
dates on dirty streets,
and love through dirty glares.
Different hands that fit too perfectly
as they walk in unison
through the dark, dimly lit streets.

Benjamin Sobel is from New York City. He is grateful to his best friend, muse and role model, Desmond Niegowski. He will study psychology and law at Ohio State University.

Still Winter Comes

Ashley Huang, 14
Doerre Intermediate School, Klein, TX, **Mike Keimig,** Teacher

Quantum theory states:
We are all earthbound matter, and yet
We act as dreamlike waves
Two bundles of ignorant energy: us
Felt not on skin, but deep in our souls
Those protons bombarding our half-solid forms
And yet we remain the same.

You and I were science-children:
Our mouths followed the Bohr, and yet
Your head already drifting to clouds
Parents and science: our covalence
But perhaps you were more ready than I
You shed your shells, that calm winter
And yet I remain the same.

Quantum and Schrödinger and us:
We are all earthbound matter, and yet
We act as dreamlike waves.

I tried to hold on to those slippery quarks
I tried to hold on to you, and yet
Those neutrinos pass me by.

Ashley Huang is from Houston, Texas, where she is interested in astrophysics, art and indie music. Her ultimate goal is to win a Pulitzer Prize.

Unleashed Steel

Joyce Freitag, 17
Hunter College High School, New York, NY, **Kip Zegers,** Teacher

In a yellow house
my father sat
on roughly grainy carpet
small fingers stumbling over
smooth metal model
titanium, aluminum fused tingles of excitement

In a room of whirring beeping monitors,
his father sat
with headsetted men
and combined intent to soar.
From his seat he etched calculations
into air
steely, precise
despite his big belly ho-ho laugh
this must be exact
for so much at stake.
Months away for this,
so no single rupture or pucker
in his strand of thought
can escape.
He sees that error would be
waste, leaving matter lost
in rubble orbiting the earth.

His father left the spot of yellow
peaceful in his early morning departure,
in perfect place amidst groomed green blades,
creamy golden sky glow.

His mother's hand raised
in a wife's wave

fingers twirling softly in the air for hours afterwards.
Already missing the months,
dreading cold sheets beside her lonely darkness.

My father took apart his father's space shuttle,
layers at a time
learned precision
in the motion of his father's faraway phantom fingers
observed in grasped moments every few months.
When his mother
dripping words, angry with loneliness
in drippy liquor haze
returned to airy smiles.

Left to his thoughts and
shiny models,
rich rumbling chest pounding at memories
of watching
giant machines lift up.

Joyce Freitag is from Brooklyn, New York. "Unleashed Steel" was inspired by her grandfather, a Navy captain and NASA employee who was part of the space race. She will attend Oberlin College this fall.

Miss Hiroshima-Nagasaki Says Her Piece

Christine Hirata, 15
Magic Pen Kids, Laguna Hills, CA, **Clarissa Ngo,** Teacher

Japanese-American soldiers get no credit for their valor against their own ancestors during World War II, but that's only because textbook historians forget to tell the stories of people who don't look like them. How many history chapters are dedicated to the Japanese-American heroes of WWII or the Navajo Code Talkers? Zip. Zero. *Nada*. I mean, the 442nd Regiment, whose infantrymen were all Japanese-American, is the *most highly decorated regiment in American history*, but has anyone ever heard of them? I don't think so.

We talk about getting an education in this country, but what kind of lopsided education are we getting if we only celebrate people of one skin color? I mean, America is supposed to be a melting pot, not a Ralph Lauren advertisement. I remember when "diversity" to Cover Girl meant three white girls with different hair colors. We've come a long way since then, but we've still got a long way to go.

And another thing! The whole Pearl Harbor incident was blamed on Japanese-Americans, but in reality, *the American government knew about the incident before it happened*. Tokyo even sent a WARNING to America basically saying, "Hey, we're gonna attack you guys soon, okay? So be prepared!" But that message never got to the admiral of the U.S. fleet, so the attack was a surprise. Did I mention that FDR knew that this was happening, but lifted not one finger to stop it? So, in his quest for a scapegoat, he pointed at Japanese-Americans and soon everyone was jumping on the hate train! Don't get me wrong; I'm definitely *not justifying* the bombing of Pearl Harbor or saying that FDR was all bad. I'm just pointing out that a *miscommunication* was blamed on the hapless Japanese-Americans, who then were robbed, dispossessed and forced to live in horse stalls they called "relocation camps." And the worse part of it is, nobody even knows about it or cares. Oh, we make a big deal about the Holocaust, but nobody cares when something bad happens to the Asian-Americans. Sure, Asian people are quiet. We're the model minority. Hurt us, and we won't say a thing.

"It couldn't be helped," my grandfather once told me. And so, he enlisted to fight his own ancestors—his own people!—to prove how American he was. The whole Japanese-American regiment did. They were the bravest, toughest, shortest group of American soldiers out there, and they achieved acts of heroism that are unsung to this day. The 442nd Regiment boasted 21 Medal of Honor recipients and the Congressional Gold Medal, yet does any American school kid know about them?

The Peculiar Institution. The Jewish Question. Executive Order 9066. All euphemisms for hate crimes that kill. You may argue that interning and dispossessing Japanese-Americans during WWII was hardly in the same atrocity category as slavery and the Holocaust, but in reality, it was a crime just as fatal. Formerly interned Japanese-Americans suffer twice the chance of heart disease and premature death than those who were not interned, primarily Japanese-American plantation workers in Hawaii. Ironically, sugar saved them.

President Roosevelt himself called the bleak barbed-wire horse-stalls Japanese-Americans were sent to inhabit "concentration camps," yet no one bemoans this crime. We flay ourselves for separating African slave families, but no one even realizes we did the same thing to Japanese-Americans during WWII. Our government possessed proof that not one Japanese-American, citizen or not, had engaged in either espionage or sabotage. Yet we robbed and "relocated" them, putting up signs that they were enemies of the state. Some Japanese-Americans suffered heart attacks upon seeing these notices, feeling betrayed by the very country they loved. Among these "enemies of the state" were WWI vets who had served the country honorably. One, James Wakabe, was even shot for walking too near the internment camp fence.

Imagine yourself a proud American. You are perhaps a farmer or a shopkeeper, just going about your business in the country you call home. One day, the FBI knocks on your door (or maybe you see a sign on your street) and announces that you have 48 hours to pack your whole life in two bags. They give you no information about when you will be allowed to return home. When you arrive at Camp Harmony, you are herded like an animal into a barbed-wire pen, and guards are set on the perimeter of your cage, ready to shoot you if you come too close to the wire.

The government suspects you of being a spy, even though you're just a pistachio farmer. Newspaper headlines accuse you of being a saboteur, of treasonous fifth column activity. Even your own Congressman hates you, saying:

I know the Hawaiian Islands. I know the Pacific coast where these Japanese reside. Even though they may be the third or fourth generation of Japanese, we cannot trust them. I know that those areas are teeming with Japanese spies and fifth columnists. Once a Jap, always a Jap. You cannot change him. You cannot make a silk purse out of a sow's ear....

Do not forget that once a Japanese always a Japanese. I say it is of vital importance that we get rid of every Japanese, whether in Hawaii or on the mainland. They violate every sacred promise, every canon of honor and decency. This was evidenced in their diplomacy and in their bombing of Hawaii. These Japs who had been there for generations were making signs, if you please, guiding the Japanese planes to the objects of their iniquity in order that they might destroy our naval vessels, murder our soldiers and sailors, and blow to pieces the helpless women and children of Hawaii.

Damn them! Let us get rid of them now!

By this reckoning, shouldn't we intern the British-Americans, too? After all, the Brits threatened our freedom at the dawn of our country's birth, and who knows, they might still be harboring plots to overtake our country and reinstate the Intolerable Acts. Once a Brit, always a Brit. You know how it goes.

Such reasoning may sound crazy to you, but it's the same rationale the American government used to intern 120,000 Japanese-Americans, half of whom were innocent children. But no one talks about this injustice, partially because Japanese-Americans still follow *bushido*, the way of the warrior. In this chivalric code, citizens are expected to follow their leaders with unwavering loyalty, regardless of the injustice of their orders. In this case, the American government was the Japanese-American leader, and this was why Japanese-Americans adopted a code of silence with regard to the injustice perpetrated against them.

My grandfather's silence and desire to prove his patriotism infects me still. To this day, I can't stand anything Japanese. My family eats Texas-style chili and cornbread for dinner, not ramen and pickled vegetables. I refuse to learn about Japanese history. I refuse to know about my ancestors. I am American, and I dare anyone to prove me wrong.

Yeah, in fifth grade they called me names like "Hiroshima Nagasaki"—racial slurs I won't forget. To be taunted by an event that is one of the worst inhumanities against man is interesting, even more so that it happens in a place where enlightenment is supposed to reign. What are we teaching kids at school that they can so easily fling around words like atomic bombs? Whatever. I am an American to the core, and I dare anyone to say otherwise.

Christine Hirata is from Aiea, Hawaii, where she plays trumpet, sings and writes songs. She is inspired by the perseverance of her grandfather, who survived the Great Depression and fought in WWII in the unsung legendary 442nd Regimental Combat Team's 522nd F Artillery Battalion.

America's Favorite Cookie

Kamry Goodwin, 17
Governor's School for the Arts and Humanities, Greenville, SC, **Scott Gould, George Singleton and Mamie Morgan,** Teachers

I'm watching a group of black kids play a game of Spades. (Note: This isn't meant to be funny. Until someone pointed it out to me, I thought Spades was only a card game, not a racist epithet for black people. Which, you'll see, is my problem.) Most are around my age, maybe one or two a couple of years younger than I am. But they all speak the same language: rappers and the BET Awards, Air Jordans and Chris Brown. I sit quietly, only listening, not contributing much. In the middle of their conversation, Tiana, a heavyset girl with fresh cornrows tied to her scalp, asks me how I feel about Waka Flocka.

"What is that?" I ask.

The table goes silent. Everyone looks at me, a few snickers here and there. I'm confused and Tiana just pats my hand and shakes her head.

"Oh, sorry. I forget you're an Oreo," she says.

Table of Black Kids laughs. At first, I don't understand. If you don't either, then let me save you a trip to Urban Dictionary:

Oreo (noun): A black person who is accused of betraying their race by acting "too white"; branded Oreo because he/she is "black on the outside and white on the inside"

Now, I wouldn't mind if she had been joking. I wouldn't mind if she said, "Just kidding," and went on to explain that Waka Flocka was indeed not a Pokémon. (In fact, he's a rapper.) But she isn't kidding. I can tell by the looks around the table what everyone is thinking: *I pity you for not being black enough.*

According to Richland Memorial Hospital medical records, I am legally "black enough." And I clearly remember the three years of middle school when Darrell Gibson and Louis Martel made my life a living hell by addressing me as Tar Baby and Powder Burn, as if I didn't already know I was darker than the "normal" black person.

Let's put aside the fact that I think BET (Black Entertainment Television) commercializes the plight of black popular culture, that I don't exactly have the famous "apple bottom" often associated with black girls, that I don't know the name of that ridiculous rapper, and I'm absolutely positive if "black person" were a legitimate dictionary term, my picture would sit proudly beside the other 40 million African-Americans on the page.

Tiana isn't the first person to deem me unfit for my race. Once, a couple of years ago, my own mother called me out for acting "too white." She had company over the day it happened, middle-aged, blue-collar, African-American men and women. I was playing my music over the computer speakers before they arrived, so I tried to select tunes they would be familiar with. It was just my luck that the moment I left the music unattended was also when my playlist shuffled to Lady Gaga's "Bad Romance." Gaga was a much-needed interlude between the "oohh"s and "baby-come-back"s of the '90s R&B groups that had played for the past hour. But my mom's friends disagreed. They complained loudly about my so-called "cracker music."

"What in the world…" one friend shook her head at my mother.

"Is this that crazy heifer with the meat dress?" another friend asked.

My mom came over and turned the music down, clearly embarrassed. "I don't know why she listens to all this white people stuff," she said. "Her dad got her into it."

She said this like an apology, as if I were something to be ashamed of. To think, I could've easily revealed that whenever she is in a bad mood, my mom blasts "Don't Stop Believin'" in our car, windows up, head bobbing with the thrum of Ross Valory's bass guitar. But I didn't. That would've taken away any credibility of blackness that she has accrued over the years.

* * *

I'm riding in a white BMW convertible, top down, with my boss Frank, a black criminal defense lawyer who pays me $230 a week for licking envelopes. I'm the summer intern, but I only have the job because Frank and my dad went to high school together in the '80s. We're on the way to pick up lunch for the entire firm when he turns to me and says, "You know what you need?" He smiles, turning his head away from the road to reveal the alien flash of the Bluetooth in his ear. "You need to be niggerized."

He says it the way a dentist would tell you to floss more. Like it was the answer to all my problems: get niggerized.

"What do you mean?" I ask.

"If you want to become a lawyer, then you've got to speak all languages. You think when I'm talking to a drug dealer or a child molester I'm speaking in perfect sentences like this?" Right now, I'm only thinking how much I *don't* want to be a lawyer. He looks at me, expecting an answer to his question. I just shake my head. "Damn right. If I'm sitting across from a crack dealer, I'm going to ask him, 'How much beat they get you with?' Not, 'When you were apprehended, how many kilograms of crack were you found with, sir?' You understand what I mean?"

"Yeah, I guess."

"So say you're working the front desk. Drug dealer walks in for a consultation, gives you a hard time, messing with you. You can't just sit there like you are right now, all prim and proper. You get up in his face and say, 'Nigga, you better back up off me and sit your ass in the lobby.' Try it, repeat what I just said."

"I don't say the n-word," I say, keeping my eyes on the white lines of the interstate.

"And that's your problem right there. You can't be...*white* all the time, you have to know when to turn it on and off. Get niggerized. Say it."

The rest of the car ride continues on like this, Frank trying to get me to say the n-word, me refusing. It's not that I haven't said it before. I've recited Childish Gambino (better known as Donald Glover, an actor on the NBC show *Community*) lyrics with the n-word, but more for the sake of artistic integrity (I'm black enough to respect at least *one* rapper) than for the sake of simply being vulgar. But saying the n-word isn't the issue. Frank tells me that if I don't recover the "little nigger" inside me, then I'm a sellout. That if I don't unlearn the mechanics of "being white," then there was really no point in being born black.

So I try to change. I decide to take a chance and be black. One Labor Day weekend, I resolve to watch nothing but Black Entertainment Television. Usually when my family gathers to watch *Soul Food* or *Beauty Shop* or other all-black-cast movies that the network uses to "promote black culture," I fabricate some excuse to get out of suffering through it. But I realize that if I want to study the art of being black, I have to start somewhere. And if that means staring at a television for two days and consuming only Red Bull and Snickers to keep myself awake, then so be it. Friday night, I lay my comforter and pillow in the front of the TV, and prepare to understand my race.

I sit through two hours of *College Hill* and a few reruns of *106 & Park* before I give up. Because I don't understand. I don't understand how reading JET magazine and addressing every black girl as shawty (or is it shorty?) defines a real black person. Is this confusion the result of private school and magnet programs, of Disney Channel and mainstream radio? Should I check the "Race Unknown" box when I register to vote? Have I become completely desensitized to what it truly means to be black? For the longest time, I've assumed that meeting the minimum requirements of the black community—being unable to swim, watching every Tyler Perry movie, consistently running on CP (Colored Peoples') time—earned me some black credit. But maybe it isn't that simple. Maybe I've wasted too much time trying to walk a gray line instead of black one. Maybe my "blackness" has really left me.

Despite my self-diagnosed racial ambiguity, I don't give up. I apply to the University of Notre Dame's Seminar for African-American Scholars, a week-long, all-expenses-paid minority recruitment program. Despite Notre Dame's reputation as a conservative, predominantly white, Catholic, private university, I had sufficient black reasoning behind attending the program: it was free. No race likes free things more than black people, right?

I thought the seminar would be Black Boot Camp 101. I thought I could learn by living with 39 other black kids stuck in South Bend, Indiana. I thought I would finally get it right. Instead it turns out to be more of what Tiana would call an Oreo convention. After the first few hours with the group, I begin to feel sorry for the person who planned our week. If his goal was to attract low-income, down-on-their-luck, born-on-the-wrong-side-of-the-tracks black kids to the Catholic Wonderland of Notre Dame, he must be crying in his office right now. These "African-American Scholars" are the types of kids who brag about GPAs the way my dad does about the Dallas Cowboys, who drive Mercedes-Benzes and Audis, who talk about SAT scores the way children compare action figures. Over the course of a week, I meet 16 black Catholics, 11 kids who can't "Wobble" (a line dance that now dominates black wedding receptions and birthday parties across the South) and a kid named Jesusislord.

But an idea occurs to me. What if the point of this week is to bring together the worst of the Ding Dongs and Oreos, the Uncle Toms and Aunt Jemimas, for the ultimate black conversion? What if Notre Dame is just the bait to attract the most black-deficient of us all? Are we here to restore what we had lost through compulsive education and No Child Left Behind, institutions that helped us become "too smart" to be black? That's what it seems like when all 40 of us are stuffed into a room with current black students at Notre Dame for a Q&A session. I think this is where the magic will happen. I think now is where I truly become black.

Jesusislord raises his hand to ask if a 5.3 GPA is enough to get into "as illustrious and astral" a school as Notre Dame.

"I was thinking the same thing," a girl named Ashley whispers to me.

As people ask more questions, I grow impatient. I want my great conversion, I want to walk out of this room knowing that people will lock their car doors and clutch their purses as I pass by. Instead, near the end of the session, one of the current students, a sophomore named Adam, stands up and tucks his hands into the pockets of his pleated khaki pants.

"Listen guys. You won't be just *any* black kid if you come to Notre Dame. At other schools—Duke, Brown, Harvard—you'll just be another fish in the sea, another black person." He raises his hands toward the ceiling like an orant. A bronze crucified Jesus hangs on the wall behind him. "But at Notre Dame it's *because* you're black that everyone will want to be your friend. Most of the kids here have never had a friend look different than them. But here, you're everyone's 'black friend.' Why? Because in their minds, you're just like them, you're just as white as they are." When he says white, he makes air quotes, as if the word hangs above him. "And that's why you should come to Notre Dame."

***

I'm looking for a seat in my school's dining hall. People sit in cliques. But the members of the newly formed "black table" are infamous for their constant loudness and sad attempts at beat boxing. I usually don't sit at the "black table," mostly because I'm unfamiliar with a majority of the new members of the small black population at my school. But one of them, a hefty boy with a voice like Barry White and the type of guy who never calls a girl by her first name, sees me wandering around and yells from the other side of the room, "'ey, sweetheart! You can sit over here with us!" I have no choice.

I listen for a place to enter their conversation. I think Usher's coming to town. Or is it Ne-Yo? The UniverSoul Circus? Then it happens again: Do I plan on going to the Wiz Khalifa concert? I stammer over my words, trying to remember snippets of *Hip-Hop World* magazine covers in order to piece together this mysterious Wiz person. Finally, I just come out with it.

"I don't know who that is," I say.

"You know. The rapper. Black and yellow, black and yellow," one girl says, fluorescent lights reflecting off her glossed lips.

I open my mouth to speak then shake my head. I've got nothing. Again, Table of Black Kids laughs. But this time, I'm aware. I know they're laughing at me, at how oblivious I seem. But I laugh with them. Because to a less politically correct eye, I am just like them. I still have coarse hair and thick lips and dark skin. I am still black. But this girl's gone full Oreo. Double-stuffed.

Kamry Goodwin is from Columbia, South Carolina. She is grateful for her father's encouragement and motivation, without which she would never have sustained her passion for writing. This fall, she hopes to study linguistics, Japanese and computer science at Duke University.

Mustangs and Thunderbirds

Jessica Lalonde, 16
Saginaw Arts and Sciences Academy, Saginaw, MI, **Rachel Reid, Jared Morningstar and Deanna Lalonde,** Teachers

On a veiled, misty morning in June 2004, a man was running through the backwoods of Caro, Michigan. He wore a tattered black Tucson bandana that pushed his mass of long brown hair off his brown face. His dark eyes were wild with excitement, his bare chest heaving from the distance, his legs pumping as he jumped over rotted logs and dodged the slaps of pine branches as he ran through the woods. He was free as life pulsed through him while he was running, like an untamed horse set loose to run to the horizon. The man ran now away from Caro's police and the howls of their search dogs after breaking out of the county jail. A television crew would soon capture his image as he dashed from one clump of trees to another, enough of a glimpse of him to send to the man's mother on television. He would later say that that moment was the freest he had ever felt. His name was *Bominadawa Mgningen*, the Running Wolf. He is my Uncle Dominick.

Of the six of my grandmother's children, Dominick, or simply Nick, was probably the one who experienced the most "freedom." Of course, it was probably hard to feel free while he was sitting in jail, but all of his brothers and sisters had prisons of their own, some more binding than others. When he was not confined or running for his freedom, he was studying Native American philosophy, the religion of our ancestors. Feral creatures and divine spirits of the earth filled his heart and led him to have faith in the ultimate peace that could be found if humans embraced the natural world. My uncle was a die-hard advocate of recycling, in both physical things, like plastic and paper, and emotions, returning to find pleasure and fun when a routine had run you dry. He embraced wind, water and solar energy, as well as filled his body with narcotics and hallucinogens. His love was for the heavenly nature of fire and its cleansing powers, reasoning that the flames that lit the beautiful rolls of *seema*—tobacco—which he fashioned himself, naturally, proved that fire could bring peace. He wore dreamcatcher earrings when he spoke about fire, and looked like a monk in his white hoodie and with his grin missing one tooth. He spoke often of the tattoo emblazoned on his chest, and once, when he deemed me old enough, he showed me the little black etching of the words *Party Animal* on his sun-soaked skin. My uncle told me that he had gotten it as a matching mark with his big brother, my other uncle, Darrin, whose name was *Oha Muckwa*, the Laughing Bear.

Darrin was a warrior in both mind and body. He was not a silent man, not in the voice that rang out at the countless weddings and receptions I'd seen him where he would dance and sing, or in the selfless, organic ways he would help those around him. At his funeral in November 2011, the leaves shuddered off the trees and fell to the gray cement, blowing away like color being scratched off a canvas. His young, handsome son was there, built just like he was, brandishing a clean white shirt and black tie, smiling at me. We sat together and he held my hand when the water fell from my eyes in tears at the songs Darrin loved. A week, a month later and my days fall back into place, the hours still pass and time pours forward, pulled by fate. I remember hearing a testament at my uncle's eulogy of his kindness, a trait displayed in a story where he had given a beggar on a street his winnings from a lottery ticket. The kindness I knew, and the memories I'd never seen, showed me that Darrin never needed a fine car to prove he had found his own freedom.

When they were teenagers, my uncles and aunts would fantasize about the glamorous cars they knew they would never have. There was the Camaro, the Ferrari, the Corvette and, the most desired of all in my family—the 1985 Ford Thunderbird, with its glossy sides and design that made it a car of the future. My grandma would complain about their pleas for the T-Bird and recite the old wisdom of ages past, when a thunderbird was the divine spirit that sacrificed itself for the survival of humanity. Lucky to share one beat-up old AMC Gremlin with its cracking blue paint, my uncles and aunts settled for a brand that was what they needed rather than what they wanted. Each of them accepted cars that drove them, instead of the other way around, until my mom bought herself a used, red 1982 Mustang after she left high school. The car took her away from Michigan and into Arkansas, college and the man who would become my father, running in ecstasy until she made her way back home. The cars were their dreams and eventually their freedom, and the mustang and the thunderbird became symbols of my family's passion. Some day, I hope to find a mustang of my own, be it material or somewhere inside me, that allows me to run wild in a world that's been paved over.

Jessica Lalonde is from Caro, Michigan. She believes art and science can together unlock powerful new ideas that revolutionize the way people see and interact with the world. She hopes to incorporate her writing in a career in science or engineering.

I Need to Practice My Farsi; Man Bayad Farsi Ro Bishtar Tamrin Konam

Erika Jobson, 17
Hathaway Brown High School, Shaker Heights, OH,
Scott Parsons, Teacher

It's a place I have never visited—never smelled, grasped, touched or inhabited—yet I consider it to be my home. I live a gaping 6,346 miles from my home, yet instead of a void of cultural disconnect, deep within me there burn the embers of an intense, fiery pride that crackles and sparks, the thick black smoke twisting up in my soul, wafting from my being in the whisper of a soft, balmy "Salam." For me, this Farsi greeting evokes the lush, rolling hills of northern Iran, the cosmopolitan vigor of the capital city, Tehran, the glittering, azure Caspian Sea, and the sweet, pungent aroma of neighbors sharing an afternoon meal of chelo kebab—not images that usually come to the minds of most Americans when they think of my mother's country. Yet this is the image of Iran I see.

From hearing of my mother's childhood and her plush upbringing in Tehran, before the 1979 revolution, I have a very different view of Iran than most people and one that precedes the constant news coverage that lumps the Middle East into one terrorist-driven, Muslim conglomerate. My view of Iran is colored by an intense appreciation for the exalted Persian Empire and its highly sophisticated, tolerant early civilization (one of the earliest and most advanced, in fact) continuing on into the reign of the late Shah. I think not of stereo-typical nomads, or sand dunes, deserts and radical suicide bombers that come to the minds of many. Instead, I think of my mother's rigorous French-Catholic education, her memories of ski trips to the northern mountains of Persia, of ancient Persian Zoroastrianism (the most accepting of the ancient religions) and the great Persian king Cyrus the Great, well recognized for his achievements in human rights, politics, military strategy and far-reaching influence in both Eastern and Western civilizations.

The irony of my admittedly idealized obsession with my Persian roots is that, to the uninformed onlooker, I look absolutely and uniformly white. My milky, ivory skin ranges from alabaster to pearlescent in color and verges on the brink of translucency during the winter months. In fact, when I was born, my Mamanjoon (Persian grandmother) uttered an excited cry of "boulouri!" meaning "porcelain," marveling at my pale skin that is so prized in my self-declared "homeland" of Iran.

This discrepancy between the girl I am perceived to be, a homogeneously white-washed prepster of strictly European descent, and the girl I know I am, an ethnically diverse mix of Eastern and Western cultures, is perhaps what drives my fervent infatuation with my Persian pedigree. I remember hungrily asking my mother from a young age if I would be recognized as a real Persian in Tehran, if I would be spoken to in Farsi and invited over for tea and rice at lunchtime. I remember feeling my spirit plummet as she laughed, caressing my face as she gently cupped my blanched, cherub cheeks in her hands and affirmed that I looked more German, English and Scottish than Persian. Crestfallen, I would dream of letting the Caspian Sea whisk me away in a swirl of cerulean curls, rolling and molding my lithe frame until I emerged from the foam changed somehow, like Cro-Magnon evolved to a higher state of being, finally able to grasp his full potential as man.

Although I have not yet traveled there, being able to call Iran my homeland certainly has shaped and elevated my thinking, much like the intellectual progression of Homo erectus to Homo sapien. With each story my mother tells me and each Farsi phrase she teaches me, I feel as if I am provided a fleeting glimpse into an elusive, enlivened and sonorous world. This world is so estranged from my suburban life in Shaker Heights and so foreign to the nuclear-driven frenzy chronicled on the news that it has enlightened me to the cultural complexities that lie beneath the facts of a history book and opinion of a news article. Unlike what is broadcast in an evening news bulletin, a nation cannot be summarized and packaged for public consumption within a 30-minute period. A sound bite will not suffice to explain the myriad of differing cultures, customs and ideas that exist, like gleaming treasures waiting to be unearthed and understood, within a population. When I visit my Persian grandparents in Texas and see Iranian

President Ahmadinejad on the news, my Mamanjoon emits a low clucking noise, shaking her head, as my Babajoon (Persian grandfather) sighs audibly. The reporter onscreen pinches and minces his syllables until my exalted Iran morphs into "I-Ran," a skewed, nasally interpretation of my country interspersed between words like "nuclear" and "threat." I-Ran, as it is pronounced on the news, is a country from which Persians ran, a country to be fled and feared rather than visited. I-Ran is not the country attributed with the archaeologically advanced ruins of Persepolis, the ceremonial capital of the influential Achaemenid empire, or the first-ever bill of rights declaring human freedom, created by Cyrus the Great in 539 B.C. after his humane, bloodless conquest of Babylon. I-Ran is not a country remembered for its great leaps in math and chemistry; the creation of the alphabet and the numeric system; and revolutionary architectural advancements, like the construction of roads, cement and brick, and sewers that rival those of the Roman Empire.

As I sit pensively in my grandparent's home, my Mamanjoon's creased hand snakes across my lap and intertwines with my own, as if sensing my frustration with the misrepresentation of our Iran. I press my translucent toes into the brightly hued Persian carpet at my feet, gently tracing the intricate designs until my limbs are awash in the striking cobalt, amber, and forest hues of the handwoven rug. I focus on molding the arches of my feet into the crisp, geometric print below, envisioning my ankles stretch beyond the depths of the navy threads until they rest in the rolling waves of the Caspian Sea. As I inhale the sweet perfume of medjool dates, pistachio nuts, pilau, kebab, beryani and rosewater that envelops my Persian family, I am reminded that this land, rooted in hospitality, history and tradition, is my "E-Rahn." My Iran will be as I define it, and only through learning and living the language can I connect further to my beloved homeland.

Erika Jobson is from Shaker Heights, Ohio, where she is a coxswain, coaching her crew teammates on the water. This piece was inspired by the negative conversations and media coverage about Iranian culture. She will attend Cornell University.

Ghosts of Another Land

Emily Green, 15
Appomattox Regional Governor's School, Petersburg, VA, **Patricia Smith,** Teacher

I.

When I was about 2 years old and living in Japan, they said I looked like a doll, my eyes large and always open, my skin pale and without the freckles I have now. Every girl in Japan is supposed to be given a set of dolls before the coming of *Hina Masturi,* the girl's day festival, and I was no exception. I am only half Japanese, but before March 3, 1997, I had my own *hinakazari.* They sit in a glass case on red velvet levels, dressed finely in traditional Japanese dress, their faces solemn and a stark white. All that can be seen of them are their faces, necks and hands; everything else is covered by thick layers of cloth. They stare forever forward in their glass tomb, lying somewhere deep in my grandmother's storehouse in Japan.

They are supposed to be taken out for the festival day, and mine were released and displayed for as long as I lived in Japan. I don't have any memories of taking out and setting up my dolls on their stages, or placing cherry-blossom rice cakes in front of them, but my mother found it important. I was her daughter, and I was going to understand. She taught me the song of the girl's day festival, and I learned it quickly.

My grandmother was supposed to take the dolls out in my absence, but if she did not, I do not blame her; it would have been quite the hassle.

I cannot remember ever seeing the dolls except in a picture. The picture where a laughing toddler sits in front of her dolls in the glass case, her expression nothing like the ones they hold.

These are not the dolls I was once compared to; these dolls are reproductions of people who never truly existed.

Three pale-skinned court ladies on the second tier, an emperor and empress on the first, all with royal countenances, all white as snow.

II.

"Momma, my *yukata* is too small."

"No, it's not, Emi. Look, I sewed it so that there is fabric left when you grow, see? Look now."

The seams snapped one by one.

"Now it fits perfectly."

Every summer before I turned 7, I would open the same bottom drawer in my dresser, the biggest one that held the yukata that I had had since I was 2. Japanese children would wear them as pajamas in the summer, and I did too, though my American grandmother protested that I shouldn't wear my pretty kimono to bed. I did not correct her; she did not know. It went down as something that I would always just ignore. Something had always told me not to say anything, to just leave it as an unknown mistake. I once described it to her as a summer kimono, but she soon forgot.

I would revel in the smell of my yukata, unlike any of my other clothing, and I would run the length of my hallway over and over, arms straight back, like a ninja. Running in a dark forest from ancient Japanese spirits that I had learned about throughout my childhood.

Akari o tsukemasho bonbori ni,
O hana o agemasho momo no hana.

III.

During the winter of 1979, my mother was a 14-year-old girl, and a dedicated volleyball player. She walked home each day after practice into the cold ocean breeze that snapped at any exposed skin. Night closed in rapidly, and twilight seemed nonexistent, the darkness coming quick and fast. That same year, something else swept across Japan like a cold wind: the *Kuchisake ona*, the slit-mouthed woman.

They say that she was the wife of a samurai long ago, and she was beautiful beyond compare. Her beauty, however, made her susceptible to evil gossip, and after rumors of adultery reached the ears of her husband, he cried, "Let us see if anyone will find you so beautiful now!" and slit her mouth open from ear to ear with his sword. Her ghost wears a mask to cover her scars, and approaches people on the streets at night.

It will be cold and dark, and you will see a woman coming to you with her head down. She will have beautiful, shiny black hair, large expressive eyes, and a white surgical mask on her face. The mask is not uncommon in Japan in winter; no one wants to get sick. She will come nearer until she stands before you, bathed in the light of an old streetlamp, and she will ask, "Am I beautiful?"

Gonin bayashi no fuetaiko,
Kyou wa tanoshii Hina Masturi.

IV.

I lie in the white lacquered bed I chose for myself after my permanent move to America. My mother sits next to me, and I say, "Momma, when I am older, I will plant a crepe myrtle in my backyard."

She replies, "But Emi, ghosts are all around crepe myrtles, you know. Crepe myrtles are a ghost's tree."

I am silent as I mull over this thought. I decide against planting any crepe myrtles.

"Ghosts come to you like this, Emi," she says, her neck bent, her arms folded into a praying mantis's prayer stance.

"*Urameshia! Urameshia! I envy you! I begrudge you!*" She leans toward me slowly, and I shy away. In this moment, she is not my mother. I try to conceal my fright, but I feel as though it shows.

"Like that, Emi. They come because they are unhappy that you have what they don't."

What she says scares me.

I am 9 years old, and I feel sympathy for ancient ghosts.

Odairisama to ohinasama,
Futari narande sumashi gao.

V.

The traditional dolls are all adults, all solemn and distinguished, but my Japanese family compared me to the dolls of little girls: rounder, and without the sharp edges of an adult's face. My father says that when my mother cut my hair into a bob, I looked like *Okiku-chan,* the doll housed in the Mannenji temple in Hokkaido.

The doll was supposedly bought in 1918 by the older brother of three-year-old Okiku Suzuki. The girl loved the doll and played with it daily until she died suddenly of a cold a year later. Her mourning family placed the doll into the household altar and prayed to it in her memory. As time passed, the family realized that the doll's hair had begun to grow. Bewildered, the family took it as a sign that the girl's spirit had taken refuge in the body of the little doll.

> *Oyome ni irashita neesama ni,*
> *Yoku nita kanjo no shiroi kao.*

VI.

Every time I reached the end of the hallway, the light of my parent's room would cast a white glow on the fabric of my yukata, covered in butterflies and flower petals of all colors. All colors, because a 7-year-old would like that.

As I turned to face their doorway, the light would shine in my eyes, I would see their quilted comforter, and then, only for a moment, I was back in reality. I would catch my mother's glance at me before I swung my arms around with me, my long sleeve covering my face, and I was gone again.

All in a split second, back into the forest, running from a monster that had no name in any language. The white walls on either side of me growing and changing into something more. I ran only to be a heroine. I didn't know the objective of the mission that I had to complete, but I knew that running was the only way to keep the mission going. It was just a monster, a scary thought for a Japanese princess to run from, her arms thrown behind her, stiff and straight like a ninja.

> *Kin no byoubu ni utsuru hi o*
> *Kasuka ni yusuru haru no kaze.*

VII.

"Am I beautiful?"

Before you can answer, she will rip off her mask and ask if she is beautiful now.

"You have seen!" she will say.

You must answer quickly.

If you say she is beautiful, she will take the scissors from her sleeve and cut your mouth from ear to ear, like hers. If you say no, she will cut off your head. If you run, she will track you down.

This is the urban legend that my mother knew, and all of Japan was talking about. Unbeknownst to my mother, a woman chasing her children out of the street was hit by a car, causing her to have her mouth slit open, leading to the resurgence of the myth.

My mother walked home in groups with her friends after volleyball practice, scared even more by the fact that it was winter, and many people wore white surgical masks. The group ran home, the wind cutting at their faces; the Kuchisake ona is not just myth, but also a possibility.

Sukoshi shirozake mesaretaka?
Akai o kao no udaijin.

VIII.

Summer is the season for ghosts in Japan; they come back during the summer festivals and roam the streets more often than at any other time in the year. And this summer as I visit my Japanese family, I hold going to the bathroom at night, and I do not wander the dark parts of the house alone. I listen closely to the creaks and groans of a house settling instead of sleeping, and see the supernatural in everything.

I watch the television, and it scares me with paranormal shows and ancient depictions of spirits. Pictures go across the screen and forever etch themselves into my memory. I do not remember the stories behind those images, but I know they frighten me. I celebrate my birthday in Japan and return to America, leaving behind all the ghosts with it. I am in the U.S. now, and the rules of the Japanese no longer apply.

All except one: At night the bathroom remains off limits.
Kimono o kikaete, obi shimete,
Kyou wa watashi mo hare sugata.

IX.

The Suzuki family gave the doll to the Mannenji temple because they had to move to Sakhalin, and it stays in the temple, its hair being cut occasionally, short, like mine was. A scientific study was supposedly conducted, and it concluded that the hair was that of a young girl. Some say the expressions of Okiku-chan change, she shifts positions, she blinks and she smiles. Others say it's a trick of the eye, but my mother still feels uncomfortable talking about it, and wished back then that my father wouldn't make such creepy comparisons.

My father retaliated by saying that it was creepy that a 2-year-old knew the song of the girl's day festival by heart. He said it was a rather haunting song to start with. My mother didn't and still doesn't understand what he means by that, but the lyrics, he says, are just haunting.

I have long since forgotten that song, and I have long since ceased to look like the doll of a little girl. I am 15, and however much I would like to remember my short time in Japan, I can't; memories I don't have haunt me.

My mother, however, can recall her childhood in Japan. She remembers the girl's day festival and how her friend in elementary school had once claimed to have seen the doll of Okiku-chan in person. She remembers the Kuchisake ona and tales of the ghost of the girl in the last stall of the girl's bathroom, and tells them to my father and me. My father laughs and tells her that a haunted toilet is silly, and she smacks him and tells him that it's not funny and that bathrooms in the Japanese culture are scary, toilets especially. She looks to me for confirmation.

"He's an American, right, Emi? He does not know!"

My father laughs again, and I sit, looking at both of them, unsure of which world I stand in.

Haru no yayoi no kono yoki ni,
Nani yori ureshii Hina Masturi.

Emily Green is from Chesterfield, Virginia, and attributes her love of writing to her father's passion for the subject. Growing up in a multicultural family helped her appreciate the value of language. She hopes to teach English in Japan or become a translator.

10:23 Tuesday

Morgan McManus, 16
Charlotte Christian School, Charlotte, NC, **Jessica Ramsey,** Teacher

An incoherent scream pierces the silence—the epitome of suffering. The sound chills me to the bone; I exhale loudly, heavily, as my heart rips. A tremor rocks my body, and I arch my spine, bringing my head to my knees, face buried in my hands.

It cannot be.

No, no, no...

The world is a menagerie of sorrow. And we have become a part of it.

I'm only a few steps out of the locker room, and Kayla's already crying. At first I think she's laughing; in a few seconds, I realize this is not so.

This was odd. For the past two days, the sight of this girl annoyed me. She didn't know how to shut up; the sound of her voice was obnoxious, it was loud, and when it wasn't obnoxious and loud, her giggling was (for this reason, I was glad to have persuaded Allie to bunk next to me; Heaven forbid I spend my week trying to sleep with Chatterbox—inevitably running her mouth—two inches away). But this was different. With her face flushed, the lips that were usually pulled into an aggravatingly large smile had curled into a frown. Tears gushed over her cheeks. Suddenly, I didn't care about how aggravating she'd been. Even Kayla deserved to be comforted; somehow, there was compassion left in me yet.

How *utterly* hypocritical.

In a few steps, I've crossed the gym. In these moments, I assume nothing's really wrong—so someone must've insulted her. Okay, that person's a jerk, people say mean things, I'm sorry (but you might've deserved it). What could possibly be so serious?

No, it's far worse than that.

"Ian Webb," she manages between sobs, "has been hit by a four-wheeler."

I search my memory for his face. *Ian Webb? Ian, Ian, Ian...oh!*

The kid whose name I can never remember...

The image of a body flying after being struck by a vehicle appears in my mind. I quickly shove it away.

"What?" I stutter. It was almost 11 at night and storming violently outside. Who in their right mind would be out there? *Impossible.*

The Parey twins, who stand on either side of me, prove equally dumbfounded. "What do you mean?" Allie finally asks.

"There were a bunch of kids lying down out there," Kayla gulps. "And Mr. Kevin didn't see Ian...and, oh God, my sister saw it." In a fit of crying, she crumples onto her blow-up mattress.

I can't think. *This is a mission trip.* Things like this don't happen on mission trips. They just *don't.*

At a loss, my eyes wander about the gym. There are so many obliviously smiling faces; this sickens me. Darkness shrouds the complexions of the girls who know. They stand in tightly knit circles, telling their friends the same news I've just heard.

Suddenly, words come to my mouth. "I'm sure he's fine," I say in a voice that reassures even me. "You hear about these things happening. If his muscles were relaxed, maybe nothing serious happened."

Kayla nods with a whimper. "It's just, if anything happened to him, church wouldn't be the same. Oh, God, Ian..."

I offer Kayla a hug, and after promising I'll be right back, I slip into the main corridor. Almost instantly, my eyes are greeted by the sight of people praying in groups. They have seen, or they know someone who has. Staff move anxiously about the hallway; their blank faces offer me nothing, so I edge toward the front doors— something they prove too busy to notice.

Blue and red light colors the raindrops clinging to the windows. It reflects off the pavement, becoming a wildly uncoordinated collage, one that would fascinate me in other circumstances. For now, my line of sight rests on the police officers. Even as thunder rocks the building, their faces are eerily still, so still that they could be ghosts. It wouldn't surprise me. Tonight, the heavens are angry.

I sit on a bench, pretending to pray—I figure this way the staff won't shoo me out, so as to not interrupt piety. This works no longer than two minutes, and then I'm back in the gym again.

Singing and praying fills the facility. The information has spread like the plague; they *know*. All of them.

Tension hangs in the air. Eleven o'clock.

With a sigh, my eyes flit to Kayla; the Parey twins have distracted her enough to keep her from crying. Good. But I don't want to go back—I'm not ready to. I want to be anywhere but here. The singing and pleading and sobbing have me feeling claustrophobic; the sounds prove themselves impossibly stifling, and the walls close in without moving.

Lord, have mercy...

To my left, a group of girls discuss the accident, whispering, almost as if it were some big secret. I edge toward them.

"There was blood everywhere..."

Oh, God.

The emotion is oppressively heavy; I move back toward the double-doors, unable to take it, my nerves falling victim to the anxiety suffocating the room. I stick my head into the corridor, peeking both ways. The coast is clear; I hang a right past the vending machines and dart outside, curling against the glass of the door, so as not to disappear into the darkness. Lightning illuminates the sky, highlighting the back fence. I remember the graveyard on the other side of it and shudder, realizing the frailty of the situation. Like a small child, I pull my knees to my chin, eyes watching with dead awareness as the raindrops strike the sidewalk, thoughts far elsewhere while my mind reels. Distantly, I know my body's shivering—from fear or cold I'm not sure. But I am acutely cognizant of one thing: *powerlessness.*

"Let him be okay," I murmur. "Please, God, let Ian be okay."

I groan inwardly, fingers digging into the cloth of my sweatpants as the prayers spill from my lips. For once, I don't know what to say to Him—my disjunctive thoughts have silenced me. I ramble, knowing by instinct that I need to pray, that I should be praying, but the proper words remain out of reach. I am lost. And God feels so very, very distant.

Lord, I feel so helpless...help me, help us all.

"Or, if it is Your will, don't let it be too bad..."

And help Kayla to be okay. God, I can't watch this...let me bear her burden. Or part of it. Or...

Something.

The door cracks open behind me.

"Morgan."

I turn my head and look over my shoulder; it's Emily. *Please don't make me go back there.*

"You need to go back inside."

For a moment, I want to shake my head, but I willingly submit, knowing tonight is not the night to make trouble. Emily offers me a small smile—a contradiction to her emotionally drained physique—and disappears after I'm through the doors.

I pause for a moment and sigh, eyes scanning the empty hallway. Thunder rumbles.

Lord, give me strength.

My hands push the gym doors open. "How Great Is Our God" crosses the threshold and ruminates in my ears.

How *sickening,* a beautiful song trying to chase out a greater darkness. It is a disgusting paradox—the complete opposite of this disconsolate mood—as if those singing wanted to believe that everything was okay, that nothing had happened. As if they had the gall to manipulate the somber ambience of the room.

…like cramming broken puzzle pieces together, trying but failing to make them fit.

The sound fades to aggravating white noise as I switch my focus back to Kayla. She doesn't have to say anything for me to recognize her increased angst. I sit directly across from her and peer into her eyes; pools of terror stare back at me.

"Kayla…?"

"I need to get out of here…" she breathes, fingers running through her fawn-colored hair. "I need to get out of here, I need to make sure Ian's okay."

I exhale, momentarily at a loss. "I know. I'm sure they'll tell us something soon."

She shakes her head and groans. "It's just, the Webbs are close family friends, and I've known Ian for a long time…and…I just need to know." A lone tear trickles down her cheek—she's fighting it.

God, what do I do now?

Suddenly, I get an idea. Considering the circumstances, I almost think it's mundane. But it's *something.*

"C'mon—are you hungry? I'll get you something out of the

machine." She stares at me blankly as I reach into my suitcase for my wallet. "You know, they say chocolate releases endorphins...endorphins make you happy. I mean, really. And you don't have to get chocolate! I'll get you anything you want."

"But are we allowed to go out there?"

I sigh, and suddenly, she understands. Kayla jumps to her feet and follows me into the hallway, willingly purchasing a Hershey bar with my dollar before settling into the crevice built into the wall. Her eyes scrutinize the corridor, looking for a sign—for something, anything—yet all is still. Even the storm seems to have moved off.

Kayla gazes half-heartedly at the immense pools of water sitting on the tile floor. "I'm so glad I didn't kiss him..." she mumbles, softly popping a square of chocolate into her mouth.

I furrow my eyebrows. "What?"

"Yeah, he asked me to—we were coming back from a party. And I wanted to...I just didn't. I couldn't ruin our friendship like that."

I say nothing, unsure of where her musing's headed.

She continues. "The last time I saw him—we were in the Dock—he checked to see that no one was around, and then he gave me the biggest bear hug." Kayla smiles. "The funny thing is, I wasn't sarcastic to him all day, and I'm always sarcastic to him. I'm so happy I did that."

As if God was letting her say goodbye...

The thought lingers in my mind. "I'm sure everything will be okay," I reply, very careful to substitute 'Ian' with 'everything'—I have not told her about the blood. And I cannot lie to her now. She is motionless for a moment before finally nodding, but it is a mystery as to whether she believes me. I want to change the subject—to make her smile again.

"Do you want anything else?"

Kayla shakes her head, holding up what's left of the Hershey bar. And then she says something that shocks me.

"You're a good friend, Morgan."

If only you had known what I thought of you earlier.

My mouth falls into an O; I recover quickly and hug her. "You don't deserve to be alone."

Tears begin to roll down her cheeks; she tries to dismiss them, smearing them with the back of her hands before backing from my embrace, a short laugh being emitted from her mouth.

"It's okay to cry," I say, my tone hushed, soothing.

She sighs heavily. "But I have to be strong for my sister." Her eyes desperately peer into mine. "What am I supposed to tell her?"

I cover my mouth with my palm, unsure of what to say. My lips draw into a line; I remain mute a moment longer before finally speaking. "Only God knows the answer to that."

Sniffling, Kayla gets up suddenly and grabs a rag, joining Sam— who has just worked his way up the hallway—on the floor, taking her frustration out on the puddles. I mimic her. We work rhythmically, silently, all the while pounding our weary hands against the tile; in no time, the water is gone. The anxiety remains.

Twelve o'clock—midnight.

Kayla mumbles a quick greeting to Sam before turning back to me; her blue eyes have faded to empty shells of color.

Why haven't they told us anything yet? It's been—almost—two hellish hours; people deserve to know.

"I hate that they're singing," she groans quietly, referring to the choir that has formed in the gymnasium.

"So do I."

They're treating it like he's dead already.

Shaking her head, Kayla takes a step toward the door, peering back at me before entering. "I...I need to go check on my sister. I'll see you later."

I nod, and she disappears; while my back was turned, Sam had sauntered upstairs. I am left alone, exhausted and angry, feeling as if my own emotion has weakened me. Who knows—it probably *has*. In these moments, I am nothing but hormones—upset, but respectably so.

With my feet lifeless beneath me, I shuffle back into the gym and head to my mattress. The Pareys sit next to me; Allie stares at the wall in the backdrop. Becca smiles, inquires about Kayla and then falls unusually quiet before babbling to someone else.

Christi's voice breaks over the intercom. *Finally.*

"Ladies." She sounds weak. "I need you to all move to the back half of the gym. Pick up your stuff, please make sure you're dressed modestly—the guys are coming in."

Her statement further frays my agitated nerves. *Dress code—*

really? You're worried about that? And then my stomach knots; the realization of what has—inevitably—happened seeps into the corners of my being.

Oh...no, this can't be good.

I look to Allie. "Something bad must've happened."

Her lips gape for a moment.

"They wouldn't put us together like this for any other reason."

The fear begins to bubble in my stomach as the boys file in and take a seat. Our pastor appears from nowhere, and my gut hits the floor. No one has to tell me what's happened. I know...

...And yet I hope to God I'm wrong anyways.

No one makes a sound; the tension is unbearable. Dr. Moss takes the microphone, lifts it to his lips, hands quivering. His eyes droop like raindrops.

"I'm sorry to tell you this..."

Don't say it...

The word "died" hits us like a sledgehammer as it leaves his tongue.

An incoherent scream pierces the silence—the epitome of suffering. The sound chills me to the bone; I exhale loudly, heavily, as my heart rips. A tremor rocks my body, and I arch my spine, bringing my head to my knees, face buried in my hands.

It cannot be.

No, no, no...

The world is a menagerie of sorrow. And we have become a part of it.

Tears spill down my cheeks.

But you couldn't even remember his name...

My heart aches. Shrieks. Not just for Ian—the stranger I knew—but for everyone else. The ones suffering who don't deserve this.

Time becomes irrelevant, and I wander blindly, vanishing into the bathroom, staring into a mirror and at my own eyes as if I was peering into the eyes of God.

As if I was asking Him the Question.

{Sixteen hours later}

The flag flies at half-mast as I cross the parking lot of the church. My heart weighs heavy in my chest, seemingly adding a hundred pounds to my body as I step across the asphalt, slowing me down. Having never been in this situation before, I don black out of respect. I know nothing else.

The sanctuary is full when I walk in, but the noise level rests only at a whisper as the debriefing and remembrance ceremony begins (for this is not a funeral).

Nothing could be done, or so we are told.

And then, we begin to sing. It is the same as last night—but now the most beautiful sound in the world. The church swells with music.

The mission trip continues. In memory of Ian.

Written in memory of E.W.—the kid whose name I always confused with Hunter, who sat in the back of my Sunday school class, and who played football. I only knew your face. And yet you changed my life. Thank you.

Morgan McManus hails from Matthews, North Carolina. She wrote this memoir as both emotional release and a tribute; few things soak up her emotions better than ink on a blank piece of paper. She is considering studying journalism or law.

Blueberry Whispers

Johanna Bear, 13
Lamberton Middle School, Carlisle, PA, **Jason Griffith,** Teacher

My great-grandmother is dying. The hopelessness is in the wrinkles that have formed over the years, surrounding her deep-set eyes. She has given up the hope that the rest of my family seems to have, the hope that she will live to see another Maine winter, with sparkling, glistening beds of fluffy white snow, and beautiful cardinals hopping about, making slight indentations as they flit across the landscape, their deep-red coats a gorgeous contrast in a white world of snow. But I see in the shake of her hands, trembling under the weight of the expectations of our family, that she knows what I know, that her days in this world are numbered, and that winter is too far away. She won't make it to fall.

My mother sits on a chair next to Great Granny's seat, holding one of her shaking hands, talking gently and telling her that all is well. What lies. My dad sits on Granny's other side, looking happy and engaging, supporting everything Mom says. I sit alone, hunched in the corner with Granny's ancient cat beside me, my eyes reflecting a sadness running deep in my veins. The more I stare at Granny, however, the more that sadness becomes an anger. After a few mere seconds, my heart is pulsing with this anger, blaming Granny for what her daughters have done to me, to all of us, blaming her for being old, and blaming her for sitting there, while my world crumbles around me.

At last, after many long minutes of a staring contest between my burning eyes, full of anger and tinted with guilt, and her deep ones, staring back, emotionless and desolate, and maybe even scared, it is time for us to leave. I get up with a sigh of relief, glad to be leaving this prison. No longer would I be trapped by those eyes that said, "You, child, out of everyone else, you know, you know my life is ending, tell them, help me." But I could not help Granny. I am a child, she, an old lady, on opposite ends of the spectrum, but each begging the other through our eyes. Mine, begging for her to change the drastic decision her daughters have made that will change my life in all the wrong ways. Hers, begging for either peace, or death, whichever comes her way first, begging me to make the family understand that it's hopeless, to give up the fight. But I am just a child, and no one ever listens to a child, even when the child knows best.

During the car ride home, my mind floats to the house, my house, my sanctuary, and my life away from home, Yellow Shutters, the reason that my anger at Granny exploded. Her daughters, my great-aunts, decided that Granny needed money to support her in her decline, for health care, and to pay the nursing home. They sold my place, my friend, the house where I have gone every summer that I could remember, the cottage of dreams, hopes, crystal-clear water, and blueberry bushes, intertwined with the beautiful mossy trees that led down to the wooden dock, bouncing along the gentle waves.

Now, every night I spend with the sweet, salt-tinged smell in my nose, cuddling against the cold in the warm blue blankets around me feels like an absurd luxury. My mind wanders, wondering how many more nights I will have here before it gets taken away, just as Great Granny will inevitably be. Another friend who is abandoning me. I feel the gentle quaking of the old cottage, almost as if it were turning in its sleep alongside me, mimicking my movements, as though trying to reassure me that everything would work out. The truth though, is in my mind. The cold, hard, unforgiving facts that can never tell a lie, the facts that say that the end is coming. The "for sale" sign is being manufactured, and a realtor will come, treating this magical place as just another job, when it deserves so much more. It deserves owners who know how to preserve its forest of trees, and the fairy houses that I had created all those years ago.

I almost wished I could join the fairies in those miniature houses, to escape from the conversations everyone thinks I cannot hear. The talks of moving, selling, tearing down and renting. Stripping the cottage of its owners and all the beauty and memories it once represented. They talk in low whispers, believing I have drifted into sleep, but I lie awake, trying to shut out the words from my ears, trying to believe it isn't happening. Trying to keep the gullibility and innocence of childhood, when I know I must grow up to deal with this problem. A problem I have no control over, because who listens to the child? Nobody. Not even when the child knows best.

The day is coming, the salty air whispers, as it caresses my ears gently, more gently than the truth. The day is coming, murmur the blueberry bushes, chuckling at the blue stains on my face, but there is no humor at this prospect. Leaving. Be ready, sing the waves, dancing over my toes as lightly as the prancing of a doe in the forest. I'll always be here for you, sighs the cottage, shifting, as though trying to move closer to me in spirit. It cannot though. It is permanently entrenched in my heart.

Yellow Shutters is, and always will be, my proverbial happy place. Untouched by time, by progress, and by economy. Timeless and strong, standing there for me in times of need. A connection stronger than any other. Love. Binding and free. The one place where I can come to be heard, the one place, the one thing that listens to a child. A desperate child, in need of a hug. Who knew blueberry bushes could hug so well? I knew. They were my friends. Who knew how beautiful the songs of the waves were? I knew. They taught me to dance. Who knew that a house could carry such an emotional bond with a child? I knew. I knew because it did. And still does. Goodbye, Yellow Shutters. I'll see you in my dreams. Always.

Johanna Bear lives in Carlisle, Pennsylvania, where ballet keeps her mentally loose and natural, which carries into her writing. Rather than choosing the craft, writing chose her—she began writing to deal with the emotional turbulence surrounding her grandmother's passing during her childhood.

Final Apology

Claudia Fang, 16
Hunter College High School, New York, NY, **Kip Zegers,** Teacher

[I could have gone back, but I was afraid.]
Once, I watched a bird die.

It was a dark little crow, perched delicately on a thin laundry clothesline that hung high above the pebbled ground below. It was ruffling its feathers as the soft summer wind swept under white sheets and a pink silk dress. I thought it had looked like some kind of hopeless romantic. I thought it had looked all worn around the edges, like a frayed black ribbon pulled too taut too many times. Its head was cocked curiously as it opened its beak and let out a shrill trill, the notes brittle and tremulous. Then it gently rearranged its wings, tucking them in carefully, and shivered, as if the thin morning breeze was seeping into its feathers and dancing through its fragile ribcage. It leaned forward, just a little black blot of ink splattered against a backdrop of dull purples and rosy pinks tinting the sky. I was tired and sweaty, sitting on the curb in a lonely little village in China watching dust dance in streams of sunlight, when the crow teetered *ever so slightly*, and plummeted through the air, landing with a little *poof* on hard stone. It didn't move.

I scrabbled to my feet, startled. The bird was a mess of rumpled feathers on the ground. I was frightened by that, and darted through a little alley until I reached my grandfather's house, a dusty little nook with cracked wooden walls and kitchen lights that didn't work.

I didn't look back.

* * *

[Is it too late to apologize?]
You died when you were 10 years old. Teetering on the edge of 11.

I'm sorry I didn't say goodbye, but I loved you too much, and I was mad. I'm sorry that I was grateful that they shipped your ashes back to China so I wouldn't have to see you. I'm sorry, but I've come this time, to *try* to make things right.

You're buried on the side of a mountain, a rugged little one that tilts a bit to the left, and that's home to some very thirsty mosquitos.

Now, carefully treading down the crumbling steps carved into the side of the mountain, I think about that pretty little crow, about why it might have killed itself when it could have gone anywhere, could have flown through the wispy bodies of clouds if it wanted to. I wonder why it didn't open its wings. I brush aside thick branches and think harshly, *maybe it didn't die. Maybe it wanted to see what it was like to fall just once, wanted to feel the warmth of the ground against its cheek just* once. I'm broken out of my reverie when my ankle twists a bit and I almost trip myself. I think that you would have found that hilarious: me, falling down the side of a mountain. The dragonflies float lazily near daffodils that struggle up from under some of the gravestones, their wings beating a thin symphony against the humid air. I finally find your stone; it's tucked away behind a looming tree that has shed its leaves onto your grave. I sweep off the dirt and let out a breathless laugh, although nothing's funny.

You know I'm like that.

I set up a metal bowl, placing some Chinese yuen into it, and light it up with a match. The inside of the bowl bursts into flames and I watch for a while as the paper money turns to ash. The smoke wafts up lazily, slowly dissipating as it intertwines around the branches of a thick maple tree. The sun blooms a little bit from behind the edge of the mountain, and thin golden strands start to unravel across the sky. It was supposed to rain. But the clouds have been chased away, and I feel a little more confident, standing in front of your grave like this, dirtied and sweaty and a wreck. Then I take a square of blue paper—your favorite shade of blue—and write.

Talking is hard for me.

But you know that already.

So I'll write.

* * *

[Because it shouldn't have gone like this—]

The hospital room is a quiet little space with polished floorboards that sometimes creak when stepped on. The dregs of afternoon sunlight filter in through the window shades, and I breathe in and let the warmth seep into my lungs. You're sitting by the window, fingers chasing the shadows that flicker occasionally across the bedspread. A little halo of dust dances around the tufts of your hair; it looks especially wispy and soft today, and I think that it looks a lot like the smooth sleek feathers of a raven. You tilt your head toward me, lips curling up into a sweet smile as you push yourself up against the pillows. I take a seat beside the bed and you press a milky-white hand against mine. I lean forward and wrap my arms around you; you smell like lilacs and crisp innocence. You giggle into my embrace, and my throat clenches. Your hair tickles the bottom of my chin as you rest the crown of your head on my collarbone. I think you look real small, like I could fold you up and tuck you into my pocket if I really wanted to, think you look too fragile, like I could crumple you up if I really wanted to. Your eyelids flutter a little, and I stroke your cheek. You smile shyly up at my face, and say, "Haven't visited me in a long time." You pout a little, and I laugh, trailing my fingers up and down your wrist, thinking *too skinny, too skinny.*

There's something about your eyes that's always scared me, something about them that unhinges me, and makes my world career just a little off its axis. You look at me sometimes, in a way that makes me feel too warm and makes me wonder, *what are you thinking?* "I've been busy," I reply. "How's the chemotherapy?"

"Busy with what?" you interrupt, and I stiffen a little, because your tone is detached and your fingers are very cold.

"Busy with school," I reply, and I let you wear my mittens, because you love to curl your fingers inside them. You frown a little, but tilt your head away and both of us are silent for so long that I thought you had fallen asleep.

I'm just about to get up and leave when you mutter, "I'm lonely," and I get all tight-knuckled and tight-throated. I lean over you and let your breaths tickle my collarbone. Then you go and look at me like *that*—god, what does that look *mean*—and you tell *me,* "Don't be lonely. Even after I die." My breath leaves me in a rush, because, god, you're only 9, don't think like that, don't you *dare* think like that.

"John," I say quietly. You doesn't respond. Anger begins to thrum impatiently throughout my veins. "John," I repeat. You look at me, and tilt your head curiously, as if you don't understand why my voice is trembling, or why my fingers are tightening around the pools of fabric on the bed, and that makes me furious.

"John," you repeat. "That's an ordinary name. A lot of people have it. You'll find another John." You look down. "David says I'll die," you murmur softly, crying now, and I think of David, that little boy in the room down the hall from yours, who has Ewing's sarcoma. I try to get you to look at me, but you're fascinated by the pattern in my mittens, and I abruptly lift your head off my shoulder and lower you down on the pillows. You're startled, and your mouth parts a little as I shove the chair back and stand up.

"I've got to go," I say flatly, and you whimper a little. "I'll tell your mom to come see you." Your eyes catch mine, and the silence in the room is so thick it starts to suffocate me. I can't *breathe,* and maybe tomorrow I'll feel guilty, maybe tomorrow I'll feel horrible, but for now, all I can concentrate on is *getting out.*

Maybe you were still crying. I wish I could have wiped those tears away.

*   *   *

[*If only I had known—*]

I didn't visit again. Time whisked by, and soon I forgot about the little boy in that dusty hospital room with the little window and the groaning floorboards.

You died a year later. Broken snippets of your mother's voice through the telephone: *died...leukemia...wasn't...alone when he... talk to me?* No, I couldn't talk, could barely even breathe. I couldn't stop wondering what would have happened if I had stayed, had wiped away those hot tears, had stroked the soft curve of your cheek and folded your small hands, still wrapped in my mittens, between mine. I couldn't face you even after you died; in fact—*I'm sorry*—I was relieved when they told me you were going to be buried back in China beside your grandfather. I was 13 then, weakhearted and cowardly. I thought that you were never alone.

But being alone and being lonely are completely different things.

*   *   *

[*I would—*]

I think about that little black crow I saw all those years ago, on the ground with its feathers all rumpled and its head resting on a smooth gray pebble. I wondered, if I had gone back, would it have changed anything? Would it still be alive? Or had it already died? And then I think about you, *you* with your soft hair and shy smile.

Maybe you would have still died, but I shouldn't have left you like that. I couldn't stop regretting. The flames are dying down now, the sparks jumping erratically around the edges of faintly charred metal. I've finished writing, and start to fold the square of paper into a little origami crane. I pause after I'm done, and cough. "I—I'm sorry, you know," I start, feeling stupid, but I know my mother's talking just a few rows over to her own father, so I try to continue. I can't though, because my throat gets all funny and my hands twist themselves nervously, so finally, I just toss the crane into the flames and watch the fire eat it up. Wisps of white smoke curl up from the wings, and I watch them drift up into the sky until they've completely faded away.

I brush the dirt off my knees, caress the side of your gravestone, and walk away, taking a seat on the steps of the mountain and watch as the sun slips languidly behind the mountain.

Claudia Fang is from Little Neck, New York, where she enjoys drawing, painting and piano, different ways of expressing emotion. She uses writing as a means of releasing tension; this piece helped provide feelings of closure about the death of a close relative.

Bing

Kristina Hu, 16

Thomas Jefferson High School, Alexandria, VA, **Jennifer Seavey,** Teacher

My grandmother kneads the dough between her knuckles. Dipping her fingers into the flour pot, she releases a pinch of powder onto the board, spreading the particles in an outward motion with her fingers. The making of Bing, or traditional Chinese pancakes, is an art that combines gentle handling with strength and firmness of touch, a rhythmic application of pressure that permits the dough to rise with just the right consistency.

"Six and six?"

"...is 36!" I shout, grinning so Wai Po can see all of my teeth. Wai Po laughs and wraps me in a hug real gentle but firm too. Her jacket tickles my face. I don't know why she wears a jacket, because it's summer and it's sunny and it's hot outside. She smells like sesame and flour, my favorite smells in the world.

I'm five today, but in two weeks, I'm going to be a kindergartener, all grown up. Virginia is so big. We moved here one month ago because Old House was too small. The New House has so many rooms, I get lost sometimes. But Wai Po always finds me. It's okay then.

Wai Po's helping me learn my times tables so I'll be the smartest kid in class. I'm sitting on her lap, and we're on the back porch because it's nice outside. She helps me a lot. I call her Wai Po, but everyone else calls her Grandma. That's because everyone else doesn't know Chinese. Only Mommy and Daddy and baby brother and me. Wai Po doesn't understand English, so I only speak to her in Mandarin. I even know my numbers in Mandarin.

"Never give up," Wai Po says. "Study hard, and one day you'll succeed. Wai Gong would be proud. Do you remember Wai Gong?"

I nod. Wai Gong is what we call Grandpa, but he died a year ago, when we all lived in Maryland together. I count on my fingers: one, two, three, four, five, six: Mommy, Daddy, baby brother, me, Wai Po and Wai Gong. Wait, no more Wai Gong. Six minus one equals five. I think Wai Po still misses him on the inside, but she never shows it.

"Wai Po?" I ask.

"Yes?"

"Are you still sad?"

Wai Po smiles and hugs me tight. "Of course not, Bao Ber. Stop asking such silly questions."

We keep learning times tables until dinnertime.

Dinner is always very yummy. The table is always filled with tofu, spicy beef and what Mommy calls "seasoned tilapia stew." But none of them are as good as Wai Po's special Bing. Wai Po's the best at making Bing. Sometimes, when Wai Po's not looking, baby brother and I eat the crispies right off the pancake when it's frying. I have to be careful not to get burned, but it's so good I can't help it.

Sometimes we try to help Wai Po make Bing, but we're too skinny and little. When she lets us knead the dough, our arms get tired fast. Wai Po says we're applying too much pressure. I don't know what pressure means, but Wai Po says we should be gentle sometimes too. "Be both gentle and firm," she says, "and the dough will be perfect to the touch."

"Watch," she says to me in Chinese. I peer over her shoulder, observing her transform the round dough into the shape of a rope. She stretches it out to twice its length like a rubber band, each time bringing the ends together again, restoring it to its original length. I notice that the dough rope never gets any longer or shorter.

"Why do you stretch it like that, Wai Po?"

"To exercise it," she replies, maintaining her focus on the dough. Though her hair is streaked with gray and the shine in her eyes faded, I marvel at the strength of her still-supple arms. I cannot believe she is almost 75 years old. I imagine that decades from now, I, too, will shrink to her short stature, and my own existence will someday vanish like dust into thin air.

Soft lips. Square-rimmed glasses. Stern eyes, and a smile rivaling that of La Gioconda. I remember little about my grandfather apart from what I've seen in photographs, but from what I have heard, he was a good man and a rocket scientist. Together, he and my grandmother lived through the second Sino-Japanese war, the U.S.-Soviet space race, and the rise and fall of the Cultural Revolution. But after years of radiation poisoning ate away at his health, my grandfather developed a vicious cancer that, in less than five years, left him dead.

That spring of 1999, my grandmother lost one of the last members of her generation—and one of her last friends. To my brother and me, he simply vanished from our lives, taking his smile with him to the grave. But to Wai Po, he was her final reminder of home and everything she had loved and grown to trust. I could feel a sense of loneliness surrounding her.

My parents knew it, and my brother and I knew it also. She did not like living here. Her emotions filled her entire bedroom, which she kept meticulously tidy, as if she wanted to erase any evidence of her existence there. The American town we lived in was too large, too isolated and too lonely, with its single-family residences and picket fences. She yearned for the bustling streets of Beijing, where neon lights spanned the cityscape, and strangers by the thousands gathered on the streets to dance at night.

Sometimes when I came home from school, I would find her sitting on her bed, letters and photographs strewn around her, faded at the edges with wear. *From the People's Republic of China,* the envelopes all said, in sprawling, beautiful penmanship. She would then don her reading glasses, read the letter within, and pause to chuckle at some distant memory.

As I crept up the stairs, I was often unsure whether or not to disturb her reverie. So much of me wanted to learn about the world she left behind for the sake of my mother's family, and I often found myself heading toward her room. The scenario in my head was perfect: I would walk in, embrace her in a hug, and ask her everything I wanted to know about her past and Wai Gong.

But it was an impossible dream. My Chinese was worsening. Living in the U.S. under a rigorous academic schedule left little time to study Mandarin, which I now considered as foreign a language as Spanish or Portuguese. In the end, I was never brave enough to broach that conversation with her, instead heading to my room every afternoon to begin my homework. I figured if I couldn't make her happy one way, I would instead try my best to please her otherwise.

At the very least, I could make her proud.

My grandmother finishes stretching the dough. Keeping her thumb on one end, she arranges the rest so that it wraps around the center, spiraling outward. She pauses every few seconds to drizzle oil and seasoning across its surface, creating the foundations for flaky layers that would later melt on my tongue. After patting the dough into its final form, she sets it aside in a bowl to rest.

This last step is crucial. The dough, if not allowed several hours to breathe, comes out of the pan tough and, ultimately, inedible.

My grandmother moved back to China a few years later, homesick but hopeful. "She needs time to breathe," I told myself, saddened by her farewell, "but so do we." Suddenly, my family could fit into one family car, and it was just the four of us sitting at one dinner table, sharing stories about work and school and America, a country Wai Po simply hadn't gotten used to. Her duty to her daughter's family was over, anyhow: My brother and I both knew our times tables by heart, and we were well on our way to becoming independent young people.

One day, we received a phone call. The number was from the People's Republic of China.

"How are you two doing? I miss you both so much!" my grandmother asked, delighted to hear our voices.

"Great, great," I responded in grammatically incorrect Mandarin. "Stay healthy, Wai Po?"

"Of course!" she replied. "The streets are busy, and the city is full of delicious food." At the mention of food, my brother and I perked up, pleading for her return and her Bing.

"Be patient, little ones," she promised, though we were far from little. "One day."

Silence filled the space between us. We had little left in common, and little left to say.

"Wai Po?" I asked.

"Yes?"

"...Are you happy?"

My grandmother paused.

"Absolutely," she said. "Did I tell you I remarried? You should call your new grandfather *Li Bo Bo*. Oh, he's home right now. I can get him here to speak to you. *GUO LAI!*" she yelled over her shoulder, summoning her new husband to the phone.

My heart sank. It couldn't be true. No man could replace the hole my former grandfather, Wai Gong, left in my grandmother's heart. My head began to swim. I closed my eyes, breaths coming in short, hard gasps. I enter a memory.

The year is 1998. Wai Gong and Wai Po stand by my side, taking in the Maryland woods. The sky broods gray and smells of rain, and the three of us walk homeward bound, when "home" for my grandmother was still in America. Thunder: the ground resonates and it begins to pour. We begin to run. At barely four feet tall, I take three steps to match one of theirs. But I am not afraid. At that moment, my two favorite grandparents in the world hold each of my hands. I grin at Wai Po so she can see all my teeth. She smells like sesame and flour, my favorite smells in the world.

Time spins forward, and I am trapped in another memory. Wai Po is gone, and Wai Gong is dead. My mother sits at my bedside, all color drained from her face. She looks just like him. "Your grandfather just passed away," she whispers in English, a cold hand on my lap. "Did it hurt him?" I asked. "Of course," she replied. "When his lungs started to fill with water, he—"

"Hello?"

My head stops spinning. I open my eyes. My new grandfather is on the other line.

I force myself to answer him with courtesy. I know better than to question my grandmother's motives. After all, I'm sure it is possible to die of a broken heart. Wai Po almost did. With little immediate family remaining, I can't imagine what she would have to endure in a transforming China, alone.

The pungent aroma of ginger accents the air. My grandmother sweeps the slices with the sheen of her blade to a corner of her cutting board, neighboring a few cloves of garlic, a stalk of green onion, a handful of chives and a bowl of ground beef. Within minutes, all of the vegetables are diced and sliced. Soon, they will be blended with the meat to create Bing filling.

"Can I taste some?" I ask, pointing over her shoulder at the ginger root. *"You sure can,"* she says, proceeding to stir the beef with her chopsticks. *I sneak a sliver from the board and place it on my tongue, but recoil instantly from the bitter sting.*

My grandmother divorced her new husband not more than a year later.

Upon hearing the bitter news, I silently cursed myself for ever harboring ill will toward Li Bo Bo, but there was little time for reflection. Within a few months, Wai Po would be returning to the United States to live with us again, since living in China would be meaningless with no family. On the day of her arrival, I prepared her bedroom, which was still prim and neat as she had left it, installing new shower curtains and emptying the closet of the junk that had accumulated there over the years.

This was my chance to begin anew—to make her feel welcomed in the United States as the last of her remaining family. No doubt she would be proud of how tall my brother and I had grown, and of all of the academic success we had achieved in recent years. And of course, she would make us Bing.

"It tastes horrible!" I cry, stomach lurching, as if to quell a gag.
"The proper filling needs all different sorts of flavors," she reasoned, sprinkling the vegetables one by one into the bowl of blended meat. I watch as the swirl of her chopsticks pulls each sliver of onion and garlic into the beefy, aromatic abyss.
"After all, a little bit of bitterness keeps the taste fresh."

One Monday, I got home unusually early. Rushing into the house at 5 p.m., I unloaded my 30-pound backpack onto the floor only to find the house completely unlit. Apart from the idle hum of a television talk show from my grandmother's bedroom, it seemed as if no one had lived here for a long time. I let my car keys clatter to the countertop. Against silence, the sound was earth-shattering.

"Wai Po!" I called out. "I'm home!"

No response.

I knew that her right ear had grown deaf over the years, and perhaps she simply hadn't heard me. I switched on the lights, glancing around.

Several unwashed dishes and pans lay faceup in the sink, foodstuffs floating in soapy water. This was unusual—my grandmother always washed the dishes and did the chores in her ample spare time, though almost always against our will. My heartbeat quickened.

"Wai Po!" I yelled, rushing into her bedroom.

I found my grandmother snoozing contently in an armchair with a photo album open in her lap. The year is marked as 1998. My baby pictures, next to a faded photograph of the three of us—Wai Gong, Wai Po and I, linking hands and walking home under a slate-gray sky, when home for my grandmother was still America. I realized then that it never was and never would be. Across the room, the television screen blared with the drama of an American soap opera she clearly couldn't have been watching. My spirits sank.

"Wai Po," I pleaded, attempting to shake her awake. I buried my face in her shoulder and began to heave a sob. I am her little Bao Ber. She smells like sesame and flour—my favorite smells in the world. A tear fell onto the photograph in her lap, its damp mark permeating outwards in the faded ink. Rain. At that moment, I realized how much I wanted to make her happy. I wanted to bring my grandfather back to life and restore her familiar world, a place that now exists only in her dreams. But I couldn't do that. But there was something I could do.

"Wai Po," I repeated. Her eyelids lifted.

"Teach me," I began in halting Mandarin. "Teach me how to make Bing."

Kristina Hu is from Vienna, Virginia, where she engages in scientific research and regularly updates her YouTube channel, TheUnsungHeroine, which showcases her piano and vocal renditions of popular songs. She is considering applied mathematics, economics or pre-med at Harvard University.

Fourteen Months on the Home Front

Michaela Coplen, 16

Carlisle Area High School, Carlisle, PA, **Matthew Fahnestock and Susan Biondo-Hench,** Teachers

I'll tell you what it's like. Let's say you're 10 years old, and your mom ships out to a country that you can't find on the globe. She's gone for 14 months. The first six weeks are easy, comparatively. You miss your mom, but it's manageable. You two weren't particularly close anyway. "Six weeks down!" you say with a smile. It's not until about week seven that the paranoia kicks in. Every story in the news could be about her. Any letter in the mailbox could be a letter from her commander expressing his condolences. You're afraid to answer the door, because it might reveal two men whose faces are drawn in shades of red and gray. You used to love the sound of rain on the roof, but now the thunder scares you. Your dreaming hours are filled with hooded figures and trains. Time is one of those optical illusions, where the months ahead seem so much longer than the months behind, even though you know they're the same size.

After a couple of shrunken sweaters and pink-tinged shirts, you learn how to do your own laundry. You may burn your fingers a couple of times, but eventually you learn the art of the grilled cheese sandwich. You learn how to make your own doctor's appointments, and how the Internet can help with homework when your sister won't. You still hate the taste, but you learn to appreciate the way that coffee cures a bad night's sleep. You learn that patience is a lie invented by the apathetic and seldom rewarded. After a couple of failed attempts, you realize that the best way to evoke empathy is through honesty. You learn that the bonds of family and marriage are elastic, and can stretch only so far before they begin to tear. You learn that even Daddy makes mistakes sometimes.

You never mention any of this in your correspondence to your mom. In fact, you never mention it to anyone. Remember, you're 10 years old. It's your job to be sunny and happy and tell cheesy jokes and make everyone laugh so that they'll please just stop yelling at each other. You get really good at acting in front of a crowd. When you're alone in your room, you teach yourself to cry without making any noise.

For the first six months, you pray every night. It's not until month seven that you realize no one is listening.

You wonder why war exists. You can't fathom why a human being would seek to hurt another human being, to push a button or pull a trigger and kill without honor. At month eight you discover the horrible, selfish, animal blackness within your soul when you realize that you could care less who wins and who suffers and who is hurt and who dies, as long as your mom comes home.

By month nine you swear you will never join the army. You hate your mom for leaving you alone and you hate yourself for hating her. So you blame the army that has pulled you around like a marionette since before you were born. Your path was chosen for you, and you are helpless to change it. You can either adapt to this life, or end it.

You're too young to understand that this was the moment when you lost your innocence—you are no longer the carefree dandelion-gatherer you once were. You are no longer a child. Children don't consider death in lists of pros and cons.

You find little things to live for, like clocks ticking and flannel sheets and long runs and tea. As the months roll along, you do your best to keep your head down and persevere. You wait.

Finally, your mom comes home. You watch her plane land, as if the weight of your stare could steady its descent. The plane stops and soldiers file out, marching across the tarmac like a mobile forest. Then she appears, running toward you with arms outstretched. Tentatively, you let yourself believe it. She is really there, really real, and safe.

You think that this will solve everything. And it does, for a while. But rebuilding a family is hard, especially when the pieces are broken. Eventually, things seem to get better. Really, you're just better at compartmentalizing. The whole experience is walled off in a section of your mind with a sign that says, "Beware of Dogs." Sometimes the memories seep through the backs of your eyes—like when you revisit your old home, or watch that Hallmark commercial, or hear the national anthem. These moments are rare and quickly suppressed. Life demands stoicism.

You think you're doing fine, until years later you're lying awkwardly on a therapist's couch. All of a sudden you're crying again, because it's still so painful that the first person is too intimate, still so real that the past tense seems inappropriate. And you realize that no accomplishment, no dream or goal has defined you in the way that those 14 months did. You know that you will never be the same again. You have felt the way that loneliness gnaws and scratches inside your stomach, felt the hammer of heartache against your skull, and you will never forget. It seems so melodramatic that you're afraid to admit that it's true. But it is—every word.

Michaela Coplen is from Carlisle, Pennsylvania, where she acts, rides horses and plays soccer. As an actor, she believes the most natural form of expression is the spoken word; her writing process usually involves tape-recording monologues. She hopes to pursue musical theater and playwriting.

Poverty and Confliction

Brianne Sands, 17
Cab Calloway School of the Arts, Wilmington, DE, **Lisa Coburn,** Teacher

A chilling breeze combed through the black tangles of my hair. Pieces of sun rays broke through the clouds. While I sat outside my house, my worn book bag in hand, I examined the snow-heavy sky. I then picked at the soil embedded under my nails; I didn't want to go inside.

I was sure that my mother sat inside, slumped over sadly. She was probably gazing vacantly at the white plaster kitchen walls. Words like "unemployment" and "evicted again" and "no gas, no cable, and no Internet," probably echoed throughout the dark stretches of her mind. I knew she felt terribly guilty. I also knew she'd take her shame out on me. I braced myself, inhaled the crisp air deeply, and walked through the front door. I had stolen a glance at the sad woman, hunched over in the wicker chair.

Dark bags hung beneath her sunken eyes, and her aging body was sickly slender. Even her hair was brittle and graying. There once was a time when she was beautiful. She would outline her eyes in charcoal black, and stain her lips crimson. She would fix her hair so it flowed silken blond over her shoulders. But it was the Cheshire-cat smile that did it, that really made her radiant. There was laughter in her spirit, as she blasted the radio and sang along, off key, at the top of her lungs. Within minutes the whole house was filled with her infectious energy, and everyone was smiling.

But no one smiled anymore, and my mother certainly didn't sing. She lived in solitary depression. Her main philosophy was that the whole world was against her. Therefore she played her cards carefully, and deceived often. My mom liked to captivate men, then drain them for all they were worth. By batting her lashes our rent got paid. Anytime she had some money, you could be sure she had conned it out of someone. However, a charming smile and honey-sugar voice had only gotten her so far. Truth was our family lived dirt broke, and my mom was in constant anger because of it.

Sadly, I averted my gaze from her. "We'll have time to talk later," I thought to myself.

I closed the door to my room and hid beneath the warm covers on my bed. Tears were stinging in my throat. Normally after school, I came right home and did my homework assignments. My sole focus was on getting good grades, so I could create a better life for myself than what my mom had given me. However, seeing her like that, so sad day after day, was making it difficult to focus on school. Crystal droplets began spilling rapidly from my eyes. After hours of crying, I fell into a deep sleep.

Everything was shrouded in darkness once I awoke. In green numbers, my alarm clock read 3:16 a.m. Thirst parched my mouth, so I made my way down to the kitchen to get a drink.

As I entered, my gaze fixed on my mom, who was still sitting at the table. She blew a thick puff of cigarette smoke from her thin lips. In the kitchen, the lights were turned down dim, casting a soft orange glow over the room. Because it was so cold and our house didn't have heat, the stovetop burners were on at full blast. The flames unfolded like dancing, cobalt-blue flower petals. Each burner looked like a replica of the lotus flower tattooed on my mom's slender neck. She got it because it represented having the strength and willpower to overcome obstacles. In order for the beautiful lotus to have bloomed at the top of a pond, it must have first pushed through the mud-thick, murky water. The bud always emerged from depths completely pure and radiant. I wondered when my mom would finally emerge from her depths.

"What are you doing up? It's so late," she whispered quietly.

"I got thirsty."

I pried open the fridge and reached for a carton of orange juice.

"You've hated me this whole year, haven't you?"

"Off and on," I answered apathetically.

"I know I've been bad, and I think about it all the time. Don't think I'm unaware."

There was a heavy, silent pause between us. I grabbed a glass and poured my juice in it. She continued talking.

"But I'm sorry. I'm going to change, alright? I promise. It just takes some time, but I'm working on it."

"I know you are. And I know you've been stressed over money. But honestly, I could never do some of the stuff you've done. It just wouldn't occur to me. I could never sit and think, 'What can I get from this person, how can I use this person, how can I manipulate this person into doing what I want?' If I wanted something, I'd just ask. If they said no, that would be that. I can't understand how someone could manipulate someone else. I simply couldn't do it."

"That's because you've got the heart of a Girl Scout, and always have. That's because you're a good person. People sense it, when they meet you. Do you hate my guts, Brianne? I know I'm not as good as you. I know I wasn't as successful as you're going to be. I know I've messed up your life a lot. And I know you hate me. You blame me for messing up your life, don't you?"

"Mommy, I could never hate you. I'm incapable of it. I'll always love you. No matter what."

"You're lying."

A bitter silence followed.

"Are you okay?" I whispered, softly, gently, finally breaking the pause.

This faraway look clouded my mother's gray eyes. Suddenly she seemed distant and sorrowful.

"No, I'm not ok. I'm upset. Over finances. Over who I am as a person. I have no confidence in anything about myself. You should just leave me alone to—"

"Drown in your own misery?" I said, cutting her off.

"Yes, exactly."

"Fine."

With a flick of her bony hand she shooed me away.

As I ascended the steps to my room, I whispered, "I love you, Mommy, vices and all. Forever, no matter what."

Even if she didn't believe me, there had never been a truer statement.

Brianne Sands is from Wilmington, Delaware. For her, writing is meant to unlock emotion, and this was a means of healing. She looks up to anyone who expresses truth through art, even when it causes controversy.

Flight

Isabella Giovannini, 17
Writopia Lab, New York, NY, **Daniel Kitrosser,** Teacher

The breasts of the lady next to me bounce, and I stare extra hard at the list of available in-flight entertainment.

"Seat belts fastened?" The flight attendant is eye level with the handles on the overhead bins. She doesn't bend down to serve us like her twin in the welcome video. Instead, her elbows stick up like macaroni from her hand resting on my seat back. (Why do all American Airlines flight attendants have French manicures?) Everything about her is angular. Especially the cheekbones. I'm surprised they allowed such a sharp object onboard.

Every time I hear a rush of air or a whir, I straighten up, hoping the craft will glide out of the gate and slip into the sky. The "fasten seat belts" emblem glows in front of me, repeated above every other row. Beneath the signs, as far as I can see, are little tufts of hair pushing up like carrot tops. Side parts, flyaways, bald spots. It's simpler to judge people when all you can see of them is their hair.

The only person talking is a fellow teenager up front. She might belong to a messy bun in row 14, but it's hard to be sure. Her voice pushes through the sterile air, sound but not words. The sentence begins low, and she works it up her vocal register. At its highest point, she pauses—the whole cabin leans forward, hoping maybe she'll stop and everyone can stop listening and retreat back into the safety of their own two armrests. Then again, maybe she's just searching for a word.

Sure enough, she's managed to straighten out the rest of her sentence and she tumbles through it, falling back down the pitches she just climbed. In her hurry she drops a distinct staccato: the misplaced "like" that confirms her age category.

There go the macaroni elbows again.

When do we eat?

I hope they serve pizza on this flight. I've come to like those steaming slices, sprinkled with heat-exhausted vegetables and served in soggy American Airlines cardboard. Not that they smell like anything. I think they just taste good because they're hot.

I can see only a small oval of the outside world, like someone drew the inside of this cabin on hole-punched paper and I happen to be sitting next to the hole punch. The oval is filled with rainy New York tarmac.

I like how inside, the gates all looked the same. Blue and white, blue and white. But out here, they're all different, with a different-colored plane stamped with a different logo parked in front of each one. Like different species of dogs leashed to parking meters outside the deli.

* * *

I'm pretty sure Kolbie is some sort of terrier. I don't want to look too close. She's lima-bean-colored and -shaped. She's also a bottom-less font of slobber.

Jessie sits cross-legged on her bed, absently rolling a crayon stub in her oval palm. Her tongue is poking out of the corner of her mouth—the sign that means she won't hear me even if I call her name. She hasn't noticed the crushed Flamingo Pink crayon under her right foot.

I would never let a Flamingo Pink be crushed. Everyone knows those are the most valuable. At least back home they do. But maybe in this cousin-world, this Michigan so far removed from home, Flamingo Pink is just a color. A color you don't need to draw dogs.

My stomach rumbles and I push Jessie's plastic jewelry box away from me. I've tried on all her bracelets, and they all fall off because I'm too little.

"What are you drawing?"

I know there's leftover pizza in the kitchen, but I'm not sure I'll be able to reach it without her help.

"Jessie?"

Her tongue retracts and her eyes blink blankly at me. The sole of her right foot is bright pink.

"What are you drawing?"

Blink, blink. "Kolbie."

I wish I could be wise enough to understand the Importance of Kolbie. I wish I could hop down the stairs and reach for the greasy leftover slice in the kitchen, trailing Flamingo Pink footprints.

* * *

My ears pop and the runway drops away from us like a used hotel bathrobe.

This moment when the plane's nose is angled sharply up and the stubby wheels are just retracting is, I think, the only time when everyone has good posture. When every head and pair of shoulder blades is flattened against the seat back, and books close on fingers and Sudokus fall on laps.

Flying is like running your fingers over the surface of the earth. Reading the Braille of houses and trees.

I close my eyes and feel the suburbs bumping the bottom of the plane.

* * *

Uncle Carl drives us to the public pool for diving lessons. He doesn't look at Jessie through the rearview mirror. Maybe he doesn't see her. Maybe he doesn't want to take his eyes off the road. All the mirror shows are the wavy lines above his eyebrows. Like the pool after a sloppy dive—a dive that you thought better of but your foot had already slipped and *splash!* now there are waves everywhere, including in your nose, and you don't think the water will ever be calm again. That's the way I feel about Uncle Carl's forehead. Something dove in there and now the waves are there forever.

I'm also convinced the rearview mirror isn't a real shape. It sure isn't any of the ones I learned at school. But Michigan itself is such a funny shape that you can't expect the people in it to know about right angles and straight lines. Instead, they hold up their hand and say, "I live here," and point to the fold of skin at the base of their thumb. Or, "Here's Lansing," and point to the pit of the palm, the capital of their hand-home.

Jessie stands at the edge of the deep end with blue lapping at her toes, looking down at her quivering reflection.

I don't like diving, but I like feeling the water close over my head.

Turquoise silence. There's no up, no down, no lifeguard and no sunscreen. The whole world pulses with the sound of my own heartbeat. My knees curl up into my chest and I am as small and self-contained as possible. The walls of the pool are warm like a turquoise uterus.

Time slows. I spend months underwater.

Her toes break the surface and penetrate my consciousness. My head breaks the surface and penetrates hers.

We look at each other, each with one body part in the other's universe.

Water leaks into my eye. I blink and through the sting of chlorine I see my cousin blur and burst and hemorrhage across the sky. I rub my eyes, and Jessie's body reassembles itself. She suddenly looks small, standing on the edge of the water, unable to dive in.

My legs are tired from fighting to stay on the surface. I give in and let the water close over my head again. By the time I open my eyes, her toes are gone.

In the car on the way back, our bathing suit bottoms leave wet heart shapes on the seats. Uncle Carl won't be happy.

* * *

Their house was on a triangular block—are they even called blocks in the suburbs?—and there was a white picket fence marching around the tip of the block. In the yard, Uncle Carl built a giant chess set that we never played with. First we were only as big as the pieces, then we were too old. Then there were spiders and ants and the set would fall apart if we played.

I told Jessie someday I would beat her. I was on the school chess team and won a keychain at a tournament, I said. Someday we'll play and I'll win. Someday.

A plane shoots below ours, trailing a streak of debris. *Make a wish.*

But a shooting plane isn't like a shooting star. After several minutes, the streak of debris goes slack, then crooked, and then the sky forgets it.

I wonder where that plane is going. I wonder what the weather's like there. Maybe the plane is filled with people in sweaters and mittens, and suitcases packed with Hawaiian shirts. Cameras. Maybe it's a plane of people migrating south for winter break.

That's it. Jessie migrated. Just took flight.

I know the press and the posters and the Facebook group say "missing child." And I know that if someone held up their hand and pointed and said, "Here's Lansing" and "Here's Detroit," I couldn't point back and say, "Here's Jessie."

But I know Jessie. And Michigan can be cold. The waves on Uncle Carl's forehead froze solid long ago. The pool closed. Or they covered it for renovation. I can't remember.

I can imagine her, walking Kolbie in the cold-December-wet-German-shepherd smell. Suddenly realizing she could just keep walking. Walk past those suburban houses and trees. Never wanting to see that white picket fence and that sad, sagging chess set again.

She might be walking right under me, between the Braille bumps. I just can't see her.

Maybe she's stopped for a second, in the long shadow of a not-yet-lit streetlight on a peaceful square of sidewalk somewhere. She's bent down to pet Kolbie. Her hands snag on a knot or twig in Kolbie's lima-bean-colored hair. Jessie's tongue pokes out of the corner of her mouth as she concentrates on getting it out. Even if I called her name now, she wouldn't hear me.

Another pat for Kolbie, then she stands and wipes the slobber on her jeans.

And she keeps walking south, and even if I called her name now, she wouldn't hear me.

* * *

The plane is heading west and the sun has finally, after prolonged pomp and drama, dipped beneath the cloudscape. Traces of violet and fuchsia still stain the sky like a paper napkin after a particularly greasy wedge of pizza.

The sun disappears behind the horizon. For just a moment, the world flashes Flamingo Pink.

Isabella Giovannini is from New York City. She studies French, Italian, Ancient Greek and Arabic, enabling her to travel and meet new people, providing literary fodder. She also loves acting and is fascinated by math and science, which she often incorporates in her stories.

For the Birds

Francesca Longo, 17
Berkeley Carroll School, Brooklyn, NY, **Erika Drezner,** Teacher

It's astonishing that the brain can have memories without making conscious requests to our cells. How the stimulus can travel down the axon of the synapse like a meteorite flying across the sky, sending the message to release the neurotransmitters from the vesicles across the gap to be caught and processed by the receptors. All to remember for a second. I was sitting in the kitchen with my grandparents and I watched my grandfather's face fall as my grandma asked me, for the third time, whether or not I'd had lunch yet.

My mother's mother began showing signs of dementia at 81. She is sociable, maternal and has been married for 62 years. Now, she cannot remember that my cousin moved back to New York from Florida or the day of the week. My grandfather's eyes welled with tears as she repeated herself, and it became hard for me to comprehend how we can be so in touch with our emotions—so sure of what makes us feel sad or feel lost, yet so unaware of how our brains are actually working. I stared at her wispy blond hair wondering what exactly was happening under her skull.

"Epigenetics" is the study of the changes to our genetic information that occur throughout our lives. DNA methylation is an example of this—a process that adds material to and removes it from our DNA sequences, changing their expression and ultimately the function of the cell, temporarily. The result looks like a normal coiled strand of DNA—base pairs linked in the middle and a spiral staircase formation—but with "methyl groups" sitting on the outside of specific bases. It's sort of like the railing of a staircase around the holidays; laced artfully with holly clinging to certain places, changing the appearance and, inevitably, the function. All of our cells do this naturally to produce the proteins and hormones they need to carry out daily processes, but the process also occurs in reaction to conditions we are exposed to throughout our lives. Age is a huge part of the cause. New research identifies Alzheimer's and dementia as the results of the alterations initiated by plaque buildups associated with these diseases.

Later that night, I sat under the stars with my grandma and we talked about my mother's childhood. She told me stories of her children: the one about my mom locked in the screened-in porch with the bat, my uncle breaking his leg putting on his pajamas and their roadtrips to the Grand Canyon. She was coherent and she was pleasant. Between stories she kept saying, "Would you look at that moon tonight?"

I did look at the moon each time, and with the third mention of it I began to feel crazy. I didn't understand why she remembered the curtains in her old house on 86th Street but couldn't remember the syllables she had uttered moments before.

One of the most profound things to me is how rarely we question the biology in our world; how rarely we appreciate our ability to remember whether we took our vitamins, or how often we overlook the astonishing capacity of the synapses in our brains to perform tasks like boiling water for pasta. I've become obsessed with filling the scientific gaps. I exist unable to get over how much we don't know and how often we forget we don't know all of it.

In the brain, when the plaque material builds up, it modifies the expression of proteins—the things that do our cells' work, like unwinding the DNA helix or providing the energy to twitch our foot ever so slightly. When the fluid that would normally deteriorate this plaque runs dry, the deterioration becomes cyclic. Our synapses fail to generate the proper instructions. With this fluid material at low levels, the buildup threatens the memory. Why her? Their house isn't fun anymore.

My grandfather, an Italian born in the '20s, has had to learn how to manage a lifestyle previously spoiled by spaghetti and meatballs and socks laid out for him. They are still in love but he resents his life. Sitting in their kitchen, eating defrosted homemade apple pie, I see pictures of them from their 20s, 30s, 40s and 50s plastered on every square inch of wall space surrounding the table. I think about how temporary everything is. There won't ever be a transcript of their conversations or dates, there won't ever be a record of their relationship's quirks, and now there won't ever be a person in his life who can ever comprehend every detail—the experience of selling the company, watching their son be diagnosed with MS, or the nights they spent in Venice, Paris and Copenhagen. I know all of this is true for everyone, but I don't know how he accepts that.

My grandmother cries out an old Italian proverb as she maneuvers herself up from the kitchen chair. "Did I ever tell you what that means?" Yes, I think, *getting old is for the birds*. I shake my head no and let her tell me again.

Francesca Longo is from Brooklyn, New York. She was inspired to write by her older sister's personal essays. As in this piece, she enjoys writing about personal topics by using science to draw logic. This fall, she will study fashion design at Pratt Institute.

Russia

Diana Mellow, 14
Fiorello H. LaGuardia High School of Music & Art and Performing Arts,
New York, NY, **Dale Hawrylczak,** Teacher

I remember being small and thinking I was big. That one long summer when the dragonflies chased us away from the river and into the gazebo, which we painted sky blue every weekend. My mother's skin. The fat on her arms and her belly. The space between her arms and her belly where I fit. Her kisses buzzing in my hair and brushing our teeth on the porch. Drawing the tin bucket up from the well, holding on to Mama so I wouldn't fall in. Pouring the water over my hands and neck and eyebrows, feeling it slither softly over my skin. The sun drying us and chipping the paint on the door. Baba Taya cooking soup, spilling it all over the kitchen tiles. My brother, Kolya, coming home with cartons of fresh Kefir to drink. His hands and feet were muddy as he held me in his arms, our hair blonde and our features the same.

Baba Taya fainted in my mother's arms. She crumbled and melted and cooled into plastic, no longer breathing. Russian summer, cool and sweet, sat on our window fanning herself. The men came in. I cried because there were no men in this house, there had only ever been mothers and children. But now they were here: giants with muscles under their sweat stains and leather-covered flesh. The monsters picked her up by her plastic arms and legs. My mother was not plastic: she drew a deep breath. Her bones rattled within her. The men carried the stretcher through the kitchen where the soup was burning. They lifted it through the doorframe and onto the creaky porch, half-painted. The Russian summer jumped off her perch on the windowsill and ran to the plastic woman. She brought her dragonflies, flowers and well water in a tin bucket. Baba Taya smelled nothing. She did not feel the water trickling over her wrinkles, melting her again. The men carried her away. Russian summer sat down on the windowsill to fan herself.

I remember coming back one winter, after Kolya had put in

running water and a new stove that did not have the soup stains of three generations. The dragonflies were crystalized in the ice. They hung from beech trees along the edges of the highway. We took a gypsy cab from Moscow. Stray dogs followed the scent of our warmth. The gazebo and the garden were covered in snow, as if an angel had descended to grace them. The oak tree that she prayed to every day for strength. The bed she slept in with her fifth husband. The river with the giant mosquitoes where she had taught her children and grandchildren how to swim. They were iced over, preserved. Everything was silent. My mother asked me if my feet were cold, was I wearing thick socks?

Born in Moscow, Diana Mellow lives in Staten Island, New York. She is a passionate visual artist, which inspires her to write as if she's painting. "Russia" was a way to connect with her heritage and her memory of her great-grandmother's death.

Osha Roots

Rhiana Rivas, 16
Albuquerque Academy, Albuquerque, NM, **Cynthia Moore,** Teacher

When I was young, I found myself outside of a portable home in the semi-remote town of Fort Garland, Colorado, soaking my tiny foot in a baking tin filled with yellow liquid. There was some dirt that collected in the crevasses of the warped bottom of a metal baking tin, and a thick slab of Osha root soaking in there along with my foot. The bleeding had stopped, allowing the liquid to infiltrate the deep gash that was carved in my flesh. I remember the water being extremely warm when I first dipped my toe in, causing steam to rise upward and fill my nose with the strong smell of herbs. It smelled like a mixture of cough medicine, celery and dirt; my lips scrunched in distaste, but I couldn't complain—there was no doctor around for another 100 miles or so. The thick, stringy root looked like saturated bark; even before it met the water it was moist to the touch. Like a teabag steeping its contents, the Osha root tainted the water with an eerie yellow color, similar to that of a black drop of paint contaminating a whole bucket of white.

A few days before I was acquainted with the Osha root remedy, I sliced open the bottom of my right foot while chasing a shoe down the creek. The July heat and the monotonous chats with elder relatives at the family reunion had coaxed my cousins and me to wander down by the cool waters of the creek just beyond the yard where the rest of the family sat laughing and trading recipes upon plastic lawn chairs. I could hear Aunt Paco's hoarse tobacco laugh, and the argument between some distant cousins over whose brisket recipe was the best. Cousin Ricardo, who was well into his 20s, was creeping around the food table wearing only overalls over his bare skin. When I asked my mother why Cousin Ricardo never wore a proper shirt underneath his overalls, she said, "Because Cousin Ricardo has been around a block or two," which confused me tremendously. When my mother was young, they called the creek "the crick," because she was so used to the adults screaming in their fast Spanish accents, "The kidsarepleyin the crick gan," which after a few times of hearing translates to: *The kids are playing in the creek again.* Sitting still and listening to the adults seemed like a punishment straight from the devil himself, and we kids wanted nothing more than to escape such a fate. Butterflies of pure childish excitement flew around in my stomach as the crisp, gushing sounds of the water beckoned us like the hand of St. Peter.

Though shallow enough to wade through, the water still came up past my knobby knees. The surface of the water glimmered like a fish and rushed by quickly. Water had gotten between my foot and my sandal, lifting the shoe away. The blue rubber swam away from me, like a bride eloping with her groom. In a desperate panic to catch my sandal, I went after it, pushing the current back to propel myself forward. I thrashed about, slapping the water in an attempt to catch the fast-moving object. I remember feeling the slimy smoothness of a boulder beneath me, and then slipping like a wobbly fawn. In an effort to save myself from a terrible plunge, I lunged sideways to the right and came down hard. Suddenly, I was stabbed.

When I pulled the knife-like stick out of my foot, I did not cry. I did not shed a tear, because my poor foot was numbed from the water, but I cried when my mother examined me because she had rough hands.

"You're going to have to get a tetanus shot. Who knows what was in that water," she said as she shook her head. "There's a pharmacy not too far down the street, I saw it when we drove in. I'll go buy some antibiotics to hold you over until we can see a doctor."

Word had spread of my injury, and my family, being the self-diagnosing, self-medicating, self-acclaimed physicians they are, offered me a feast of remedies. My grandmother's sisters, identical to her in voice and stature, tend to provide the most medical "knowledge" out of everyone. Rama and Vicky, though different in appearance, sounded the same as they enlightened me with descriptions of various ointments and goos that have spared them from wrinkles and laugh lines. They silenced abruptly, as my great-uncle, dressed only in his pinstripe night shorts and gray T-shirt busted through the early morning haze with a handful of dark, scraggly Osha root and a steaming baking tin.

* * *

My Great-uncle Phil pushed through the crowd of people to get to me, sloshing hot water onto the ground. Uncle Phil smelled like the night: smoke and wine. And he was in need of a comb to fix his gray rooster tails. He claimed the root was a miracle, and had countless times spared him from painful toothaches, flu symptoms and assorted scrapes and wounds. He tore off my cloth bandage, eager to share his "miracle" with a new patient, unaware of my wincing as he manhandled my delicate foot. The gash, lined with dead white skin, looked foul with a yellow pus oozing from the opening. It was perhaps the ugliest foot I had ever seen.

When the brew had cooled, I eased my wounded limb into the tin, hissing at the sting of the medicine.

"This is Osha root. It is a very old, very rare root that heals. The bears eat it," he explained. (Although years later I discovered that the root is quite common and used for a variety of reasons, none that really emphasized using its power for toothaches.) I peered down into the water, where my skin was quickly becoming prune-like. The man's eyes were bright with pride, as the pureness of the water was tainted with the sunlight of the root.

* * *

There is no scar, not even a trace or a hint of damage on the healthy pink flesh. The skin is tough, like the fibers of the mountain plant, and although I swear by the power of the Osha, I believe another kind of root aided my healing. I was at a family reunion that summer, becoming reacquainted with those whom I originated from, those with whose germinated seeds I've grown from over time: those self-diagnosing, self-medicating, brisket-cooking, pinstripe-night-short-wearing people—they are all Osha roots.

Rhiana Rivas lives in Albuquerque, New Mexico, where she belongs to a group that creates awareness about women's issues. Her role models include J.D. Salinger, Naomi Shihab Nye, Sonya Sotomayor and her family, whose melting pot of humorous characters inspired "Osha Roots." She hopes to become a neurologist.

Excerpts From an Experiment With Shakespeare

Taylor Geu, 18
Bishop Heelan Catholic High School, Sioux City, IA,
Charlotte Clovis, Teacher

0 year Experiment Date

It is beyond an honor to receive this test from the Ministry of Curiosity. With the success of my Experiment Derived from Molyneux's Problem—If a blind man knows things by the touch of them, such as shapes, would he be able to recognize them by sight? Answer: Not without assistance—I can only assure that the Ministry's faith, funding and honored gift of immortality will not go unwasted. I shall prove or disprove this theorem in quick succession. I have bought the Monkey; I have bought the typewriter; now all that awaits is Shakespeare or the lack thereof.

.005479 year ED

We have reached an impasse rather earlier than hoped. The Monkey typed 30 A's before quitting and redesigning the device as a hefty nutcracker. Worse, the interns have developed a poor rapport with the simian, and now we must pay for both a new typewriter and Young Phi's medical bill. Shame they couldn't save his toes, and the new ones will cost us a small fortune. I will go before the Ministry with a proposal for slight "Modifications."

.16667 year ED

Despite complaints of itching, the Monkey seems to enjoy its new brain. He should; I understand the donor was very optimistic by nature. We have given the Monkey a new typewriter and told it to type whatever it wanted. Although hesitant at first, that expensive brain of his soon decided to go for it. We have given him books on grammar with the hopes that his writing will be somewhat legible.

1 year ED

The Monkey has penned two poorly written erotic novels (*Jorje's Big Banananana* and *Eerotik Addvanchures of a Yung Orangyutan*.) Despite having a horrible grasp of grammar, spelling, plotting and character development, the Monkey does seem to be grasping the concept of metaphor and foreshadowing. The passage where "Jorje" must choose between the sultry, flexible gibbon and the tender, supportive gorilla with a thing for tire swings was particularly full of social commentary with regard to Objectivist Individualism. Although the Bard was, ahem, "bawdy," I feel the Monkey is barking up the wrong tree, much like the young orangutan's incident with the koala bear.

6 year ED

I had to tell the Monkey today that he had to give up the ghost on his memoir. I don't know where he even came up with the idea to write one, seeing as he spends all day in a clean white room with a typewriter. He grew a bit upset, saying I had no artistic soul. He said he wanted people to understand him, that his life story, with its small triumphs (convincing me to give him a stick of gum), was worth telling. He is now quite moody, chewing my gum with venom in his eyes. Oh well, I knew this would be a slow project when I accepted it. Hopefully, the Monkey snaps out of it. I don't want to suffer through another self-pitying bit of poetry. God, if Shakespeare had not written sonnets, I'd taser the Monkey for trying. I mean, how do you rhyme "Tailless cat" with "Tossing poo"? I sent it to a few poetic journals for evaluation, and they assured me that it was poor enough to win a special category in their annual competition: "Torturer's Pick." I understand the winner is actually read in a torture chamber to break the subject's will to live. I guess that it's progress.

53 year ED

The Monkey has not touched his typewriter for five weeks. Some of the interns are getting nervous since Chief Scientist Laser has undertaken Schrödinger's Cat and is already publishing interesting treatises. All we have is a collection of essays: *Cat Really Does Rhyme With Poo: Letters to a Fascist*. When asked why he abandoned writing, the Monkey said it was as if a block was in front of his creative output. The

Interns, amazingly, spent six minutes debating surgical techniques to remove the blockage in question. To work in the Ministry of Curiosity does require a certain literalness of thought, but there is a line between literal and imbecile.

Oh well, this too shall pass.

70 year ED

It has been 17 years since the typewriter became quiet, and bloody Tom Laser has proven the bloody damn cat doesn't die unless a person has an IQ higher than three (and people say my research is corrupted due to mental realignment). What's more, the Ministry asked when the project will see results. I told them that the nature of the experiment would require perhaps millennia to find a result.

It became very quiet.

They told me that funding would not last that long.

In fact, it would last only until 200 years ED. After that, the project would be disbanded.

Stunned, I could only nod when the Ministry offered me an invitation to Laser's award ceremony. Apparently, many people think he's the Dominion's sexiest bachelor.

I won't tell the team; best to let this debacle run its course. I see this as completely fair because they, in turn, have not mentioned Tom's award.

75 ED

With a mere 125 years to finish the project, there is no time to coddle the Monkey and his muse. After much consideration, we have given him a laptop computer with wireless. Many people believe the Bard was "inspired" by outside sources. It is hoped that the Internet, coupled with our hints of "You know what's fascinating? Scottish history. All the Macbeths and Macduffs and the murdering of kings to ascend to the heights of power only to fall to insanity and death is fascinating! Someone should write about that! Or Kings Henry IV through VI!" will tip him off. We wait with bated breath.

75.50579 ED

I think for my next experiment, I will test whether or not online games steal a man's soul, for it has certainly left a mere husk of our Monkey. The once-moody ape has become a zombie that requires only nachos, energy drinks and diaper changes. When I ask how the writing is going, it grunts vaguely and returns to killing pixilated foes. In response, I have tossed out the computer. The typewriter has returned, and the Monkey has begun to write again.

True, these are graphic descriptions of what he would do to my elbows, but at least he's writing again.

114 ED

The Monkey has completed his fantasy epic. I'm not much of a fiction fan, but even I can see that it's moronic. I mean, does this magical realm of Cri'snichtk have a shortage of vowels? For example, how do you even pronounce Hngs'ajgvn-i- stnsoigb'hk? He's thinking of making it a trilogy. I asked if the next one might center on, say, a midsummer night, but he confidently told me that in Cri'snichtk they do not use the Julian calendar. Instead, they are using one with 32 months split into six seasons, each month split, as well, into seven mini-months called Blts. The Monkey asked if instead, it could be a MidFreepinlock Night. I told it not to bother.

116 ED

An e-mail says some man named Hugo wanted to give the Monkey something in regards to his new science-fiction novel. I deleted the message. I will not be fooled by another scammer.

150 ED

A mere 50 years separate us from the deadline. In desperation, I have analyzed the great writers of the past—Poe, Fitzgerald and Hemingway—for signs of that mysterious spark of genius. What separates a laureate from a hack? What mysterious key opens the floodgates of inspiration?

Pouring over the results, I think I have finally discovered the secret of the muse. Could it be so simple, so obvious? All these great writers had one thing in common, one uniting thread for anyone to unearth.

They were alcoholics. Our Monkey must get drunk.

The alcohol is worse than the online game. At least then he stayed still. But what's the point? The team found out about the end of funding and how this experiment will be marked as incomplete, worse than a failure. They were understandably upset that I had not told them 80 years ago. Now, on their permanent records for all employers to see will be a century-and-a-half-long exercise in fruitless exercises. They left me alone in the facility.

Late that night, I walked into the Monkey's room. Taking a seat on the antiseptic bleached floor, I stared at the walls. I couldn't help but think. Over the past century, I had something of a life. My marriage fell apart, I attended my great-granddaughter's birthday, and I saw almost everyone I loved die in front of me or else grow old. I have not aged a day. My grandson and I could have shared a birthday. But sitting there, looking at the wall, empty as the experiment it contained, I suddenly realized how much I had. What was it like to live in this room for 152 years without a bed, with only a typewriter? Could I be happy, knowing there was a world out there I could never be a part of? Should I be jealous that the Monkey was shielded from pain, or pity it for never feeling the loss of love?

Something was held in front of me; it was a glass of whiskey that shone like embers. I looked to my left to find the Monkey offering it, an empathetic smile on its face.

For the first time, I talked to the Monkey. As the whiskey drained away, I finally told it what we should have told it from the start—its purpose in life. The Monkey was silent for awhile, then told me it knew why the experiment wasn't working. Something amazing, something beautiful could not be produced randomly in a lab because it was never random to begin with. A balding, bisexual genius took up the quill and crafted every sonnet and soliloquy from the soul with deep feeling. He had a vision that he wept blood to attain. Every meter was weighed with a pound of flesh.

I thought, and realized it was right. I felt no better hearing it, but in my soul's secret cell, I knew it to be true.

To the Ministry of Curiosity,
I write to inform you that I have decided to resign my post as

head of the Shakespeare Experiment. I understand Uruguay is hiring a new Proactive Paradox Disabler in their National Space and Time Association. I want to say that it was an honor and have no regrets in my pursuits. The only other thing I ask for is my Monkey, for nostalgic reasons.

Best of luck, sirs,
Professor Benjamin Planck, ex-head of Existential Affairs
P.S. Kiss my ageless ass.

Taylor Geu is from Dakota Dunes, South Dakota, and was thrice awarded South Dakota State Champion Cat Showman. He maintains a "fiery loathing of elves" and other clichés, preferring science fiction that isn't afraid to explore the human condition. This fall he will attend Kenyon College in Ohio.

St. Jude's Center for Ticking Time Bombs

Emma Hastings, 15
Thomas Jefferson High School, Alexandria, VA, **Judith Bello,** Teacher

Hrep-078. Grp1. Grp2. Jt-432. Vorg5. Rort2.
These are the letters and numbers that dictate my life.

They're the names of genes. My genes, to be exact, and the genes of the other hapless souls incarcerated in this hellhole. The government and the social workers and the doctors call it St. Jude's Center for the Protection and Rehabilitation of At-Risk Youth, but they're the only ones. The rest of the world has a different name for it.

St. Jude's Center for Ticking Time Bombs. That's where I and a hundred kids like me go to school, eat, sleep and exist within tall barbed-wire fences that, we are assured, are for our own protection. But they're not, of course. Like the locks on every door, the canisters of pepper spray tucked away in anxious teachers' purses and the (and this is my personal favorite) thick leather straps the nurses believe they've cleverly hidden under the mattress of every infirmary bed.

But why all the security in a facility meant to house and care for mere children, you ask? Simple. We're not children. A hundred or 50 or maybe even 10 years ago, we might have been mistaken for something so unstained and innocent, but thanks to the endless march of science, the world will never make that mistake again.

Perhaps I should explain.

Do you remember those genes I told you about? Those seemingly meaningless little jumbles of letters and numbers? Well, in reality, they are far from meaningless. In fact, they are all that separate a normal, functioning member of a community from monsters like us, locked away from the free world for the safety of its more-deserving inhabitants.

Throughout the process of uncovering and analyzing the human genome, the geneticists of our time made a shocking discovery: 99% of violent criminals possessed more than 4 out of 15 unique genetic markers that are virtually nonexistent in the average population. Every kid living at St. Jude's has at least five of these indicators. I have six, which means that I'm 100 times more likely to commit armed larceny, arson, kidnapping or murder. So you see, we're not children. We're liabilities, dangers to society, the absolute scum of the human race.

So, you know, lucky us.

* * *

I could tell that Zeke, the newest inmate of St. Jude's, was a different breed of guy the first time he walked into the mandatory weekly counselor meeting that we all unwillingly attended. Mostly because he actually *walked* in—most newcomers had to be dragged in, kicking and struggling. But Zeke calmly strode into the counseling session and took a seat without a fuss, staring expectantly at the front of the room, where Ms. Stein was hustling about, setting up her presentation for the day. He caught my eye as I studied him out of the corner of it, and smiled shyly at me. I would love to say that grand notions of an enduring friendship formed in my mind then, an alliance to show that a few unlucky genes didn't determine the course of a life, but they didn't. My first thought was that it was T minus 24 hours until this guy was torn limb from limb. I turned my attention away immediately, focusing on a point on the floor as the snickers of the other kids flooded my ears. Even with my gaze averted, I saw Zeke shift awkwardly in his chair. Good, I thought at the time, maybe he'll wise up and toughen up. But when the cruel laughter started, and the other guys began to harass Zeke, I still felt oddly guilty.

Ms. Stein was halfway through her usual spiel about *free will* and *making our own choices* (and all that other stuff that, if she truly believed it, would make her protest our being locked up in here). She displayed a frighteningly cheerful attitude that couldn't be the result of anything other than prolonged delusion, severe psychiatric damage, alarming overmedication or any combination thereof. I felt a tap on my shoulder and whipped around, bristling and ready for a fight. I didn't get one.

"I like your necklace," Zeke said quietly, leaning in close so that Ms. Stein wouldn't hear us talking.

"How wonderful for you," I snapped back, as rudely as possible. That's one of the first things you learn when you're among the ticking time bombs—any attempt to make friends is met with hostility at best and blows at worst. Zeke might seem different now, but that's how all the newbies started; a few weeks confined to St. Jude's, and they became just as angry and uncontrollable as the rest of us.

But even so, I couldn't help but let my hand creep up toward my throat, couldn't stop my fingers from worrying the familiar metal cross and beads. The piece of jewelry was given to me by my mother on the day she sent me to this forsaken place—my tenth birthday. It's been four—no, five—years since I've seen her.

Zeke was unphased by the venom in my reply. "Do you know what it is, exactly?" he questioned softly. I ignored him, focusing on Ms. Stein. "It's not just a normal piece of jewelry. It's called a rosary, and it's used in prayer."

I steadfastly held my gaze forward, hoping that Zeke would take the hint and shut up. And then Ms. Stein pulled out a couple of god-damn *puppets,* and I decided it was time to pick the better of two evils. I swiveled in my chair to face Zeke, and I would be lying if I said I wasn't surprised at what I saw. The expression evident in his eyes...it was almost *sad,* unlike the practiced caginess and, too often, muted fury in the all the other teens with whom I spent my time. I blinked, and cleared my throat slightly before speaking. "Prayer?" Zeke nodded. I thought about that for a few seconds. "Do you pray?" I questioned.

He nodded. "Sometimes. If you want, I could—"

"Then take it," I cut him off sharply, tearing the rosary from my neck. The clasp snapped with a sharp *ping!*, and I threw it unceremoniously onto the wide-eyed Zeke's desk. Several of the little beads rolled free of the string, which seemed to distress him. "You'll get more use out of it than me."

Zeke hastily began to restring the beads, shaking his head as he did so. "I can't take this, it's yours."

I rolled my eyes, feeling a prickle of annoyance at his insistent conversation. "Not anymore," I hissed back. Zeke opened his mouth to respond, but Ms. Stein spoke before he could.

"Excuse me," she said loudly, a tiny crease forming in her Botoxed brow. She put her puppets down and strode toward me and Zeke, the insipid smile somehow remaining plastered to her face. "But I'm the only one who should be speaking right now." The spark of irritation generated by Zeke suddenly ignited into a roaring fire, and I decided it was time for our favorite game—Stein-baiting, or seeing how quickly we could get the counselor to drop her cheery façade.

"You're excused," I shot back coldly, flicking a strand of hair out of my face. I was rewarded with a blotchy flush invading Ms. Stein's face, and a collective noise of interest rose from the other teens as they realized the game was on.

"I would appreciate it if you didn't speak to me in that tone, Morgan," Ms. Stein said through gritted teeth, obviously trying to keep her composure. All the kids in the room save Zeke leaned forward excitedly, waiting for my next move.

"You know," I retorted, "you should get the puppets to tell me that. I might take it better from them."

Scattered snickers reverberated throughout the room. I smirked as dozens of heckles rose from the crowd, and sat back, satisfied. The scent of anarchy was in the air.

"Now *really*," Ms. Stein stammered, attempting to retain authority. "You must all calm down." She took a step back, betraying her fear. I scowled in disgust, and as she made a couple of desperate, last-ditch grabs for peace, I stood and left the room. Zeke followed me out as I stalked onto the grassy lawn.

"Why'd you *do* that?" he asked incredulously, trailing after me as I went. The repaired rosary was clutched tightly in his fist.

"The same reason that everyone else is following me out of there," I replied sharply, stopping and gesturing toward the stream of kids trailing out behind us, chortling at their triumph over the counselor. "Because we can't *stand* that woman."

Zeke paused and glanced over his shoulder. "I guess that's a good reason. I mean…puppets? Really?"

An involuntary laugh tore from my throat, and we both looked at the other in surprise. Before either of us could speak, a knot of guys surrounded Zeke, cornering him against a nearby tree. I stepped away as Russell, the oldest one of us, approached him.

"So," the teen growled, crossing him arms over his chest menacingly. "How many?"

It was the first question posed to every newcomer to St. Jude's: how many of the 15 genetic markers for violent crime do you have?

Russell was the current holder of the highest number, at nine.

Zeke didn't seem to understand the question. He blinked, mystified, and looked at me questioningly. I gritted my teeth, unwilling to ally myself with him in front of the meanest guys at St. Jude's...but as Russell's eyes flashed dangerously, I realized that if I didn't want any bloodshed, I had to help him.

"He means how many genetic markers," I clarified quickly. "How many did the geneticists tell you that you had?"

"Oh." Zeke nodded uncomfortably, running a hand through his long black hair. "Uh...I think they said...11?"

My jaw dropped. *Eleven?* Everyone was stunned speechless.

Zeke glanced between us uneasily. "What?" he asked, shuffling his feet. "Is that bad?"

"It certainly isn't good," I grumbled under my breath as I overcame my shock. Russell suddenly grinned, clapping Zeke forcefully on the shoulder.

"You're never going to get out of here," he said, grinning ferally. As he began to wander back toward the dormitories, I heard him laughing darkly. Zeke shot me a look of bemusement, and I just shrugged. Then the laughter abruptly stopped, and Russell threw back his head and let out a warning cry.

"She's back!" he sang out, pointing toward the main gate even as he broke into a run in the opposite direction. I followed his finger and sighed.

"Who?" Zeke asked, yet again turning to me. "Ms. Stein?"

"Nope," I replied, sticking my hands into my jeans pockets. I nodded to where a teenage girl was walking toward us. She had a large, bulky bag slung over her shoulder and a visitor's pass (a rare sight in St. Jude's, as few people ever visited) clipped to the front of her shirt. "That's Allison." Zeke stared questioningly at me, and, with a begrudging sigh, I explained.

"She's a student at the local high school for the normal kids. Wants to be a psychologist and comes here for volunteer hours." I had mixed feelings about Allison—she was nice enough, and without the infuriating air of fake cheerfulness of Ms. Stein. But I still had that nagging feeling that she didn't think of us as equals, but rather as fascinating objects to be studied. The other kids felt that way too, which was why they scattered like spooked horses as she approached. Everyone, that is, except Zeke.

"Hi," he said, waving awkwardly at Allison as she approached. Allison blinked in surprise; that was easily the friendliest reception she had ever received. A startled, but pleased, smile spread over her face.

"Hi," she replied eagerly, hurrying for the last few steps. She offered her hand for him to shake without any sort of hesitation (a point in her favor), and he shook it. "I'm Allison."

"Zeke." He smiled kindly at her, and she returned it, curling a finger in her hair. I turned to leave—I had no interest in watching the two of them flirt—but Allison called me back.

"Hey, Morgan, wait a second." She sounded urgent, and, against my better judgment, I stopped and looked at her expectantly. She pulled a thick packet of paper from her bag, offering it to me to look at.

I frowned. "I'm definitely not going to read that."

"Alright, fair enough." Another good thing about Allison—she doesn't take offense easily. "What I have," she told me, tapping the packet, "is a petition."

"A petition for what?" Zeke leaned over to examine the paper, and Allison handed it to him.

"To close this godforsaken place, of course." Allison watched as Zeke leafed through the pages. "What they're doing here, locking you all up in these secure facilities...it's not right."

I narrowed my eyes at her. "You don't have to argue that point with *me*."

"Right, right, I know," Allison blushed slightly. "But really, these places do nothing helpful. It's counterproductive to their mission statement. They shut you all up in here, tell you that your genes are supposed to make you violent...and then they act surprised when you exhibit bad behavior. It's...despicable."

"No kidding," I grumbled. I wasn't really impressed—a lot of people came in here preaching that they would close St. Jude's. If none of them could do it, why should I expect anything different from a teenage girl?

"You think that you can get us out of here?" Zeke asked, sounding very intrigued.

"Maybe so." Allison grinned enthusiastically. "I'm going to collect signatures—you know, from politicians, psychologists and you guys too, if you're willing."

"Of course!" Zeke grinned. He flipped through to the end of the packet eagerly, looking for where to sign.

Allison cocked her head to the side, watching him. "Have you..." she began tentatively. "Have you been here long? I mean, I've never seen you before," she added hastily. But I knew it was more than that—Allison could tell from his demeanor, like I had, that he was different.

"I just got here today," Zeke admitted.

Allison's eyes widened. "And you've never been in a secure facility before?" He shook his head. I was a little shocked by that too. Most of us had been incarcerated by age 9 or 10; Zeke had to be my age, at least. The idea that someone with 11 out of 15 could have gone unnoticed for so long was nothing short of astounding.

"No," Zeke said, shaking his head. "A couple weeks ago my family moved to Virginia and we all had to undergo mandatory genetic screening. That's when they told my parents I had to come here."

"And you'd never had any, you know...problems before?" Allison asked, carefully posing the question so as not to offend.

"None."

It was a familiar story, sadly. Most of us were sent here after undergoing genetic screening for some reason. Some had had behavioral problems before, but only some.

"That just proves my point," Allison replied, crossing her arms over her chest. "Places like these create criminals, they don't rehabilitate them." She held up the petition that Zeke had signed, presenting it like some sort of sacred relic. "But I'm going to change that."

Poor Allison. I know she meant well, but in the end she created more problems than she solved. Far, far more.

* * *

Months had passed before Allison got back to us. In the first few weeks, Zeke often talked grandly of her efforts contacting important people, collecting signatures and trying to right the grievous wrong we'd all been subjected to...and I relaxed my rules on our friendship just a little. But as more and more time went by, I noticed a change in Zeke. St. Jude's was really getting to him—the confinement, the mistrust of all those around him, the anger that was palpable everywhere you went. It seeped under the skin and just stayed there. It was all too much for a nice guy like Zeke, and I saw him change right before my eyes.

When Allison finally did return, it was in defeat. Despite the work she had done, the experts she had consulted, the government ignored her efforts and St. Jude's remained open. And the first time I saw her was from the window of my dorm room. She was out on the lawn, fighting with Zeke.

"I'm sorry!" Allison said, her arms wrapped protectively around herself. Zeke was standing in front of her, bristling. He was furious. "Look, I tried, but—"

"Maybe you should have tried harder, then!" He shouted back, taking a step forward. Allison flinched slightly and stumbled away from him. I cursed under my breath. There was nothing, nothing Zeke hated more than people fearing him. "What, are you afraid of me?" he demanded. "Afraid that I'm going to hurt you, like the violent criminal that I am?"

Immediately, I was on my feet and running out to the lawn, out to stop Zeke before he did something monumentally stupid. I could still hear his shouts, even as I sprinted through the halls and outside.

I burst onto the grass to see Zeke pull back his fist. I screamed a warning, sprinting forward as Allison stood frozen in horror. I ran forward, terror driving my every step. But the only thing I got there in time to do was feel Allison's blood as it splattered on my cheek. The time bomb had blown.

* * *

Hrep-078. Grp1. Grp2. Jt-432. Vorg5. Rort2.
These are the letters and numbers that dictate my life.
And it doesn't look like that's going to change anytime soon.

Emma Hastings is from Vienna, Virginia, where she studies biology and Latin, and particularly enjoys science fiction because it incorporates her other interests, throwing her imagination into overdrive. For inspiration, she surfs her school's scientific journal databases for new discoveries to get her creative juices flowing.

The Room

Carter Jimenez Jenkins, 14
Home Schooled, Dallas, TX, **Clarissa Ngo,** Teacher

There was a room they never entered. Some called it the Room of Sinister Thought; others, the Room of Trepidation. Something had happened there a long time ago, but no one remembered exactly what. The House had been in the family for generations and was so large entire wings were closed off, with the furniture hidden under sheets. The house was owned by the Léglise family, whose noble ancestor had invented the guillotine. Thus they were the most hated people in France.

The Léglise family members were not the only occupants of the house. They had cooks to bake escargot pie, chauffeurs to polish the Léglise collection of Bentleys and chambermaids to scrub the chamber pots and dump their contents. There was a gardener who trimmed the hedges into a maze for the children, an ancient doorman who greeted you with a morose look every time, and finally, an 8-year-old boy named Thaddeus who polished the silver.

Thaddeus was a curious and fearless young boy who loved to explore the unoccupied wings of the mansion. He was the son of the cook and the chauffeur, which meant his mom always snuck him the leftovers and his dad taught him everything about cars. Thaddeus was not the only inquisitive one in the house. The 6-year-old Léglise twins, Odil and Celie, were his fellow adventurers, and they spent many a rainy afternoon getting cobwebs in their hair when they weren't getting beaten by their dad, who stomped around the house with a bottle in his hand.

The games helped the children forget, for in creating imaginary terrors, they forgot their real ones. There was one room into which they would never venture. There were claw marks on the ancient wood door, and brown patches that looked eerily like dried blood.

"What is it?" Thaddeus had asked Odil and Celie the first time he had seen it.

"Papa says it is a sign from the devil and to stay away."

Of course, the warning only made the children more curious.

They played games of Chicken, daring each other to touch the door. Once, Odil claimed something reached out and tripped him as he ran past the door. When he looked down, he noticed an angry claw mark raking his leg, forgetting it had been inflicted when he had accidentally spilled his soup.

The children stayed away for a week after that. Then it rained, and the children were so bored they craved even the terror of the Room of Trepidation. Master Léglise was away on a trip, and the children enjoyed a rare week of peace. They played their usual games until it was time for the twins' dinner.

This time, instead of going to his room to wait for the twins or for his mom to bring him some scraps, Thaddeus stayed behind. He looked around to make sure no one was there, but all he heard was his racing heart. The creeping shadows snuck up behind him as he reached for the door.

Just do it.

He squeezed his eyes shut and pressed down on the handle.

Click.

The sound was a gunshot in his head.

Thaddeus ran. He was tempted to look back; he could feel a breath of cool wind coming from the open door. Was it the devil tempting him, or was he missing out on the most wonderful thing in the world? It was terrible not to know. He wrenched his head back just enough to see a shadow flit across the room and the door slam shut.

The next rainy day, when Odil and Celie decided to play their game, Thaddeus hung back. Celie had a new black eye, and Odil had a new limp when he walked.

Thaddeus's heart sank as he looked at his two friends, but he didn't say anything. They would just say they had fallen down the stairs. Perhaps he could take their minds off their troubles with an adventure. Thaddeus lowered his voice to a conspiratorial whisper.

"The Devil lives in that room. Last night I opened the door."

The children's eyes were as large as watermelons.

"You saw the Devil? What did he look like?"

"He was purple."

"No!"

"Yes, and he's not a very fast runner."

"Really?"

"Oh, I easily outran him in the halls."

Odil screamed. "I saw you! You looked like you were going to pee yourself."

Thaddeus reddened.

Celie tugged on her friend's sleeve.

"Thaddy, you can't actually open the door. The last boy who did that disappeared, and his whole family vanished soon after."

Thaddeus froze.

"Why didn't you tell me?"

"We wanted you to play Chicken with us."

* * *

The children avoided the Door after that. They ventured into other wings of the house, but never found anything as fascinating as the Room of Trepidation. One day, when Thaddeus was sent on an errand to retrieve an old silver ewer for a winter ball, he found himself near the Room. He couldn't help himself. As he passed the Door, he threw a glance over his shoulder, and that's when he saw it—a golden light, spilling out from under the Door like salvation. The delicious scent of apples wafted from the Room's inner sanctum. Thaddeus felt the Door pull him toward Her like a magnet, and he lifted his hand toward the iron handle. In his head, he could hear sweet music now, a melody to a song that was familiar but which he could not place.

"Thaddeus!"

They knew his name.

The word jolted him out of his trance. With horror, he looked down to see his hand pulling down on the handle. The Room had almost tricked him again.

* * *

The next evening, Thaddeus was determined to enter the Room. He snuck out in the middle of the night in his pajamas while everyone was asleep. Sliding among the shadows, he stealthily crept toward the forbidden Door, his heart thumping. Without giving himself time for thought, he launched himself at the Door and swung it wide open.

When Thaddeus sauntered in feeling like a brave explorer, he discovered from where the aroma of apples had emanated. A giant apple tree spread its wings in the middle of a lush endless garden.

There were no walls to the right or to the left, just a green orchard that spread as far as the eye could see. Thaddeus looked up and saw the cloudless sky shimmering above him like an ocean. He breathed in the fresh apple-scented air and closed his eyes.

When he opened them, he was not alone. On either side of the enormous tree stood a tall young man and woman, so beautiful he could hardly look at them. The lady's eyes were a piercing sapphire blue, and her golden hair rippled about her face like water. A serpent coiled up her torso with a gentle hiss.

"Hello, Thaddeus."

A lump blocked his windpipe.

"W-who are you?"

"I am the First and the Last."

The man stepped forward.

"Have you eaten, son?"

He held out a shining golden apple in his hand.

Thaddeus shook his head. There was something about the scene that seemed familiar, and he wanted to share it with Odil and Celie. He found his voice.

"If I need to leave and come back, will you and the garden still be here?"

The lady smiled.

"That's a chance you will have to take—if you want your friends with you."

Thaddeus looked around the garden. He was in an orchard of peaches and golden apples, but it was unlike any fruit he had seen before. The plump peaches were the size of basketballs, and they looked like they were about to burst with cool sweet juice. The trees were beautiful for climbing, with branches that stair-stepped to the sky. He could see another world up there to explore—a floating castle that called his name.

"I want to stay."

The lady nodded.

"Shall I show you around then?"

"Yes, please."

The lady took him down a cobblestone path to a lake of shimmering topaz.

He wondered, what if the stones were gold? Suddenly, they were. He hunkered down and started clawing them out of the ground to fill his pockets.

What else could he change? A tree caught his eye. Thaddeus imagined a chocolate tree laden with saltwater taffy and then, there it was. He charged over and peeled a strip of chocolate bark, plucked a taffy apple, and stuffed them both into his mouth.

There was a symphony in his mouth—of the sweetest, darkest, richest chocolate and the juiciest saltwater taffy he had ever tasted. He was in Heaven.

Maybe he really was.

"Would you like to go for a swim?" The lady pointed to a glistening blue lake fed by a waterfall that poured from the sky. "The water is warm."

Thaddeus looked down at his grimy clothes, remembering that he hadn't bathed in days. Celie and Odil had just taught him how to swim, and he was eager to try out his new skills.

He ducked behind a bush to strip as the lady politely turned away, and with a splash, he was in.

"It tastes sweet!"

The lady nodded and smiled. "There may be other surprises as well."

He dove back down to the bottom, through water clear as shimmering, blue glass.

There was something there, glinting at the bottom of the sea. He pushed his way through a forest of sticky seaweed, reveling in the fact that he could breathe.

"I wouldn't go there if I were you," a voice whispered in his ear. A beautiful girl with the body of a fish shimmered beside him, her face grave.

"Why?"

"You will see things you will wish you hadn't."

"What do you mean?"

The mermaid shrugged and disappeared with a flick of her tail. Thaddeus thought to himself for a moment, then swam down anyway. He stopped five feet short when he saw a giant yellow eye staring at him.

It belonged to an octopus—the biggest one he had ever seen.

It was the size of a room, and it didn't look friendly. To Thaddeus's surprise, the octopus plucked its tentacles off the glowing orb and floated away.

Thaddeus placed his hand on the shimmering glass and the cloudiness gave way to stars. Even though his face was pressed to the glass, he felt as though he were moving through time and space as the stars shot past him, and with a shout of surprise he realized he was seeing home. There was his mom picking herbs in the garden, and there was his dad polishing the Léglises' collection of Bentleys. It made him realize how much he missed home. And that is when he saw himself, laughing and shouting with Odil and Celie as they ran around the old wooden kitchen.

A shadow darkened the door.

"I told you to play outside!" Master Léglise shouted, boxing Celie's ears.

Celie dropped to the floor, clutching her ears. Odil ran to her, screaming at his father.

"You hurt Celie, Papa!"

Master Léglise shrugged and lumbered off. Odil knelt before his sister.

"Are you alright, Celie?"

She didn't answer.

A few moments later, she looked up at him and pointed to her ears. "Why can't I hear anything?"

Odil stared at her in horror, then took her in his arms.

I don't remember this happening.

Thaddeus felt someone tap his shoulder, and he whirled around to see the lady Eve gazing at him.

"Did that just happen?"

"It hasn't yet."

"So if I go home, I can stop it?"

The lady smiled. "Do you want to go home?"

Thaddeus nodded.

"Just know that if you leave now, the Door to this world may never open again."

Thaddeus swam to the surface of the lake and gazed at the paradise around him. He was free here and nobody's servant. But at home, Odil and Celie needed him.

"I want to go home."

Eve looked stunned. "Are you sure?"

"Yes." Thaddeus squeezed his eyes shut and tried not to look at everything he was about to lose. Before, all the good he had seen had made him forget about the bad. But now, all the evil he had seen through the glass had made him forget about the good. He couldn't ignore it, and when he opened his eyes, he was home.

***

"You clumsy clod! Get off the floor." The Master was glaring at him, his red eyes bulging as he swung an empty whisky bottle over his head.

"I'm sorry, Sir." Thaddeus clambered to his feet and hurriedly bowed.

"That's more like it. Just stay out of my way." Master lumbered off.

Odil and Celie came tearing around the corner.

"Thaddeus! We've been looking for you." Odil gave him a gap-toothed grin.

"We've waited to play tag with you all day."

Thaddeus froze. "I don't think—"

But Odil and Celie had already disappeared. Thaddeus tore after them, but he was too late. The shadow was already darkening the door of the kitchen.

"I told you to—"

Thaddeus didn't even think. He grabbed the nearest object, which happened to be the Master's prized crystal whisky decanter, and hurled it to the floor.

The Master whirled on him. "What the—?"

"Run!" Thaddeus screamed as the Master descended upon him with blazing fists. He knew what was coming, but he still wasn't prepared for the pain. It was like being pummeled by a train that never ended. All he could think was that he was glad it wasn't Celie. He hadn't realized how much he cared for her until he gave up paradise to come back and save her. He just didn't know what his new feelings meant.

* * *

He woke up in the Room, which was back to normal again—just

four walls and a rocking chair. His head felt like an exploded bomb, and he couldn't hear a thing. The strange thing was, Celie was crying, and Odil's mouth moved with no sound.

He must be deaf then. The knowledge had been sitting in the back of his head waiting for confirmation, but now that he knew it, he felt utterly alone.

"I can't hear anything." Thaddeus pointed to his ears.

Odil and Celie stared at him in horror, then took him into their arms. Thaddeus could smell Celie's hair. He smiled.

And then he realized something.

"You opened the Door."

Celie pulled out her little chalkboard and quickly wrote. *We had to. It's the only place Papa won't come.*

Odil tugged at Thaddeus's hand and pointed at his rucksack. It was stuffed with cold salamis, pieces of cheese and baguettes. *Food,* Odil wrote on the chalkboard. *We're not leaving you.*

Thaddeus's heart swelled as he hugged his friends. He wished he could take them to his Paradise, but he didn't know if the Lady would return.

"I have a secret."

The twins' eyes widened.

"I have been to another world, and the entrance is here."

The twins looked around, wide-eyed.

"The last time I was in this room, a giant apple tree spread its golden branches here, and there was a man and a woman who showed me Heaven."

When can we go? Odil scribbled on the board.

Thaddeus's face fell. "I don't know. The Lady said the Door may never open again."

The children looked deflated.

Just then, the children heard a familiar voice call to them from outside the door. "Children, come outside."

The children froze. It was the Master.

What shall we do?

"Pray."

Thaddeus took the twins' hands in his own, then clutched them tighter when he heard the axe smash the door.

"Dear Lord, please help us—Papa knows not what he does…"

"Hail Mary, full of grace…"

"Our Father, who art in Heaven…"

CRASH! SMASH! BASH!

The door splintered, revealing an angry sliver of the Master's face.

"Forgive us our debts, as we forgive our debtors…"

Another door panel hurtled to the ground, and the Master was barging in.

"Thy Kingdom come, Thy will be done…"

The children clutched each other as the Master descended upon them, fists swinging. They cringed, preparing to feel the force of his blows, but instead, they felt a warm wind on their faces. They looked up to see the most beautiful man and lady they had ever seen smiling down at them, and their fear melted into joy. The couple lifted the children in their arms and flew through the wall into the open sky. There, Thaddeus heard singing.

Carter Jimenez Jenkins lives in Dallas, Texas, where he has raised $30,000 for his nonprofit, Students for Safe Water, to build a well and sanitation project in Nicaragua. He hopes to study business and perhaps one day start his own.

Four Angry Horsemen

Alexander Valdes, 17
Lakewood High School, St. Petersburg, FL, **Barbara Palmer,** Teacher

[Lights up on a large table center stage, four chairs face the audience with one on each end angled toward the audience. Seated at the table are two men and a woman. The first man is dressed in a dirty off-white wife-beater and sweatpants. He holds a box of tissues and frequently uses them. He is Pestilence. The second man is wearing faux military fatigues, the kind bought in a store and not actually used in combat. He grabs items around him and pretends they're weapons, much like an 8-year-old-child. This is War. The woman is wearing stylish clothes but is very thin. She has the air of someone with an eating disorder and has a small salad in front of her, which she stares at hungrily but seems only to move around her plate. She is Famine.]

WAR
[over mouthfuls of food] So what I'm trying to say is that if Napoleon had actually looked in his left pocket first, he would've never lost the Battle of Waterloo. I had it all…[swallows noisily] had it all lined up, and the little French dick thinks, 'Oh well, my pen must be in my right pocket,' and screws the whole thing up.

PESTILENCE
You know, War, you always blame the pocket thing, but you and I both know if you had let me start that pox in those Russian army camps, the whole battle would've gone just the way you had wanted.

WAR
Pestilence, I've said it before, and I'll say it again. I don't need you to fight my battles. You always gotta poke your nose in my business, spreading gonorrhea or cholera or some other ridiculously named disease, and it always messes up my plans.

PESTILENCE
Stop being a baby, you know I just make the diseases and after a while they take on a life of their own. Maybe if all your soldiers properly washed or actually used their heads and didn't drink from the same stream they pissed in, then my wonderful diseases wouldn't take hold. I mean, look at the Jews.

WAR
What do you mean "look at the Jews"?

PESTILENCE
Well, you know when I went through that "hating all of Europe" phase? I tried to wipe the whole place out with the plague?

WAR
Yeah, good times.

FAMINE
Great times—people starved in the streets.

PESTILENCE
Well, the whole thing hinged on how filthy all those Europeans were, but the damn Jews had to go and have all the religious cleanliness. They didn't even know why washing their hands kept the Black Death at bay.

FAMINE
Hey, speaking of Death, he's late.

WAR
Every time with that guy, I swear. Should I call him?

FAMINE
He never has his cell on.

PESTILENCE
Yeah...it's always... [rimshot] dead.

[an awkward beat]

WAR
Ha! I get it.

FAMINE
Yes, very clever. Pestilence, give him a call anyway.

PESTILENCE
All right, one second. [Pestilence dials.] 6...6...6...why isn't this working?

FAMINE
You forgot the area code.

PESTILENCE
Oh, right...7...2...7...6...6...6 [The phone rings and is projected to the audience so they can also hear the call. It continues to ring until it sounds like Death has picked up, but it's a voicemail recording.]

DEATH VOICEMAIL
Whaddup, it's Death.

PESTILENCE
Wow, you picked up! Great, so lis— [He's cut off by the continuing voicemail.]

DEATH VOICEMAIL
Psych! Ha! No way I'm at the phone. Oh, and if this is Pestilence, you can go fu—

PESTILENCE
[Pestilence hangs up the phone, cutting off the message.]
Goddamn it.

FAMINE
Sounds like that worked out well.

PESTILENCE
Shut up and eat your food.

FAMINE
You ass! You know I can't do that! [Famine gets up in a huff and storms off stage left.]

PESTILENCE
Aw, c'mon, Famine! Hey, come on!

WAR
That was kinda mean.

PESTILENCE
Shut up, War.

[Death walks in from stage right; he's dressed all in white with some heavy shadowing around his eyes, giving him a mild skeletal look.]

WAR
Well look who decided to show his bony ass.

DEATH
Hey, guys, sorry I'm late. Got tied up at the hospital.

PESTILENCE
What were you doing at the hospital?

DEATH
The usual, standing over old people and freaking them out.

PESTILENCE
You're aware of the importance of this meeting, right?

DEATH
Chill out, Pestilence. You shoulda come with me—you love hospitals.

PESTILENCE
I do love hospitals... [He has a wistful look on his face.] But that's not the point. We have a job here.

[Famine comes back onstage, sniffling.]

DEATH
Hey, Famine, where were ya? Doin' a bit of... [points at his open mouth and makes gagging noises]

[Famine starts to cry again and rushes offstage...again.]

Hey, what'd I say? Thought you were into that!

WAR
You guys are dicks. I'm gonna go get her.

[War hurriedly walks after Famine.]

PESTILENCE
Nice going.

DEATH
Ah, she'll be fine. So...any word from the guy upstairs?

PESTILENCE
Not yet, think he's waiting for a few more signs. He mentioned something about a black dog running through a cornfield or something.

DEATH
I don't think that's right.

PESTILENCE
Well, whatever, looking for signs isn't our job.

DEATH
I guess. [fidgeting] So does War still have a thing for Famine?

PESTILENCE
What?

DEATH
Oh, come on, you haven't noticed? I mean he was like a horse outta
the gate when I made her cry.

PESTILENCE
Hm. Guess I never really paid attention. Is that even like...possible?
Are we allowed to, you know...do that with each other?

DEATH
I'm not sure...I mean, you know I'm more of a banshee guy. I guess I
never even thought of dating in the office.

PESTILENCE
Me either. Well, I guess if there's no rule against it, they can do what
they want.

DEATH
Guess so. [beat] So like, is he gonna call us when it's time? Like on
a cell phone?

PESTILENCE
I think the Almighty's a bit above using cell phones.

DEATH
Well then what?

PESTILENCE
I don't know, Death, we just gotta wait.

DEATH
Fine.

[Death and Pestilence sit in silence. Death pulls out a list from his shirt
pocket and looks it over, while Pestilence coughs without covering his

mouth then blows his nose into his hands and wipes it onto his shirt, and Death watches him while looking above his list.]

DEATH
Really? That's disgusting.

PESTILENCE
What?

[Suddenly, Death's phone rings. Death scrambles at his pocket and takes out his phone. Even Pestilence seems interested.]

PESTILENCE
Well, who is it?

DEATH
It says unknown number.

[They share a look.]

Do you think?

PESTILENCE
Just answer it!

DEATH
[answering the phone] Hello? Oh...no sorry, wrong number. Wait, is this David Masterfield? It is? Oh, man, no way! You went to Florida State, right? Yeah man, go Noles! Weren't you the second-string quarterback? Who am I? Oh, I was just a frat guy, I saw you play though....I was in Delta Epsilon Delta...yea, man...well, what are you up to now, wife and kids?...No? Well that makes this easier. [He snaps his fingers at the phone.]

PESTILENCE
Did you just...?

DEATH
Kill him? Yeah.

PESTILENCE
Why?

DEATH
He was on my list for today; this whole waiting for the Apocalypse
thing has thrown off my whole schedule, so I figured I'd just take
care of it over the phone.

PESTILENCE
You make me sick.

DEATH
Everything makes you sick.

[As Pestilence begins his rebuttal, War and Famine walk in, looking
a bit awkward, almost like a child going to its parents to ask a question
they know won't go over well.]

Well, well, looks like the lovebirds have returned.

FAMINE
What?

DEATH
Nothing, beautiful. [studies them] Why do you two look so guilty?
[A smile spreads across his face.] What took you two so long, eh?

WAR
Well, we were kind of talking about something.

DEATH
[looking deflated] Oh.

PESTILENCE
[apprehensively] About what?

FAMINE
Well... [struggling]

DEATH
C'mon, spit it out.

FAMINE
[blurting] We don't want to do the Apocalypse.

[A long beat passes as Pestilence and Death stare at Famine, while War stares at his shoes like a scolded child.]

PESTILENCE
[dumbfounded] What?

FAMINE
Well, we were just saying that—

DEATH
You don't want to "do" the Apocalypse? Are you serious!?

FAMINE
Well, yeah! I mean...kinda. War and I just got to talking, and we figured some stuff out.

PESTILENCE
Like what, War? Elaborate.

WAR
[looking like a deer caught in headlights] Well...uh...you know, it's like...What happens after, you know? I mean, Famine and I don't have anything lined up after this.

DEATH
You're really serious. I can't believe you're getting cold feet.

FAMINE
He's not getting cold feet! He's actually making sense. I mean what about you, Death? With everyone in Heaven, that doesn't leave many souls to reap.

DEATH
Yeah, well... [He falters; she has a point.]

FAMINE
And you, Pestilence!

PESTILENCE
What about me?

FAMINE
What are you going to do after the Earth is engulfed in flames? Last I heard, bacteria don't really go hand in hand with hellfire. All your work will be gone.

PESTILENCE
That's not the point! We were made to do this! We're the Four Horsemen! The Harbingers of the End Times, ushers of Armageddon, Death, what about your pale horse!? What are you going to do with him if we don't go through with the Apocalypse?

DEATH
Actually, I sold Muffin eight years ago. I bought a Camaro.

PESTILENCE
You sold your horse!?

FAMINE
You named your horse of the Apocalypse Muffin?

WAR
Bro. A Camaro? Nice.

[A beat, Pestilence glares at War.]

I'm just saying, Camaro's a nice car.

DEATH
Hell yeah.

PESTILENCE
You're all unbelievable!

DEATH
Pestilence, stop being so narrow-minded; they make a good point. I mean, I wanna see the End Days as much as the next guy, but I really enjoy reaping souls. There's just something special about stalking an elderly woman down the road until she keels over, then leading her to her afterlife. I mean, the look on their faces when they see me, it's priceless, like they didn't know.

FAMINE
And all of that would end with the world.

DEATH
Exactly. I'm not sure I want that. You know what? I'm on board, no more Apocalypse.

PESTILENCE
You too, Death!? Come on, you should want this more than I do.

DEATH
I'm not saying no Apocalypse; just...let's wait a bit longer. Maybe a thousand more years?

PESTILENCE
But we've waited so long!

WAR
Pestilence, bro. It's just one more millennium; it's been like, two billion years. Another thousand will pass like the blink of an eye.

FAMINE
Trust us, we totally want to bring suffering unto men with fire and brimstone and all that, let's just savor human suffering a bit longer. This year's crop of high school girls looks really promising.

WAR
Yeah, and Iran is gonna boil over any second. That could mean nuclear war, and you know how much I love that.

DEATH
Not to mention, aren't you working on that megaflu, Pestilence? You'd really be ok with seeing all that work go to waste?

PESTILENCE
I don't...I mean, I guess not. I am really proud of it. It makes people throw up their own stomach.

DEATH
That's great, man, I'm sure it's going to be a blast to reap all those stomach-less souls.

PESTILENCE
Yeah, it would be really fun to have an old-school pandemic.

WAR
So, you in, Pestilence?

PESTILENCE
Yeah, I guess. Just a thousand years right? Then we do this...right?

FAMINE
Totally.

PESTILENCE
Alright then, I'm in. No Apocalypse.

DEATH
Great, man.

[a beat]

So what are we gonna do when the big man comes a callin'?

WAR
I forgot about that. Think he'll be cool with it?

PESTILENCE
Knowing him? Most likely not.

FAMINE
Maybe I could reason with him?

[A light from above begins to descend on them.]

DEATH
I think we're about to find out.

[The light glows brighter, then a booming voice is heard. God never shows up in person, but his voice should be booming and echo throughout the theater. He is God, after all.]

GOD
Hey, guys, you ready?

DEATH
Oh...hello...sir.

GOD
Death, please, call me God. What's up?

DEATH
Nothing much...God. [hurriedly] So, Famine has something to say.

[Famine looks stricken and hesitantly cranes her head toward the light.]

GOD
Famine? What's eatin' ya?

FAMINE
[nervously laughing] Hey, sir...uh...God.

GOD
That's me.

FAMINE
It...it sure is. So listen. We've been talking and, well...how important
is this Apocalypse thing?

GOD
Uh...pretty important.

FAMINE
Well, we were talking, like I said and...we don't want to do it.

GOD
Do what?

WAR
The Apocalypse.

GOD
WHAT!?

DEATH
Hey, no need to yell, let's just talk this— [He stops and clutches his
chest.] Agh!...oh...you bitch! [He slumps onto the table.]

PESTILENCE
Hey, there's no need for that! Come on, bring him back.

GOD
Why should I?

FAMINE
Because he'll come back anyway?

GOD
Two sure things...

DEATH
[suddenly jerking up] TAXES! [panting] Oh...you jerk. You know how I hate tasting my own medicine!

GOD
Stop being a baby or I'll do it again.

DEATH
Try it!...AGH! [promptly drops dead again]

PESTILENCE
Let's all just calm down. We just want to wait a thousand more years. That's all.

WAR
Yeah, that's like, nothing.

PESTILENCE
Now bring Death back so we can talk like reasonable, omnipresent deities.

DEATH
[Death gasps back to life.] ...Touché.

GOD

There'd better be a damn good reason for this.

PESTILENCE

Well...I personally have spent a lot of time in this place. You know all the suffering and sickness and itchiness? That's me. Those are my creations. I hate to say it, but I've kinda grown attached to those little, deadly microbes. They're like my kids. I just need a bit longer to say goodbye. Plus, to be honest, the plague I've got for the End Days could use a bit more incubation; I haven't really perfected the simultaneous projectile vomit and diarrhea part. It's more alternating right now, and that's just not that special.

FAMINE

And you know, there's really nothing for us after this. No hunger in the afterlife makes me wholly useless, and it's not like you've set up a job for us after this.

WAR

Yeah, what am I gonna do once the Apocalypse wraps up? I was created from the chaos of nothingness; I don't have a college degree or anything. This is all I know.

DEATH

Not to mention, we already have so many souls in Heaven. All these new angels are going to kill the job market. You already had to downsize and fire Gabriel. You need to expand before we're ready to take in all these new people, and you know that.

GOD

But most of the souls won't be going to Heaven, and with all the new labor in Hell, prices will be lowered and we'll see increased spending in the third quarter.

DEATH

To what end though, God? You and I both know the balloon that creates will burst in a few months and we'll enter an economic depression the likes of which we haven't seen since the Flood! We couldn't stand to keep all those souls then, and we can't take them now, our economy isn't ready. You could lose your job.

GOD
The board would never vote me down; my decision to deposit all those extra souls on Earth saved us a fortune.

DEATH
Still, an Apocalypse now would bankrupt us and you know it.

GOD
[God sighs.] I just feel like all this preparation was for nothing.

DEATH
It wasn't for nothing, just get a bit more preparation in and I promise we'll bring about the End Days in a millennia.

GOD
A thousand years...that's really depressing.

WAR
Hey, cheer up. Like we told Death, the time will fly.

GOD
[sighing] I suppose that right now the death of every person on the planet wouldn't be very financially prudent.

PESTILENCE
I respect that.

GOD
[genuinely touched] Thanks.

FAMINE
[tentatively] So I guess we'll do this again in a millennium?

[A beat passes as God considers the proposal.]

GOD
Yeah, fine. See you then.
[The light slowly fades.]

[The group all looks at each other and breathe a sigh of relief.]

DEATH
Well, there ya go.

PESTILENCE
That actually went pretty well. Guess forgiveness is in his job description.

DEATH
Yeah, he's a cool guy. So you guys want a round of drinks?

WAR
Actually, Famine and I kinda made a pact that if this all went smoothly, we'd go see a movie. [pause] Together.

[Death and Pestilence share a look.]

DEATH
[to War] Let me guess...*Twilight?*

FAMINE
How did you know!?

[Pestilence coyly leans behind Famine and makes a whipping motion to War.]

DEATH
That's adorable...well, you two have fun.

WAR
[bashfully] Thanks.

[Famine and War stand up and leave; Death and Pestilence remain at the table.]

PESTILENCE
How nice.

DEATH
Yeah. So, Pestilence—since it's just us, wanna hit up that hospital? There's a guy in there whose eyes just kinda popped out one day.

PESTILENCE
Oh, yeah? That's been a little pet project of mine. I'm game, let's go.

DEATH
Awesome! Come on, we can take the Camaro.

PESTILENCE
[scoffs] That thing's a death trap. [He exits.]

DEATH
[to himself] Why do you think I bought it? [chuckles and walks out]

[lights out]

THE END

Alexander Valdes, from St. Petersburg, Florida, loves reading G.R.R. Martin, Dante and Homer. Before writing this script, he read the entire Book of Revelation. He will study public relations at the University of West Florida.

Use It or Lose It

Nicole Narea, 17
Convent of the Sacred Heart, Greenwich, CT, **Matilde Larson,** Teacher

North Street Elementary School on a Tuesday morning is perhaps an anticlimactic setting for my first act of true adulthood. It will be as I have always pictured it. I will roam the deserted landscape in search of the murmurs that echo through the cavernous hallways. My car keys will jingle in my pocket as I take another step toward that ultimate expression of my individual freedom in this country. And then I will see it, gleaming in metallic brilliance. So shall begin my long-anticipated first rendezvous with the ballot box on November 6, 2012.

Some may regard this moment as insignificant, a mere rite of passage. However, I view it in a different light. I have witnessed the political process as an onlooker on many occasions, first as a child tugging at my mother's sleeve as she penciled in her vote during the Gore-Bush election, and most recently on behalf of the *Greenwich Time,* interviewing voters and volunteers at the local precincts. But to actually participate—to think that I will have invested myself in maintaining American democracy as a mere 18-year-old, a wide-eyed freshman in college—is nothing short of extraordinary.

My awe, however, is not universal. According to a March 8 *Washington Post* article that went viral after its publication, New Hampshire's new Republican State House Speaker, William O'Brien, claimed that college students lack "life experience" and "just vote their feelings" in a recent speech to a Tea Party group. He viewed them as "foolish" because they vote overwhelmingly liberal, as evidenced in the last presidential election, as Barack Obama garnered a whopping 66% of the youth vote, according to a Pew Social Trends report.

O'Brien's comments are a reflection of the recent push in the New Hampshire legislature to impose voting restrictions on college students that could effectively bar them from the polls. One bill seeks to restrict voting in college towns to students who establish permanent residency there, meaning that most would have to return to the polls in their hometowns to cast their vote. Another could end Election Day voter registration. Other expected battleground states in 2012, like Wisconsin and South Carolina, are also mobilizing to initiate similar legislation.

Any effort to limit youth voting should be condemned, but O'Brien's comments are alarming on a different level—they paint a portrait of a generation that is dangerously ambivalent and uninformed. According to a study by "Rock the Vote," a non-for-profit organization that works to build the political power of America's youth, eligible young voters number 40 million strong as members of the largest and most diverse generation in history, the Millennials. We are indeed a potent demographic, capable of swaying the course of history, just as the Egyptian youth proved to wield more power than the people actually in power, quenching a nation's thirst for revolution. We have all the tools to make change. We have the advantage of an established democracy in which our revolution can take place silently, in so innocuous a setting as a public elementary school.

And yet, in spite of that, we have become increasingly disengaged in the past two years. The youth vote decreased dramatically in the 2010 midterm elections, with only 11% turnout, the lowest percentage for the youth segment in two decades, according to *The Washington Post*. Are we so disenchanted with the political process as to not even care enough about going to the polls with an informed opinion? We, too, have a responsibility to democracy. All it requires is a five-minute date with the ballot box. Our counterparts in the Middle East are dying, literally, to have such a date.

But, midterms aside, the experience of the Obama campaign in the last election was a wake-up call for Democrats and Republicans alike. The youth vote can make a difference. Besides, I have faith in my generation, so watch your back, Speaker O'Brien—Mubarak didn't see us coming either.

Nicole Narea is from Greenwich, Connecticut, and a special correspondent for the Greenwich Time. *This op-ed was inspired by her desire to rally her generation in the next election, valuing a privilege her father's family lost under General Pinochet in Chile. She will attend Yale University.*

Gimme Shelter

Alexa Horwitz, 18
Buckingham Browne & Nichols School, Cambridge, MA, **Rob Leith
and Jean Klingler,** Teachers

"Who wants to dance with a sexy, gorgeous 58-year-old babe?"
Linda Burston asks, with her trademark laugh, which starts somewhere
deep in her belly. "I'm a burnin', churnin' love machine, and I want
to get down."

It is shortly before noon at the Women's Lunch Place on Newbury
Street, and Linda is getting her groove on, belting out an off-key
rendition of a Gloria Estefan hit. But, despite her high energy and
some funky Latin disco moves, Linda isn't getting any takers among the
dozens of homeless women scattered throughout the lunchroom of the
day shelter. The regulars at the shelter are used to Linda's outrageous
behavior, but some of the other women stare, open-mouthed, at the way
she gyrates to the salsa-infused beat.

Everything is big about Linda: the sound of her booming voice,
her oversized personality and her ample behind, squeezed into a
pair of skintight jeans. Even the Mohawk wig she likes to wear, the
one with a big red stripe down the middle, is enormous. It adds another
six inches to her sturdy frame. But nothing about Linda is quite as
big as her smile. It starts at her generous mouth, and then spreads
across her weathered face, making her eyes sparkle like dark amber
jewels. Her skin is smooth and the color of dark, rich molasses. A
missing front molar completes the picture, but Linda is completely
unself-conscious of her gap-toothed grin, or the bump on the bridge
of her nose, broken, years ago, in a barroom brawl.

"Let's get down, girlfriend." Linda has finally found herself a
dance partner, a schizophrenic named Sally, who has been living on
the streets of Boston for more than a decade. Sally's hair is a matted
mess, and her tattered clothes are crusted with layers of grime and
grit, but her face is filled with joy, and for a moment, she looks like
the queen of a homecoming dance.

Welcome to Linda's World. Her official title at the Women's Lunch
Place is Support Coordinator, which means Linda is responsible for

helping to make sure the homeless women who come to the day shelter get the assistance and advocacy they need, whether it's an appointment with a social worker, or just a chance to do their laundry. Executive Director Sharon Reilly hired Linda, giving her the mission of being a link between the guests and the volunteers. She trains each volunteer so that each is ready to react to some of the painful images they might see at the shelter, such as a woman crying about being pregnant or getting hit in the face by a drunk guest.

Unofficially, Linda is much more than her title implies. She is equal parts Mother Theresa and Doctor Phil. Along with a hot meal, Linda serves up heaping platters of advice and encouragement to the women who wearily trudge through the streets of Boston in search of comfort and kindness. The women listen to Linda because she knows their pain and she knows their demons.

"My father was an alcoholic. My mother was an addict until the day she died. When I was 12, my dad shot my mom in the stomach." Linda recites the facts of her life story without a shred of self-pity. "Instead of gettin' hugs, I got beaten. I used to see my father beat my mother. What he did to her, she did to me."

And what Linda did to herself was just as bad. Her descent into the abyss of addiction and crime began early. "I always drank, even as a child." Linda recalls that her parents would give her liquor to put her to sleep.

When Linda says she's "been to hell and back," she isn't exaggerating. "I was raped when I was younger, and I started using drugs when I was 13 going on 14." Dropping out of school in the seventh grade, Linda had her first daughter at 15. By the time she had a second daughter, Linda was an IV drug user, strung out on heroin and cocaine.

"I was in and out of jail and detox so many times I've lost count," she admits. "I was arrested for being drunk and disorderly, and for bein' a prostitute. You could say I was a common street hooker." Linda's eyes are trapped in a memory that is light-years away from the dingy church basement—reliving those raw memories in obviously painful detail. Her face shows it all: These memories have made her who she is today.

"You know what's ironic?" she asks without expecting an answer. "I used to sleep in abandoned buildings and in abandoned cars. I can remember eatin' out of dumpsters. And I'd come here to the Women's Lunch Place, lookin' for food, a shower or a place to crash." She pauses for a moment, before continuing. "I came looking for hope and, somehow, I ended up at this church."

The Church of the Covenant is an impressive building, rich in architectural detail and history. It was built in 1865 in the neo-Gothic revival style in the heart of Boston's trendy Back Bay. The stained-glass windows were designed by Tiffany & Company and the steeple soars skyward more than 240 feet into the air. The church sits on the corner of the second block of Newbury Street, next door to some of the chicest boutiques in Boston. The homeless women, who flock to the privately run day shelter, shuffle past elegant window displays featuring the latest designs by Christian Dior and Giorgio Armani.

The women enter the basement of the church through a side stairwell. The smell of lingering cigarette smoke fills the air, and graffiti covers the metal door to the entrance. Linda's is often the very first face they see, and she greets everyone with a warm smile and a hug.

"What you lookin' for, Marsha?" Linda turns to welcome one of the regulars, a woman who might be in her 40s but appears much older. Exhausted, she looks worn out as she shakes the snow from her jacket.

"I see ya comin' my way," Linda says with a friendly chuckle.

Marsha avoids eye contact, but Linda is nothing short of relentless.

"You look great, Marsha. You aren't pickin' your face again, are you?" Linda reaches down to grab one of Marsha's blistered hands. "You need gloves, honey. Your hands are cracked from the cold."

Marsha follows Linda into the cramped walk-in closet that is tucked into the corner of the basement, carefully maneuvering around the organized chaos. The long rectangular room is jammed with bins and boxes of donated clothing and toiletries. The closet is ground zero for the women who come to the Lunch Place, because most of them, like Marsha, need extra layers of warmth. Linda reaches into one of the boxes, and lets out a hoot. "Just what I was looking for!" She holds up a pair of fleece-lined gloves and hands them to Marsha.

"The next time, Marsha, I'm pinnin' those gloves to ya, sweetheart.

I don't want you to lose 'em."

She has an upbeat way of looking at life at the shelter without a shred of judgment, a core value of the Women's Lunch Place. The homeless women are referred to as guests and treated with respect, dignity and kindness.

That distinction means everything. These are the poorest women of Boston. Many of them sleep outside or in temporary overnight shelters, forced to carry all of their belongings with them wherever they go. They come to escape sexual abuse, get sober, have a hearty meal or, perhaps, see a doctor. But mostly they come to get warm and to find some peace and quiet. They know that between the hours of seven in the morning and two in the afternoon, Monday through Saturday, they'll be able to get off the streets for at least a few hours.

Today's lunch is chicken cacciatore, and the smell of garlic and onions fills the basement. A team of volunteers has been prepping, chopping and cooking all morning in the newly renovated, stainless-steel industrial kitchen. Promptly at noon, the volunteers go from table to table, serving steaming platters of food to the guests, restaurant style. And, like a restaurant, a small glass vase with a bouquet of flowers sits on each cloth-covered table.

"The fact that we serve the women, instead of makin' them walk through a line in a soup kitchen, speaks to who we are," Linda says, referring to one of the biggest differences between this shelter and the Pine Street Inn. "I can tell you, that kindness made a real difference to me. Even on my worst day, I could come here and get a smile from someone and it would change absolutely everything."

Like Linda, nearly half the women who come to the Lunch Place are women of color. Many of them are mentally ill or addicted to drugs and alcohol. Because the shelter does not receive any government funding, the women are not subject to many of the rules that other shelters impose. They are not turned away if they are high or drunk or having a psychotic episode. The only serious infractions include stealing or engaging in violent behavior.

The shelter is committed to accepting each woman for who she is. Linda remembers what it was like to come to the Women's Lunch Place and be treated with dignity. "I felt human again. I was treated like somebody special." This feeling of acceptance is precisely why Linda is so beloved to the guests who come to the Women's Lunch Place.

Linda is off again. She continues to make her rounds. Starting in the big square lunchroom, she helps the volunteers stack the folding chairs in the corner. The staff have tried to make the shelter appear more cheerful, but it's hard to ignore the exposed pipes, fluorescent overhead lights and scuffed linoleum floors. A piano, missing more than a few keys, is pushed off to the side of the main room, near the closet. The nap room might be cramped and dark, but for the 150 women and children who rest on the array of futons, it is a safe place to catch up on some sleep. Today, the art room is a hub of activity. One of the women has her 4-year-old daughter with her and many of the guests are making a fuss over the picture the girl has painted. "What a beautiful artist you are," Linda tells the little girl. "I'm gonna hang your picture on the wall." The youngster beams with excitement from the attention.

Later, Linda acknowledges that it is poignant how many of the pictures the women and children draw are of houses and happy families. "Maybe they remember better times," she says, "or maybe they're just drawin' their dreams." Linda says she is always aware how quickly good luck can turn bad. She takes nothing for granted. "One bad decision and I could be right back here as a guest," she says more than once. I have to keep my head on strong."

Linda says there was no "Aha!" moment, no lightning bolt or a sign from God that made her turn her life around. "I just got tired. Tired of wakin' up drunk or high. "In July 1993, I was a livin' nightmare. It was one of my worst strung-out periods, and I looked at my oldest daughter and told her I wouldn't get high with her again." She stops, pained to hear her words. "Yes, I used to get high with her." That summer, she decided she'd had enough, and with the help of the government, she checked herself into a Boston rehab. In this "prison," she learned how to talk about her feelings and discovered that she wasn't alone. Eventually, Linda learned new skills that allowed her to stand up for herself.

Linda believes that it was fate that made her read the newspaper one day and see the ad for the position at the Women's Lunch Place.

That was 10 years ago.

Linda is always on the lookout for those guests who are, in her words, "on the scam." "I know who shows up high or who is taking advantage of the place. Trust me, I can spot a crazy from a mile away," she says. In the library, a couple of women are sitting on the battered leather couches talking about Linda in hushed tones. She is legendary among the guests.

"Linda used to come in here all high and shit," says Shannon, a tough-looking woman with a crew cut and a spider tattoo on her neck. "She used to come in all fucked up and I swear to God, I know someone who used to do some nasty shit with her." Shannon is talking about Linda like she's a rock star. That's the kind of mythology Linda possesses at the Lunch Place. But really, Linda is more of a teddy bear than a grizzly bear. She talks a tough game, but for every guest she chases out the door for stealing from the closet or getting in a fight, she goes out of her way to hold a drunk woman in her arms, comforting and reassuring her that she can overcome all of the demons in her life. "I would do anything to make a woman feel better about themselves. A lot of these women trust me with their life."

For Linda, this job is more like a gift than work. "It is way beyond just a paycheck. I love seein' the guests. I worry when I don't see them—I go lookin' for them. Just seein' a smile on the guest's face. Just getting a hug. There ain't words for this. This job has saved my life," Linda says simply.

"You got some milk with those cookies?" Linda stops for a hug from 7-year-old Byron, who has been shuttled from shelter to shelter for the past six months. His mother, Deborah, is a victim of domestic abuse, and she has been on the run with Byron and two of his siblings.

"We're finally getting out of here and going home to South Carolina," she tells Linda. "Our bus is leaving in a few hours." Linda's eyes convey a feeling of not only hope, but also a bittersweet sadness. "God bless, Deborah, and Godspeed." She turns to Byron, "You be good to your mamma, sweetheart. I'm gonna miss you."

Deborah wipes away the tears. She doesn't need to say a word.

Linda's story is a story about redemption and about second chances. It is about how one woman can come back from the abyss and actually make a difference. "My testament helps people. My story gives them strength and hope."

Linda has hopes of her own. She has dreams and goals. She takes classes at Bunker Hill Community College and, next September, she will receive a two-year scholarship from Simmons College. Later this month, Linda is moving into a new condo, an upgrade from her current living situation—a crime-stricken, rundown apartment building in Dorchester. She describes her relationship with her children as beautiful. "My four kids are all extremely happy at how far I've come. We have an amazin' relationship—they love me for who I am. There ain't an evenin' that I love more than spendin' time with my four kids." Linda is proud of her accomplishments but mindful that one bad decision can change everything. "If I mess up, I could be right here at the Women's Lunch Place as a guest. I gotta keep my head on strong and stay out of trouble."

Linda finishes up her work for the day at 3:30 and trudges up the stairs onto Newbury Street. As she turns the corner, Linda stops for a moment. One of the guests is lying on a grate. Nearby, a shopping cart is filled with plastic bags and bundles of blankets. Linda reaches into her pocket and crouches down. The woman gratefully accepts a pair of gloves, and after one final hug, Linda continues on her way, disappearing in the crowd of people.

Alexa Horwitz is from Cambridge, Massachusetts, and is drawn to journalism because she loves telling stories of ordinary people who do extraordinary things. She is inspired by her mother, a journalist who reported from Ground Zero on September 11. She will attend Tufts University.

Let's Cancel CSI

Julia Marino, 16
Convent of the Sacred Heart, New York, NY, **Jason Vermillion,** Teacher

I love Twitter. I guess you could say I'm obsessed. I tweet wherever, whenever. Like at breakfast: "Eating fruit is very important." Or from the car, practicing for my driving test: "Speed limits. What's up with that?" or "I just breathed. Twice. Now three times." When all is said, done and tweeted, of course, Twitter is this amazing way I express myself. You see, I'll start with some attention-drawing tweets, and soon I'll be discovered by MTV or maybe even Disney Channel! It seems as if anyone these days has the chance to gain fame and acclaim within the limit of 140 characters. While my twitterverse leaves a lot to be desired, I, along with countless others with and without social-networking sites, have bought into that idea that success can just magically manifest. Today, it seems many celebrities are famous for not really doing much of anything. We suffer from Celebrity Stupidity Influence, or CSI. And it really is a crime that, thanks to never-ending media attention, reality stars, YouTube sensations and heiresses become rich and famous for simply "being themselves" (or, to put it more accurately, living a privileged life of excessive partying, binge drinking and law breaking—and that's certainly just a Tuesday). As we elevate our celebrities into positions of status, we lose sight of the importance of hard work and a good character. According to a recent Pew Research poll, the most important goal of young adults is to become rich, followed closely by becoming famous ("A Portrait of Generation Next"). But by publishing the misdeeds of celebrities, we condone, encourage and even reward their bad behavior. To stop this crime of Celebrity Stupidity Influence, we will start by investigating its two main repercussions: first, CSI leads to superficiality and stupidity and, second, it promotes the idea that it is acceptable to take shortcuts and misbehave to become successful. Next, we'll scope out some implications before finally pinpointing some smart solutions, so we can incarcerate this criminal once and for all.

Our first area of investigation is CSI's, role in superficiality and stupidity in our society. In the 21st century, the most shallow celebrities receive the most media attention. We are captivated by shows like *The Real Housewives of New Jersey* and *The Real Housewives of New York*, which feature Z-list, middle-aged women, famous for their ability to entertain us with never-ending catfights, catsuits and cat eyes. I don't know what it is, but there's nothing more fascinating than a televised facelift. The truth is that almost everyone is attracted to the drama that our poorly behaved celebrities create. Last April, Charlie Sheen was charged with criminal offenses including drug and alcohol abuse, along with allegations of domestic violence. After his scandal became a public news story, Sheen created a Twitter account. Within the first 24 hours, Sheen had accumulated 1 million Twitter followers. Was this superficial temper tantrum actual news? And why does Sheen have millions more followers than I do? Unfortunately, this common media addiction has very serious ramifications. According to a recent study by Dr. Marcus Appel, a psychologist at Austria's University of Linz, watching shows like *Jersey Shore* can actually cause you to imitate the actions of Snooki and The Situation. Dr. Appel refers to this as "media priming." He explains that humans are "cognitively influenced by the most recent stimuli in our lives." This means that watching mindless reality programming is actually causing millions of American viewers to make incredibly shallow decisions. Because we've bought into celebrating superficiality and stupidity, we are actually losing our ability to think.

But wait! CSI has yet another devastating repercussion. Our second area of investigation is that CSI also results in a societal belief that it is acceptable to take shortcuts and even misbehave in order to become successful and famous. Two researchers at the University of California, Los Angeles recently identified the most prized values in TV shows over the past 50 years. While back in 1967 the most important value communicated to children was "benevolence," in 2007, it was a "desire to become famous." Thanks a lot, Hannah Montana. According to the lead author of this study, Yahlda Uhls, "with Internet celebrities and reality-TV stars everywhere, the pathway for anyone to become famous, without a connection to hard work or skill, seems easier than ever" (Uhls and Greenfield). A direct reflection of this frantic desire for fame is the never-ending race to rack up YouTube viewers, Facebook friends and Twitter followers. And because many of our celebrities make it seem acceptable to misbehave and break the law, many people even see negative media attention as one of the fastest ways for fame to just fall in their laps. According to E.P. Mulrooney, a former police commissioner of New York, the first inquiry of the average young criminal is the amount of media coverage his crime has received (Carnegie). The prospect of spending time in prison is a small price to pay to be sharing space on the cover of magazines with their favorite movie and TV stars. The fact of the matter is that we're unrealistic about what it takes to become famous, and according to Dr. Patricia Greenfield, many teens have even given up on actually preparing for realistic careers and setting goals. Because who needs to work hard and go to college when you can just get pregnant and go on TV? That is exactly what many teenage girls began doing when MTV began casting for hit shows *Teen Mom* and *Sixteen and Pregnant*.

We are clearly suffering the irreparable consequences of this crime of Celebrity Stupidity Influence. We are praising, celebrating, and recognizing things that we shouldn't, losing our perception about what is right and wrong. Let's consider Tucker Max. Age: 35. Occupation: writer and blogger. Claim to fame: getting excessively drunk and indulging in every whim. Catchphrase: "a-holes finish first" (Max 379). For those of you who don't know, Max has become famous in the past five years for basically glorifying misogyny. A University of Chicago and Duke Law School graduate, he has made millions by writing books, touring college campuses and even making movies. Max writes about rape nonchalantly and argues, "fat girls aren't real people" (Max 211). I find it disturbing that we live in a society where a man like Tucker Max can top the *New York Times* best-seller list, but not surprising, as we live in a culture that so willingly celebrates bad behavior. A recent National Culture Values survey found that 74% of Americans believe that we have weaker morals than we did 20 years ago, and that the media is to blame *(The National Culture Values Survey)*. Although many of us know we are doing something wrong, we continue to do it anyway.

So, we've identified the perpetrators. Now, we need to crack the case and find solutions to our Celebrity Stupidity Influence. First, we have to start paying attention to the ideas and values that are actually important. I'm not proposing a nationwide burning of *Us Weekly,* but there is no reason why *People* should be America's most profitable magazine. We have to recognize that fame and infamy are very different phenomena. Reese Witherspoon recently commented, "I get it, it's cool to be a bad girl. But it is possible to be successful without doing a reality show" (Kurtz). There is nothing wrong with children wanting to become famous, but they need to be reminded from a young age that it does take hard work to get there. According to Sigmund Freud, our fame obsession originates from the natural human desire for a "feeling of importance" (Muckenhoupt). Instead of emulating celebrities, we need to quench this desire by finding our passions. Because what you do determines who you are. How you get your feeling of importance determines your character. If we follow these solutions, we will all begin to realize what is truly important, combating this crime of CSI to achieve *Law and Order*.

I'm not ready to delete my Twitter account just yet, but I've realized that CSI's superficial and lackadaisical effects are only bringing us down. We must realize that being infamous and on the cover of magazines is not the same thing as being a successful person. We have to pay attention to values and ideas that are actually important, finding our own personal feelings of self-worth without compromising our morals. We haven't solved this case just yet; now it's up to you. I've let go of my Celebrity Stupidity Influence. Just follow me!

Works Consulted

Appel, Markus. "A Story About a Stupid Person Can Make You Act Stupid (or Smart): Behavioral Assimilation (and Contrast) as Narrative Impact." *Media Psychology,* 14.2 (2011): 144-167. Taylor & Francis Online. Web. 15 Dec. 2011.

Carnegie, Dale. *How to Win Friends and Influence People.* New York: Simon & Schuster, 1931. Print.

Max, Tucker. *A-Holes Finish First.* New York: Simon & Schuster, 2009. Print.

Max, Tucker. *I Hope They Serve Beer in H—.* New York: Simon

& Schuster, 2006. Print.

Muckenhoupt, Margaret. *Sigmund Freud: Explorer of the Subconscious*. New York: Oxford University Press, 2007. Print.

The National Culture Values Survey. The Culture and Media Institute. The Media Research Center, 2007. Web. 15 Dec. 2011.

A Portrait of "Generation Next": How Young People View Their Lives, Futures and Politics. Pew Research Center for the People and the Press. N.p., 9 Jan. 2007. Web. 15 Dec. 2011.

Kurtz, Judy. "Reese Witherspoon Disses Reality Stars at MTV Movie Awards." The Huffington Post. N.p., 6 June 2011. Web. 15 Dec. 2011.

Uhls, Yalda, and Patricia Greenfield. "I Want My Fame TV: UCLA Study Finds That Tweens Receive a Clear Message From Their Favorite TV Shows: Fame Is the Most Important Value." Cyber Psychology. Children's Digital Media Center at UCLA, June 2011. Web. 15 Dec. 2011.

Julia Marino lives in New York City, debates in her high school speech team and credits writer Shawn Achor and cross-country coach Zoë Swenson as role models. After college, she hopes to join Teach for America and publish research in classics or chemical engineering.

The Limits of the Scientific Method

Eric Tweel, 16
Upper Canada College, Toronto, Canada, **Terence Dick,** Teacher

Today, science continues to grow in influence, advancing at an un-precedented pace of discovery. Although science is incredibly useful, it is crucial that contemporary epistemology is not clouded by the illusion that utility defines reality, lest the truth be sacrificed in the name of science.

This essay defends the thesis that science, in its empirical form, cannot tell us the truth better than any other area of knowledge. It will show that because of science's inability to avoid error and its inability to deal with certain fundamental questions of truth, it isn't superior in determining truth compared with other areas of knowledge.

We cannot proceed without precisely defining what we are discussing. Firstly, this essay deals only with the natural sciences—which we will consider to be grounded in empirical evidence—and is not concerned with any form of "science" that does not use expe-riential evidence to support its claims. As well, we will be compar-ing science to two other areas of knowledge, ethics and the human sciences. The human sciences differ fundamentally from the natural sciences, and thus for the sake of clarity, they will be referred to in this essay as the humanities. The most significant term here, though, is "truth." Here we are concerned with the unchanging, immutable truths, those that will never cease to be true, and we are assuming that these truths exist.

No matter how enhanced they are, our senses will inevitably make errors, and thus, so will science. These errors can be avoided only by rational thought, removed from the empiricism that constrains science. Galileo was right to believe in Copernicus's theory of helio-centrism, but there is a growing body of literature that shows that he was "scientifically wrong" to be right. In other words, based on the observations he made and the data he collected with the scientific tools available to him at the time (chiefly his telescope), he should have concluded that Copernicus was wrong. A contemporary physi-cist, Christopher Graney, has suggested that Galileo made erroneous conclusions because diffraction tricked him into believing that the stars were much closer than they actually are, and this caused him to side with the Copernican concept of heliocentrism. But the more likely explanation is that the rational idea behind heliocentrism—the law of parsimony, the principle that things should be explained with the fewest assumptions possible—caused Galileo to believe in it. Although the solar system could be explained as revolving around the earth, it is far less complicated (and thus requires fewer assumptions) to explain it as being centered around the sun. As well, heliocentrism has implications for the human condition—it rejects the notion that we are supreme beings at the center of the universe, and forces us to acknowledge our relatively low position in the astronomical hierarchy. Therefore, it is likely that Galileo's beliefs about the nature of human existence influenced his conclusions. This approach to perceiving the world is somewhat more akin to the humanities than it is to the sciences. These rational, logical concepts were probably the reason Galileo was steadfast in his beliefs when the Catholic church accused him of heresy.

Science can never be absolutely sure about any of its conclusions; it cannot tell us absolute truths. This is because of the unavoidable problem of induction, which states that just because something happened in the past, we can't assume it's going to occur again, regardless of how many times it appears to happen. This is often illustrated with the famous Black Swan example: if all the swans a person had ever seen were white, they might assume that all swans are white, but this wouldn't be true, because it would be disproven the moment they saw a black swan. Contrary to areas of knowledge such as ethics and the humanities, which determine truths based on reasoning and rational dialectic, science makes assumptions grounded in empirical evidence. This applies to all of science, including aspects that are often considered unequivocal truths, such as the laws of physics. Karl Popper, a 20th-century philosopher of science, attempted to resolve the induction fallacy by arguing that science doesn't use observations to predict the future but rather uses them to falsify theories. Popper asserts that the only way to grasp the truth is to identify all untruths. However, this assertion requires scientists to choose to believe in one of the theories from the number of unfalsified theories available, which renders Popperian science a confused and conflicting body of thought. Therefore, science involves the problem of induction, which areas of knowledge such as ethics and the humanities manage to avoid. This limits science to generalizations rather than absolute truths.

Proponents of the pragmatic theory of truth may argue that science is truthful simply because it is useful. However, science is limited even in its utility, because although it gives us the means to extend our lifespans and fly above the clouds, it can't give us useful advice about how to organize an ideal society or how to separate what is morally right from what is morally wrong. Questions of politics, religion and ethics must be dealt with using unscientific methods, with rational, logical thought processes that are separate from the empirical world. Today, the field of biology has advanced to the point where neuroscientists are bold enough to claim, in various ways, that their knowledge of the brain can suggest how we ought to live. In both the academic and popular press, these claims have sparked debates about the implications of emerging "neurotechnologies." According to conventional philosophical wisdom, there is a fundamental distinction between fact and value—between how things are and how they *ought to be*. On the basis of this distinction, one cannot draw normative conclusions from descriptive premises because there is nothing in the premises that would warrant such conclusions: from the fact that happiness is desired it does not follow that it ought to be. Whereas neuroscience might be able to identify the neurophysical correlates for evaluative notions such as preferences and attitudes, lying and the distinction between in-control and out-of-control behavior, neuroscience cannot, by itself, provide the basis for their evaluation. This is because, in the absence of factors external to these neurophysical states, one neurophysical state is no better or worse than another—internal neurophysical states are logically value-neutral. Similar problems arise when science attempts to overstep its bounds. Normative questions cannot be answered by scientific means, and thus, science is not more useful than other areas of knowledge.

Science would indicate that I am the result of a series of mutations and nothing more than a negligible mass of atoms in a vast, unfathomably infinite universe. It cannot help me discover my purpose in life, or why I fundamentally exist, and this limits how useful it is to me. Despite my fascination with science, and although I am strongly considering a career as a scientist, I still recognize that science is just as limited as other areas of knowledge. If I am to be stringent in my awareness of truth, then I must acknowledge that science is not superior to other areas of knowledge in grasping the truth.

This is not to say that science doesn't work. In the past few decades, advances in modern medicine, theoretical physics, chemistry and computer science have radically transformed our society. Nonetheless, this doesn't evince science as being superior to other disciplines in ascertaining truth. Even if we correlated truth with utility (which this essay argues would be erroneous), science isn't necessarily the most useful area of knowledge. The humanities, for example, have given contemporary society various advanced political systems that are vast improvements on the primordial tribal social structures that existed during the beginning of civilization.

Thus, because it cannot avoid the problem of induction and is prone to human error, empirical science cannot tell us the truth better than other areas of knowledge. The rate of scientific progress has been rapidly increasing in the past few decades, and this has created the illusion that science may now be more effective at determining truth than other areas of knowledge. It is crucial that this misapprehension be recognized as being illusory. We cannot allow the immense value of bodies of thought such as ethics and the humanities to be brushed aside by the aggressive 21st-century breed of science.

Eric Tweel is from Toronto. He considers writing the highest manifestation of one's basic drive to shape reality. He hopes to pursue biochemistry, join the transhumanist movement and work toward biological immortality—or study philosophy and "do the serious thinking society so weakly compensates in monetary terms."

Fun-Sized, Pocket Pal and Other Euphemisms for the Better Height

Shruthi Deivasigamani, 16
Cresskill Junior Senior High School, Cresskill, NJ,
Kathryn Peters, Teacher

"Aw, it's okay, sweetheart. You're not short, you're just...vertically challenged."

Whenever the oh-so-taboo issue of height (or lack thereof) comes up, people always—always—take a moment to spare me a sympathetic glance. The less tactful can never help but throw an unashamed snicker in my direction. You're short, they seemed to want to say, as if I wasn't aware. Although I initially begged to differ—five feet flat was kind of tall, right?—it soon dawned on me that the only time I could feel tall was when I visited the elementary schools...in heels. It took me a while to decipher the minefield of euphemisms. Vertically challenged, fun-sized, Santa's littlest helper—all of these were just delicate ways of toeing around the real subject.

Why exactly euphemisms are necessary for something that is so blatantly obvious is beyond me. In my humble and unbiased opinion, the petite end of the height spectrum is the superior end of the height spectrum. And so I present the top-five reasons why being short is better than being tall:

You have a lower center of gravity.

It's basic physics. If you have a lower center of gravity, then you will not fall as easily. This comes in handy, especially in the tumultuous halls of Cresskill High School. The student body moves as a cohesive unit, knocking over victims like a battering ram. Those with low centers of gravity will get jostled a little, but run a negligible risk of falling. Our long-legged brethren, however, are like human Jenga towers—ready to topple at any given second.

The Scholastic Art & Writing Awards **197**

You have infinite leg room.

Imagine for a moment two boxes of the same size. One box has a baby spider monkey in it, and the other houses an orangutan 400 times as large. Which creature is more comfortable? Similarly, smaller limbs allow smaller folk to enjoy smaller spaces without any cramped joints or muscle fatigue. Tall people don't have this luxury; if their legs are forced to occupy a constrained space, they have to contort their limbs into awkward and uncomfortable angles. Eventually they'll emerge with numb feet and a crazed limp.

You aren't living in the past.

It's a complicated scientific theory, one that Google could provide an extensive explanation about if you cared enough to look it up. Basically, it takes a tenth of a second longer for tall people to receive stimuli from the lower half of their body than it does for short people to. It's a longer journey. Essentially, tall people are living one-tenth of a second in the past because whatever sensation their brains receive occurred one-tenth of a second before.

You are stealthy.

If you're training to be a ninja, then this side of the height spectrum is the place to be. Small people can hide in tiny pockets of shadow—perhaps even in the shadow of an unsuspecting victim. Small people have lighter footsteps and can spring a surprise attack at any moment. Small people have the amazing ability to tuck themselves away into corners, undetected and unnoticed. For all you know, there might be a short person spying on you *right now*.

You will live longer.

This isn't so much based on statistics as it is in biology. Shorter people have fewer cells in their body than do tall people. Cells die often and need to be replaced. However, the human body can only replenish so many cells; it has a limit. Because short people have fewer cells, they need fewer replacements and thus can live longer because they take longer to use up their body's maximum amount of cell reproductions. These findings were published in a bulletin of the World Health Organization over a decade ago, so no, you can't dismiss this as foolish hypothesizing.

Short people live the life, an assertion that can be scientifically proven by biology, physics, math and common sense. An added bonus? You can have bragging rights. When tall people brag about how tall they are, they look like jerks. When short people brag about how short they are, they look self-assured and confident. Napoleon was short, after all, and he nearly took over an entire continent single-handedly. As much as tall people like giving smaller people condescending smiles and making unoriginal comments about hardly seeing us down there, they really are missing out.

Not everyone, after all, can be fun-sized.

Shruthi Deivasigamani is from Cresskill, New Jersey. She has done research in neuroscience, which she will study this fall at Princeton University with a minor in creative writing. As Carl Sagan and Neil deGrasse Tyson did for physics and astronomy, she hopes to bring neuroscience to the common reader.

The World Is Not Flat

Joel Wilner, 16
Advanced Math and Science Academy Charter School, Marlborough,
MA, **Martha Richardson,** Teacher

You've all seen the video. Miss Teen South Carolina was asked at a 2006 pageant to discuss her opinions on why a fifth of Americans can't locate their own country on a world map. After much profound thought, the beauty queen offered her...insightful explanation: "I personally believe that U.S. Americans are unable to do so because, uh, some...people out there in our nation don't have maps and, uh, I believe that our, uh, education like such as in South Africa and, uh, the Iraq, everywhere like such as..."

...Breaks my heart.

The beauty queen later went on to explain that she was "overwhelmed" by the question. But let's face it. Miss Teen South Carolina isn't the only one who is, to put it lightly, geographically and culturally inept. Just as the mesmerizing question she received stated, too many of us—and I'm looking at you, Americans out there—fall on the bad end of the bell curve when it comes to geography. But can it be true what they say? That a *fifth* of Americans can't find the United States of America on a map? *Crap.*

This is...a problem. Right!? Avoiding geography is like...avoiding food. If you do it for too long, you're going to become delirious and blind to the essentials of life. Because when we become oblivious to our world, we lose the ability to make connections.

You see, geography is not about memorizing state capitals or long, impressive place names—although knowing how to pronounce that Icelandic volcano Eyjafjallajökull (pronounced AY-uh-fyat-luh-YOE-kuutl [-uh]) will get you far in life. That is how you pronounce it, I looked it up—but I digress.

In the long run, the world looks nothing like how fourth-grade geography class made it out to be. The world does *not* cut off with the 50 state capitals song and then...fade into oblivion. The world is *not* flat. But, with our level of geographic education, soon our ship *will* fall off the edge.

So let's keep ourselves from heading into that point of no return. Let's navigate our ship around the globe safely and prove that the world is truly round—and doesn't stop at the borders of America. Our first port of call will be to discuss the causes of this pandemic of geographical illiteracy that is decimating society. Next, we'll voyage to the implications that geography has on all of us so we can cast aside our ignorance of the very world that we live in.

One of the main reasons geography is so overlooked is its unfair depiction in society. We regard it as an afterthought, placing it too far down on our list of priorities when it should be at the top. The knowledge that we glorify the most is undeserving of such attention, losing relevance in the real world, while geography will always be relevant. For instance, every year, ESPN televises the Scripps National Spelling Bee on prime-time TV, showcasing middle school contestants like athletes, complete with play-by-play commentary. According to Nielsen Media Research, it averages more than 4 million viewers a year. In contrast, the National Geographic Geography Bee ekes out a scanty public television broadcast. Furthermore, spelling bees have been glorified in several films, like *Akeelah and the Bee,* and even a Broadway musical, *The 25th Annual Putnam County Spelling Bee.* Geography? N-O-T-H-I-N-G, nothing.

So what has led to this unwarranted view? Look around you. Our schools have let geography fall off the map. For decades, geography has been taught with uninspired instruction, limited to memorization without any context, resulting in geography's being lumped into history class under the euphemism of "social studies"! And, as our schools cater to careers that are viewed as more profitable, like engineering, computer science and math, any traces of geography are gone completely. But what our education system is forgetting is that geography is arguably more important than any other subject. We can't compete on a global scale if we don't have a grasp on our global setting. But our schools' poor exposure of geography has led to adults with as good a geographic education as the health situation is in Swaziland.

An Associated Press research poll has found that three-quarters of American adults incorrectly named English as the world's most widely spoken native language, and six in ten could not locate Iraq on a map. But the saddest part of all is that fewer than three in ten even thought it was important to know about countries in the news.

America is not an island. We can't shut ourselves inside the confines of our country and let world events carry on. Our ignorance isn't just hurting our image; it's hurting our self-worth.

At the tender age of 3, I spontaneously started tracing one of those United States placemats. Intrigued by the colorful shapes on the map, I naturally learned the states, their cities and their locations. Then, I moved up to the next level: the world map. By the time I was in kindergarten, I had memorized every country in the world and each one's capital. Seven years later, I came in second place in the Massachusetts geography bee!

Arrogance aside, I can tell you firsthand that my knowledge of geography has paid dividends and much, much more. Although memorizing the world capitals and countries may seem impressive, it means absolutely *nothing* if you can't expand upon it. You see, geography has given me a unique perspective on my world because I can analyze the *why of where*. Geography is about documenting the lessons of previous generations into a modern worldview. Geography is critical to succeeding in a world that is going international in such areas as industry, business, our environment, our economy, our culture and our history.

We experience this effect every day of our lives, from video games to household items, even fashion. Don't believe me? Check the tag of the shirt you're wearing. Made in China? I thought so. Through this kaleidoscopic lens, a true student of geography can piece facts together from across all subjects to create a more enhanced view of the world.

So to obtain this enhanced view, we must first find a way to cure geographic illiteracy. Like I mentioned before, our schools are doing a dismal job of teaching geography, which translates into ignorant adults. But ignorance is no excuse for indifference.

Not surprisingly, Americans travel internationally less than residents of any other developed country. According to CNN, only 30 percent of Americans own a passport, while in other countries, such as Canada and the United Kingdom, the rate is as high as 75 percent. And while "America the Beautiful" is certainly a masterpiece, our dependence on other countries—Chinese-produced clothing, for example—makes our lack of international interest appalling.

Matt Harding was a 26-year-old kid living the American dream—he played video games for a living. Matt worked for a game-designing company in Los Angeles and spent his days cooped up in the office. After many years of this, he came to the sad realization that life was a rhythmic migration from "bubble to bubble: car, work, car, apartment, car, shopping mall, and so on." He realized that in order to be fully satisfied, he had to get out. See places. Matt quit his job and spent his life savings on a trip around the world, dancing with all the people he met.

Four videos, 80 countries and 75 million views later, "Where the Hell Is Matt?" is one of the most uplifting and influential videos on the Internet. But what Matt learned along the way is more valuable than any fame or success he may have gained. Through his travels, Matt realized that true appreciation of this world comes with actual discovery and the stories one learns along the way. Matt met tribesmen in Papua New Guinea and Mongolian nomads, but "to see the joy on their faces, and to witness a fuller spectrum of emotion, reminds us that they are no different." And you can't teach that in a school.

So laugh at Miss Teen South Carolina all you want. But we have got to start changing our attitudes about geography to avoid becoming a stereotype. Because once we abandon our planet, the stories and societies are lost forever. And somewhere between Borneo, Bolivia and Boston is a world with cultures, places and people that make each geographic experience impossible to ignore.

Joel Wilner is from Marlborough, Massachusetts, where he plays piano and captains his school's baseball and speech teams. He loves slam poetry, geography, travel and filmmaking, which he hopes to pursue in college and as a career.

I Am Noor

Katherine Fang, 16
Bellaire High School, Bellaire, TX, **Camille Quaite,** Teacher

I. Plastic surgery
"Is she bald under there?"
"That has to be it."
"Let's pull it off."
"Oh…well, hell—I guess she's not."

My *hijab* is next to the half-liquid Wrigley's someone spat on the cement hotplate a few hours ago, and they are gone when I hear their words. And because this is how it's always been, I pretend I have Botox, and I move nothing as I pick it up, not even my eyelids.

There is a girl with a tattoo and a boy with black jeans a few feet away. They were shy 15 minutes ago, but now her hand is clawing at his back, and his is inching toward her ass. Roughly 50 other stragglers in spaghetti straps and V-necks and colored tights are waiting outside after school, one girl making wide sweeping gestures as she shouts at her indifferent boyfriend with the mohawk and the earring. A black boy and two white girls practice a cheer routine. All of them clutch their phones, and I pretend I don't know what they feverishly typed before they pushed send.

II. *Aloo gobi* and praise repeated
At home, it's stuffy because Ommy starts to sniffle at nothing, so Baba compensates by not wearing a shirt. Ommy is making *aloo gobi,* her favorite dish, which means she's feeling sentimental. I know it when she starts singing the only American song she knows—she swore Punjabi music was superior for years but then one day she heard the Bee Gees playing while a commercial flashed 0% APR financing for some car. She sings American when she thinks Punjabi music and its uncertainty are too close to what she's feeling. The language itself just developed like that because the people didn't know things, she says, not like Americans, who always just knew—
"And the sun will shine, if just for you.

And the trees will talk to the skies, whispering lies.
Heaven will pass to me, yeah.
Trains walk by and the birds disappear."

I wonder what is making her so sad when it's not even winter yet, until I feel her watch me run up the stairs, and I know she knows, even though I made sure to dust the hijab off. I don't hear the sound of my back slapping against the floor until I've pulled myself halfway through the next sit-up.

When I go downstairs again, the TV that we never bother to replace is playing, and Baba says, "Noor, come and see. Come and see."

And I see the stripes and stars next to the president, and then the newscaster says how those Navy Seals flew into Baba's Khyber Pakhtunkhwa province, and the country is avenged for that atrocious crime of almost exactly a decade earlier.

"Praise," is all Ommy says as she mixes more curry into the aloo gobi and hands me a bowl. There is never enough curry in this world for Ommy. "Praise, praise, praise."

"He was nothing of what loving Allah is," Baba says.

III. Carnival-going

We go, Baba and Ommy and I, because fall strolled carelessly in with its straw hat and loose-fitting, dirtied orange jumper and eased summer out, and we all begin to taste crispness on our tongues. Ommy and I wear our burkas like always.

The Ferris wheel is turning, and a sign for the *Dungeon Drop—a thrilling ride if you dare! (must be 5 feet)* is visible from the parking lot. I resolve to try cotton candy, finally stepping away from my childhood refusal, based on the conviction that it was spun out of human hair.

Baba hands me some money to buy us tickets. The ticket guy has two days' stubble and chews tobacco from the right side of his mouth with that gum-smacking noise, and I count one-two-three flies stuck to the darkened window. I slip him the bills, but he stares and doesn't reach to take it.

"I'm sorry, ma'am. But we cannot allow you in the park."

"Are you closed?"

"No. But what you're wearin'..." He spits out his tobacco and starts cleaning his nails. "It's juss, I'm 'fraid you'll scare them children."

"What?"

"You'll scare them children, you hear? With your crazy terrorist clothes or whatever."

Baba's face always furrows up toward his hairline rather than down toward his eyes. I watch him and suddenly realize that this is too often his face.

Ommy looks angrier than when I lost all that money at that one museum.

"And what is your meaning here?" she asks. "We are here to enjoy the carnival like every person, nothing more."

Her words slur out with her Punjabi accent, which gets stronger as she continues. She moves her lips like there is bramble in her mouth.

The ticket guy cuts her off.

"Tell you what, ma'am. You let me go get someone to do a pat-down of you, and then if they figure you're a'right, then you can come in, sound fair? It's just...I cain't see nothin' but your eyes, and it's a-freakin' me out a little."

Ommy's eyes shine as she walks away. Baba and I trail behind, and all he continues to look is sad.

IV. Papers

At school, they've formed an activist club—out with the existing system. A posse of them come with their pamphlets as I glare at chemistry, and they hand one to me. Statistics and facts and an Elizabeth Cady Stanton quote.

"Read it, please. It's really informative."

"I don't know how you can stand it."

One of them says that the country should just go the way of France and ban these religious garments altogether. They talk to me like I am an alcoholic in need of rehab, and the pleasure is theirs, really.

As they are walking away, the girl with the lopsided ponytail cannot help it. "Is it hard not to trip?" she bursts.

But she is too embarrassed to wait for a response, so I remain silent and allow her to quicken her steps away.

V. Declaration

I am Noor. Seventeen and thin. Skin so barely there that you can count my veins. Dark circles under my eyes, courtesy of genes. Hair that's naturally shiny and grows hella fast. Thick eyebrows and lips that look stained with Dusky Rose from that corner drugstore even though I leave them nude. I walk with my hips first.

I chose this. I chose this so no one can see if my ass is pinchable or if I'm repeating outfits or what size cups I wear. I chose this to demand that you see that:

I am Noor. Seventeen, and I eat Pop-tarts like some people pop Tic-tacs. I always say keep the change because I hate loose coins jangling. I once ate a rolly-polly. I am always losing my pens. I have never had cotton candy. I gut-bustingly laugh at romantic comedies, and I don't very much like aloo gobi, actually. I spreadsheet everything. The ocean at night sends me into a panic. I get the hiccups too much. I think peanut butter shouldn't be jelly's twin.

I am Noor. My parents, Ommy and Baba, came to stop being dirt-poor. I rearrange furniture periodically and think maybe I can find a new identity. I stare at the sun sometimes to make sure it's really in the sky. I can't complete puzzles because I lose the pieces. I leave sticky note reminders for myself everywhere. I am always washing my keys. I burn the bread I try to toast. I never get test anxiety except when they're taking my blood pressure. I always think the moon is too small and distant to pull ocean water into tides.

I am Noor. Remember me.

And remember that when he died, we said it too.

"For Allah and country," we repeated...

Katherine Fang is from Bellaire, Texas, where she figure skates and practices languages, including Chinese, Spanish and Arabic. She hopes to pursue international relations, using language and writing to promote receptivity to cultural differences. This piece grew from observations of racial subtleties she saw cultivated in others.

My Cuba

Marcela Grillo, 17
Institute for Collaborative Education, New York, NY,
Hilary Leichter, Teacher

*June 1942. I grew up next to the river. Every day, I woke up before
the sun could appear behind the clouds. I ran, ran as my feet melted
into the mud below. I ran to be close to my river, where I grew up.
It never mattered that I was only 8 years old. I knew with my whole
soul that I had never seen anything so beautiful in my entire life. I
was convinced the blue water was full of hidden crystals. I could lose
myself in those waters, fishing in the early morning hours.*

February 1955. I'm going to see my cousin Ramón and my Uncle
Domingo today. Walking down Avocado Street, I cross to the corner
and see a policeman interrogating a woman. These days, my little
town is so unfamiliar. The streets are quiet, and nobody dares to go
out alone. We're afraid.

*When I stood there at the river, I knew I was in the safest place.
When I stood there at the river, my feet only a small distance from
those of my best friend Benito's, it was like time lost itself, the hours
hiding in the river and its sweet song.*

We're afraid. Batista's cronies have completely overtaken my little
town. They said that they were men of honor and men of uniform, but it
was all a painful lie. They use their guns every day and their consciences
are never clean. I see the policeman and I want to run down another
block, before I have to see his face. I hear him yelling. The sweet face
of the young boy I once knew disappears into the sticky air.

*"My brother! Come check out this fish!" His voice was light as it
floated along the riverbed, where he stood high and mighty, barefoot
on a flat gray stone. I went fishing every day with Benito. He taught
me all that I needed to know. He never bragged about anything
without backing it up. He was impulsive and never wore shoes and*

almost always invited himself over for dinner, but I loved him anyway. I loved him for his brotherhood, for his spontaneity and for threatening to beat the crap out of those kids who teased me at school.

I only fished with Benito. My father was always busy, my mother could care less, and Ramón was more into cars like his father Domingo. So in my love of fish I was alone, except with my best friend.

"¡Mira, mujerota! ¿Qué te pasa?"

He is screaming at an innocent woman who hasn't done anything wrong. Sensing trouble, I hide behind a parked red car on the other side of the street, occasionally peering with a pounding heart. The paint of the car feels smooth against my palm, and I can feel one single drop of sweat cross my brow. I squint in the burning heat of the sun and see a boy of about 16 years run out from behind his mother, shoving the police officer back a few steps.

One always has to stand up straight, arms without any movement. There is no speaking allowed, mouths silent in honor. My father always told me and Benito: "You are not a part of their world. You're only visiting."

I stared at the fish Benito had caught, its skin glimmering before my eyes, its eyes dark brown. I ran my finger along its scales, mesmerized. The silver colors bounced off of one another, and occasionally a reflection of reds and purples would stream in and I couldn't tell whether or not it was my imagination. I'd never seen a fish that big before. I tried to imagine all the things it had seen along its journey.

"Let's throw it back," I suggested before I could stop myself.

"No way," Benito sneered. "How are we going to eat tonight?" He stared down at the fish and his lips curled into a sly smile. "Here, gather the line. I'll take care of this guy."

I watch as the policeman stumbles back slightly. His hands curl into fists almost instantly. "Don't talk to my mother that way!" the boy screams, his dark eyes full of rage. "Watch your mouth!"

"You watch your step, boy."

I find myself praying for the boy to quiet down.

"I watch you every day, abusing and tormenting my neighbors!" the boy shouts louder. "I will not let you do it now. Get off my block! *¡Largate!*"

The boy's sun-kissed skin is dark with grime and dirt. He reaches and shoves the policeman harder, but the man acts twice as fast and forces the boy onto the concrete.

Thump. Thump. All I can see is the boy's lifeless body being thumped into the ground, a puppet whose strings have been cut loose.

Thump. Thump. My little feet were damp and I ran to Benito's side. He removed the bait and line from the fish's mouth with his deft fingers, and the fish flopped lifelessly, gasping for air on my friend's grimy palm. I realized that at any moment he was going to reach into his brown slacks for his trusted pocketknife.

I don't even feel the tears falling down my cheeks but they are there. The policeman is Benito, the boy who used to be my best friend. My fingers are shaking furiously, and I am sure my heart has dropped too far down my chest. I gasp for air, but there is none. Almost like I am not a part of this world torn apart. Almost like I am just a visitor. I watch Benito stalk down the block, blood on his baton, walking in the same direction as the flow of the river. He fades into the hot sun, and I see the boy and the man fade together and disappear right before my eyes.

When I look at the river and see the fish swimming to other worlds, I know that each of them has a different story. Where did you come from? What have your eyes seen? And then, I can't help but think: What is there of the world outside my Cuba?

Marcela Grillo is from New York City. "My Cuba" is based on her grandfather's emigration from Cuba during the revolution in 1956, an experience she values far more than any textbook fact. She hopes to study literature or medicine at Connecticut College and become a novelist.

Post-Op

Caroline Hamilton, 15
Fine Arts Center, Greenville, SC, **Sarah Blackman,** Teacher

Feed him split pea soup and clean up the green spittle off his chin and shirt collar. Respond to the way he flicks his head, twitches his lip—he needs someone who will understand. Do not cringe at the color of his stumped leg or the fluids that soak the bandages. Change them daily, or perhaps more, depending on how often his eyes glance down to see if it's really gone.

When the pain makes his nostrils flare and his hands grasp the hem of his shirt, give him what the doctor gave you for childbirth; pain is pain. Mend his clothes in front of him, but do not let him see you cut off the right pant leg; sew the end closed at the knee. Improve your strength so that you can carry him to the bathroom, help him into the tub, but do not watch his hygienic routine—he must rediscover his body alone. Sleep near him to hear him, though not in the same bed; healing takes room. Watch to see if he rolls over in his sleep, notice how he chooses to prop himself up against the headboard during the daytime. Take him outside at increasing rates, no matter the difficulty this causes you. Fresh air is good for the grieving. Feed him casseroles your mother brings. They are all brown, like his weathered shoulder blades, the mole on his thigh.

Take note of when his eyes water, downcast; this is your cue to leave him. Kneel in front of him and rub his temples slowly, sing Gaelic folk hymns. Do not make eye contact. Avoid the church, the pastor, the string of busty women with bible verses and artificial sweeteners. Wash the dishes in private, wash the clothes in private; separate him from day-to-day tasks to minimize the remembrance of amputation. Hide his razor; such clean sharpness so close to the throat becomes too tempting.

Write your letters in his presence as encouragement. Place books by his bedside about men overcoming problems. Remove them later when he doesn't read them. Make all his food from things you grow. His nourishment is solely your responsibility. When he learns to stand again, take his weight on one shoulder to teach him about balance.

Remove all obstacles from the bedroom to the living room; there must be no obstructions for him to maneuver in his path to recovery. Sacrifice to remain with him; he will always need your arms, your joints and tendons, your awareness of his discomforts. When you find him sprawled in the bathroom trying to remove the other leg, kiss the small incision and wipe away the blood. Tell him it is time to change the bandages.

Caroline Hamilton lives in Greenville, South Carolina, where she enjoys playing cello, singing and acting. Being involved in multiple art forms helps her discover her place in the world and how she should interact with it. She hopes to pursue dramaturgy or dramatic literature.

Conjoined

Nathan Cummings, 16
Mercer Island High School, Mercer Island, WA, **Susan McKay**, Teacher

This is the only thing that matters.

When I was three days old, doctors cut my brother off of my right side. As expected, he didn't survive the experience. They put him in a small box and gave him to my parents, who—not being much for pomp and circumstance—laid him to rest in our backyard. For all I know, he's still there. It doesn't matter. This is not his story. This is my story.

Funny how people have trouble telling the difference.

The word is *conjoined twin*, for the record; let's just get that out of the way. It doesn't help that my mom is from Thailand, of course. There are certain people who will never understand that that does not make me an actual, factual *Siamese twin*. Trust me, if you can make the connection, allow me to tell you it's been done before. Like on my first day of kindergarten: all the parents in the back, listening to their kids mumble their names and favorite colors. Then I got up to speak. The teacher—a gray-haired, matronly type who'd apparently been briefed in advance—took one look at me and said to the whole room, "Will is a very special boy. He was born a Siamese twin." Instantly, the room went quiet; my mom got this furious gleam in her eye. Like, *I cannot believe you just said that.* The teacher seemed to sense she'd made some sort of faux pas but stubbornly decided to forge ahead. "Will," she said to me, her voice dripping with as much syrup as she could slather, "what is your favorite color?"

I said red, and people automatically started trying to assign some sort of connection to my psychological profile, because there's *no way* a former conjoined twin could be interested in something as mundane as fire engines. One parent took a peek at my right arm, which has always been slightly shorter than my left, and he looked as if he wanted to pickle me in a jar.

School's gotten a little better over the years. Of course, I couldn't juggle quite as fast as other kids, but I was a mean shot at foosball, and I could freeze-tag with the best of them. It still goes around, though. People talk. They don't hate me for it. I wouldn't even say they pity me for it, which would be a million times worse than hate. But they identify me by it. Not Will, the bad juggler. Not Will, that kid with the dark hair and a weird sense of humor. Will, the kid with the scars.

Sometimes, when I'm lying in bed at night, I absently run my fingers up and down my right side. They are still there, impossibly faint outlines on the smooth textured plain of my skin. People used to look at them and wince, and for the life of me I can't understand why. Sure, the process must have been painful, but so is getting your wisdom teeth out, and most people sure as hell remember that, whereas I don't have the slightest memory of being three days old and one-and-a-half people. These scars, I've grown up with them. To me, they're just another part of my body. I run my fingers up and down, down and up, until I fade away into sleep.

The dreams began when I was 10 years old. I would feel overwhelming darkness, a sense of pressure from all sides, and no air. I was incredibly thirsty; my skin seemed too dry. I tried to move, and my fingers crumbled into dust. That was usually when I woke up, gasping and sweating and not the least bit thirsty.

I was stupid enough to relate this to my psychologist when my parents signed me up—nothing's too good for our little malformed darling!—and he was over the moon. He dug into my medical file, turning up all sorts of information I didn't really want to know. Eventually, he dug up a picture of me when I was about a day old. I puked when I saw it. It must sound odd, puking at a picture of yourself, but beside me lay...something else. Scientists talk about the "uncanny valley" effect with robots: the closer something gets to normal, the more eerie and unnerving the remaining differences look. Well, the thing lying beside me...it wasn't whole, not even close. But I could still see hints of myself in it, in the hair, the curve of the forehead. I was looking at my personal uncanny valley, and it was a long way down to the bottom.

My shrink asked me, "Do you ever miss your brother?"

I said that it's kind of hard to miss someone who was in a catatonic state at birth and got cut off you before either of you could form full sentences.

He asked, "Do you ever hate him?"

That really set me off. What was to hate? Poor little bundle of nerves and giblets. He hadn't harmed anything in the world. He'd kind of gotten the short end of the stick, in fact.

"Do you ever feel like you were him?"

What a question. At that point, I was done talking. I screamed, and my parents scooped me up and placed me back in the car. The psychologist snapped a picture of me with his phone as I was being carried out. Prick.

So what if I have dreams about being buried alive. Are you thinking that it's telepathic communication—that my brother's some sort of fetal zombie reaching out from beyond the grave? Bullshit. I had nightmares about being stuck in a shoebox because for the longest time, when I imagined my brother, all I could think of is that it would be pretty awful to be stuck underground while I was out enjoying the sunshine.

Maybe that's it. I'm sure that would be the inevitable conclusion that the psychologist would draw. Simplified as much as possible, it would come out to something approaching survivor's guilt: I lived, and he died. Believe me, I've thought about this—and now, after 16 years, I've finally come to terms with it.

Yes, I got lucky. Yes, I survived and my brother got the scalpel of doom. But here's the thing: If he was really my brother, I know he would have been happy for me. I imagine us having a conversation: me sitting in a folding chair, legs thoughtfully crossed, him lying in his little petri dish. *Take life by the horns, bro,* he'd gargle at me in his squishy chipmunk voice. *Don't hold back. Go get 'em, for me.* My imaginary little brother gives great advice. He'd have been a pretty cool guy, come to think of it. But then again, so am I.

And there you go. After so many bad dreams, I'm finally free as a bird, and the last thing I need is you throwing the same old paranoia back in my face. So get over the scars. Get over the photograph. Get over all your sick, twisted conspiracy theories, because if *I* did, so can you. I am a normal person. Not a person and a half, not half of a person. I am whole. I am perfect.

Yeah, right. Like you're even listening to me right now. I know what people want to hear. So step up, folks, because here I am, the freak of nature, right next to the bearded lady and the limbless man.

When I was three days old, my parasitic little lump of a sibling was carved off me, leaving me alone.

This is the only thing that matters.

Nathan Cummings is from Mercer Island, Washington, and an avid member of his cross-country and track teams. While he will always write, he is also interested in pursuing medicine.

The Only Way

Jane Wester, 16
Charlotte Latin School, Charlotte, NC, **Maria Klein and Richard Harris,** Teachers

He was 13 in 1973. Thirteen and in the seventh grade at Richard Talbott Junior High School.

There were three schools on that stretch of Finley Road—Benfield Elementary, RT and Finley Park High School, all in a line, so you just moved down the hill as you got older.

The schools were separated by chainlink fences, and when busing began in '71, the junior high kids could look through the fence to see the high school next door, see their older brothers and sisters and the fistfights and the protests. Charlotte was supposedly handling integration well, but it didn't look that way, not to the kids on either side of that fence.

But right then, all that he and his friends could see through the fence was a baseball game. They were at recess, playing in a field that faced FP's baseball field. Naturally, the high school game was the main attraction for the seventh-grade boys.

He climbed a small tree to see the game better. He had just gotten to the top when the principal, Mr. Davis, strode onto the field, walking straight toward the little boy in the tree.

The boy scrambled down as fast as he could. Mr. Davis broke a branch off the tree.

"Here, or in my office?"

"Here," he answered, trembling.

Mr. Davis began, and one of the other boys started to count. One, two, three...

Seventeen.

Late that night, after his mama had put him to bed, he came back into her room. He had been silent all afternoon, but he wouldn't admit that anything was wrong.

"Sweetie pie, what's wrong?"

He turned around and lifted up the back of his pajama shirt.

"Oh, no."

His parents believed in public education. When busing began and so many of their friends moved their kids to private schools, they kept their three children in public. Busing was an experiment, sure. Their friends said that they didn't want their kids to be used as lab rats.

He was a doctor. He understood the importance of lab rats.

At the hearing they asked Mr. Davis: Why didn't he stop? Why keep on hitting a little boy for an offense as small as climbing a tree?

His answer was simple.

"Because he didn't cry."

They asked him if he always hit his students. It was 1973, after all; corporal punishment was on its way out.

"It's the only way those nigga children learn," he said. "You can't reach 'em any other way."

He was 13 in 1973. Charlotte was handling integration well.

Jane Wester is from Charlotte, North Carolina. She runs cross-country, plays piano and is active in her school's community service program. She hopes to study English, history or religion and become a journalist.

Puna

Elizabeth Gobbo, 16
Hood River Valley High School, Hood River, OR **Gabe Judah,** Teacher

She works for herself, and no one else. Not for her mother, her dead father, her refusing-dead grandmother or her loser brothers and sisters back home crowding all together, under one sagging roof. Not for the old ways or her people or old Laos. Now, she works for herself, and for America.

Still, after 15 years, America does not work for her. She lives and works in dark grease and cinder block, and bathes her daughter each night in spindled shadows and cracked cold water. She tells her daughter that when she grows up, she will know how to care for herself, because she will be an American. She left the girl's father years ago; he did not work at all. You already are working, he would say, I do not have to work. You provide for me, you are the wife. But he is gone now, she has let him fade back into the same part of her mind that contains the rest of them, the dead and the refusing-dead and the wishing-they-were-dead, all crowded, under one sagging roof.

For five years she has made her living as a waitress in a bowling alley. The cook is from her country, from Laos, and he makes drunken noodles and basil rice next to the burgers and french fries. The drunken noodle is very good, very spicy and soft, like home. No one ever orders it, they all want pizza and Coca-Cola and M&M's to swallow between rounds, shooting terrorists with purple machine guns in the arcade. She watches the American children who play on the games and scream and drop food on the floor and sweep it into the corners with the hard heels of their bowling shoes. Her daughter could be almost their age; she will enter the first grade in September, after the summer is over. She wonders if her daughter is like them. She does not get to see her much; she is never home, always working.

On her walk to work, she passes through her neighborhood: the scattered hair salons and nail shops and closet-space restaurants and laundromats. When she arrives at the bowling alley, her boss yells about the Thai man who used to work there and did the accounts. He yells until he is red in the face. He is telling her that the Thai man ruined everything and took money for himself, and that she should have known and that she is very lucky to still have her job. She nods, but she thinks, I am not lucky. I have worked hard to get here, harder than most.

She walks home late, back through the fragmented Cantonese and Korean and Thai and Vietnamese lettering and tries to read through American eyes. The brushstrokes and neon blur into a muddy smear, spreading out under her feet and up over her head, until the sky is all black and red and beige brick. It gets colder, and she pulls up the hood on her jacket. It is a very nice jacket, green and soft and still fairly new. It was a gift from her cousin in Seattle, Washington. She has never been to Washington, but she thinks it must be very green there, and growing. She thinks soon she will take her daughter and move up there, but not to Seattle. She doesn't want another city, she wants somewhere in the country, with only houses and trees, no apartments and no crowds.

She thinks, maybe there, people would understand. Here there are too many of us, always coming and wanting and working. Maybe there is somewhere quiet where they can still see us, can hear us without losing us in the fog and the crowd. Maybe there is a place where America knows we are working.

Elizabeth Gobbo lives in Hood River, Oregon, where she plays pedal harp, Zimbabwean marimba and electric bass. "Puna" was inspired by the experiences of a Laotian woman she met at a bowling alley. She hopes to act on Broadway—or else study foreign languages and join the Peace Corps.

Witch's Lullaby

Jacqueline Knight, 16
Lafayette High School, Lexington, KY, **Carole Johnston,** Teacher

Sleep like a coiled snake on glowing coals, my son.

Don't listen to the goblins who will whisper in your ear when I close you off from the hallway light. They'll click at the back of your neck until your hair stands stiff, but cover your ears, my dove. Don't be afraid if the creatures of muck and mud visit you tonight. One may smell like bleach and another of wet garbage and their claws could be six inches long, but you are my clever little boy. Sing them a song my muse, the one of the dragon and the seven noble men. Or the song I sing when I fix your meals. The one with no words, only hums and dums and dees. They will hear your voice soft as a spider's web and let you go on your twisted dream path with your voice pinging around between their pointed ears.

The trees may be purple or green. Perhaps they'll even want to waltz with the wild roses that sprout around your socks. Our world is full of hungry monsters, dear child, so keep those ears sharp as a scorpion's stinger. They will want your golden hair and mistake your eyes for the finest gems, so your wits must be closer to your heart than your cotton pajamas. If you stumble across a rat's cold, blue tail, wrap it around your finger for luck, and if a troll steps in your way, and I'm certain one will, give it to him and he will move on.

Princes will have skin of layered rubies and their tight robes will be lumpy and coarse. Queens have hummingbird beaks and spoons instead of tongues but bow and don't stare, my lovely, for they will paint the rest of your path. Cats will talk in short riddles and dogs will chirp on top of cliffs, but you are odd in the world of the insane, so keep to yourself and they will clop into the forest of strung-up paper lanterns and blown-glass suns.

When you kneel by the river to drink, be careful not to bump noses with the merchildren. They are mischievous boys and the girls tangle plastic water bottles into their hair. They will laugh like dishes being dropped on tiles and their mouths will never move. With their tails, long and lean, sticking into the fog, they will want to show you all their tricks, but do not stay, my lamb. Keep walking or you will trip into their trance of shells and bubbles and never come back to me.

When the paint on your road has dried and begins to chip away, be quick as a salamander and jump away, for when the paint all falls there will only be a gaping abyss waiting for you. With the road gone, you must travel by boat, my love, but that is the fastest way to travel when there is no ground.

Before the sun shakes hands with the moon at the bottom of the sky, you will see a house of packed-in sand and red tapestries. The windows will be shaped like clouds and the only door will be two-feet high. Crawl through, dear prince. Do not be afraid when you see a fire burning. It is there to heat the cauldron of water hanging by the thin silver chain. Take a seat on the softest cushion by the fire and close your eyes with the steam filling your ears, your mouth, and every crevice of your skin. When you open them again, sweet boy, I will be there in the kitchen and my bowl will always have something for you.

Sleep well, my love, so that you may wake to the strangest adventure of all.

Jacqueline Knight is from Lexington, Kentucky, where she writes fiction and humor, and aims to keep her keyboard in a state of constant shock. This piece was inspired by the Wicked Witch of the West in The Wizard of Oz.

Mr. Ten Fifty

Grant Stoner, 18
Homeschool Academic Teaching Support, Salunga, PA, **Elizabeth Jones,** Teacher

A fellow with a disagreeable look walked along the grubby street. He wore black slacks, a black topcoat and a black bowler hat tilted ever so slightly to the left. He held a letter that read something like this:

Dear Mr. Finicky,

Thank you for all the years of fine work you have poured into your department. You have done an excellent job in every instance. Your work has been so good that you have literally worked yourself out of a job. The department is sad to say that it no longer needs your assistance. We again thank you for your exemplary work. We also wish you the best of luck and will recommend you to anyone you may want to work for.

What was a man his age to do? He was not old enough to retire, nor was he young enough to begin a new career. He had been with his former employer for the past 15 years. He wasn't ready to relocate and start a new job. Mr. Finicky was a man of particular tastes. He was well educated and was quite diverse in his knowledge.

His thoughts flashed back to his young adulthood. The thrill of being able to do anything, the adrenaline rush of accomplishing dangerous feats, had brought tremendous satisfaction to him in his youth. If only he could return to those days and relive the thrills. But those days were gone, swept away by the winds of time, never to return. Or were they? Could they simply be locked in a deep hidden storeroom waiting to be unlocked? Could he return to his past thrills? Could he possibly once again live a thrilling lifestyle?

But what could he do that would relight his old burnt-out torch of exhilaration? Men of his age were frowned upon if they left their comfortable lifestyles for the rompings of youth. So, what would he do? He no longer possessed the youthful body he once had. Although his body was not as strong, he was more experienced and his mind was saturated with priceless information.

He needed something that would not only give him a physical thrill but would also challenge him intellectually. It also needed to be something that no one else would know about. It did not matter whether it was legal, for that made no difference to him. For he would not be caught. Something illegal actually would suit him quite well. It would give him a thrill, and it would protect his identity.

Now, what act of lawlessness would he take up? Violence never agreed with him. Murder was out of the question. Robbery was a slightly more suitable option. It would be quite exhilarating, and his intellect would be stimulated to find a foolproof plan to protect his identity.

The money was not the goal. He was motivated by the physical rush and mental challenge that he could get from robbery. He decided he would pilfer ten dollars and fifty cents from each place. It was enough to make him feel like he accomplished something without damaging the targeted businesses.

Saturday mid-afternoon, he reached a small grocery store that was about an hour from his hometown. He simply slipped his handkerchief up over his face, pulled his hat low over his eyes and stepped into the store. He then pulled a small gun from his coat pocket. Pointing it at the man behind the counter, he demanded in a gruff voice ten dollars and fifty cents, which was quickly brought forth by the panic-stricken man. Mr. Finicky received the money, slipped the gun back into his pocket and backed out of the store. He slipped behind the wheel of a "borrowed" car and was gone.

So began the mystery of Mr. Ten Fifty. A few days later, he robbed a department store without even the slightest hint of a sniffle. Then he went on to rob a small jewelry store, taking his usual ten dollars and fifty cents without even looking at the gold. After that he went on to rob a high-class watch and necklace store. Holding the security guard at gunpoint while robbing the store, he left with squealing tires in another newly "borrowed" car.

Mr. Ten Fifty became a household name. The papers were having a field day with the mysterious identity of Mr. Ten Fifty. Many people wished the gentleman robber well, but others considered his unlawful actions to be in bad taste.

The men in the investigation office were as mad as hornets. There was no promising evidence to find the identity of the thief. There were no leads outside the store after the suspect drove off. And there was no pattern as to which stores were being hit, other than that they were constantly being more and more difficult.

A week later, a lone gunman held up a small bank, taking ten dollars and fifty cents. A few weeks later, the state bank was held up for ten dollars and fifty cents. The thief left no clues as to his identity or his location.

The department of investigation offered a small reward for information leading to the arrest of Mr. Ten Fifty. This thief was making them look bad. He had to be stopped, not because he was damaging society, but because he was destroying the investigators' public image.

The whole department was up on their feet after the national bank was held up for a mere ten dollars and fifty cents. This was the last straw for the department. They tripled the reward and put their best men on the case immediately. They went back to every store that had been visited by Mr. Ten Fifty. They had one more surprise card to play. They would bring back a hero. They would call back Mr. Finicky. He had been somewhat of a genius in the department. With him on the case, the mystery would be wrapped up in several weeks.

And so, another letter was sent. Mr. Finicky chuckled with the greatest of satisfaction as he read:

Dear Mr. Finicky,

It seems that we have parted ways a bit prematurely. The department of investigation would be grateful if you would consider returning for another one-year contract. It seems that your skills are greatly missed. You would be able to begin work immediately on the Ten Fifty case. Please send your reply immediately.

Grant Stoner is from Salunga, Pennsylvania. His favorite writers include J.R.R. Tolkien and C.S. Lewis. He would like to apprentice in wood- or metalworking, which, like writing, involve the art of creating and recreating.

The Global Origins, Evolution, Proliferation, Influence and Future of the Geek Empire

Rishi Mirchandani, 14
Fox Chapel Area Senior High School, Pittsburgh, PA,
Jessica Green, Teacher

Long ago, a speck on the horizon of human history became a stomping herd kicking up a dust cloud that has still not settled.

It marked the arrival of the first Geeks: sporadic isolated groups that eventually became an unstoppable tide. Scholars, evolutionary historians and speculators have documented this phenomenon and have offered various schools of thought regarding its trajectory. Sifting through fuzzy documentation of Geek history has proven to be a daunting task. This reviewer, who defines himself as part of the Geek genus, has put himself up to the challenge.

Contemporary Western studies claim that the first Geek was probably a bespectacled genius with a photographic memory who outsmarted his teacher, befuddled his parents and, being different, ended up abandoned in the wilderness or was consigned to an insane asylum. As more cases sprouted up in classrooms, teachers accustomed to slotting students into categories of fun, popular, dumb, corny, rich, poor, bully, bullied, et cetera, were simply at a loss. Programmed by a system where all human activity was subdivided into specialized isolated departments, they, as educators, experienced a major crisis. They couldn't neatly pigeonhole the complex types who were part charmer, part psycho, socially awkward and superintelligent. And so, after much discussion, a consensus was reached. The new category of "gifted student" was created. Into it went prodigies, immigrants and motley groups that were too different to comprehend.

A curious parallel phenomenon occurred while the Gifted Program was in the throes of birth. A whole host of behaviors, from attention-deficit/hyperactivity disorder to nail-biting, were now assumed to be giftedness in some manifestation. It appeared that all casualties of marginalization had been given newfound hope.

Some records and oblique references to the vibe of mutual incomprehension between the early Geeks and their more scattered counterparts have survived the onslaught by the Proponents of Political Correctness, the Dumb Dudes League, the Witless Protection Program and the Geek Empire Deniers and other groups vehemently opposed to the legitimization of Geeks as a significant category in human civilization.

Oral traditions have been almost snuffed out, giving rise to conflicting accounts of the Geek experience. *The Advent of the Chinese Kid and His Role in the Pedagogical Revolution* is a modern Geek fable that precedes *The Multicultural Invasion of Campuses and Curricula*. Its hero has achieved legendary status for having been the first toddler to nick calculus problems in preschool, and to have opened doors for high-achieving Asians of all stripes to outperform their peers despite being brown. While the Cool, Sporty and Entitled Rich niches vied for superiority against the Clowns, Goons and Rapping Serial Fillers of school hallways, there were simmering forces at work. From the ashes of unpopularity, type A phoenixes were rising. The nerd mentality asserted itself despite being scorned as freaky. Safely ensconced in the Gifted Programs, the nerds with drive and ambition vented their nerdy visions into exam papers, competitions and presentations. The nerd boldly stepped from the margins to the center—from fool to cool.

Geeks and nerds then entered an era of fused nomenclature. They were now part of an elite squad that participated in math olympiads, spearheaded chess clubs and got perfect scores on standardized tests. Their progeny are easily recognizable in schools today. They usually sport thick-lensed glasses and are perpetually lost in thought. They are far ahead in the time-space continuum in a typical school setting and have given a new meaning to the concept of space travel.

The ripple effect created by this subspecies of student is far-reaching. Veritable armies of militant parents routinely set up camp outside testing venues to obtain a coveted spot in gifted camps and challenger schools. Websites advocating views of gifted experts to enhance the giftedness of the gifted now abound. Embryonic cerebellum research identifies would-be Geeks, and they are promptly subjected to nonstop Mozart while in the womb. Preparatory schools proudly spawn legions of supercerebral young beings who then go on to mastermind technological, artistic and creative wonders that shape our world today.

Entrepreneurs worldwide are cognizant of the marketability inherent in this demographic. Geek-chic fashion accessories are a hot commodity, especially the techie headgear such as hats with a built-in iPhone. Despite its obscure lyrics, Geek Rock is now a popular music genre, especially the smash hit "Come on, Amadeus! Whatcha Gonna Play Us?" Geek intellectual pageants are as entertaining as they are unique. Geek reality TV has very high ratings, particularly the prime-time show "Prancing in Mars," which airs on the Show Wiz Network. Brain-Box News is a major contender in the media wars. The Geekspot blog is a significant cyberspace presence. There are Geek Cruise lines operating complete with pretravel agreements for patents on inventions or any cognitive miracles that might happen onboard the ship. Geek vacation spots are sprouting in remote exotic places where Geeks can peacefully contemplate unsolved equations and conundrums while sipping their piña coladas. In response to accusations of insularity and elitism, geeks have been passionate in their embrace of cheesiness, and have started social-networking sites like Tracebook and Glitter.

We live in a stay-connected world designed by Geeks. They stealthily rule from behind those thick lenses. Mother Nature is stupefied at her own creation. Like all things in nature, Geeks are not a monolithic entity. There are Geeks of every stripe. As they achieve success and fame, we see Geeks-turned-corporate-gods, geeky eco-gurus and a veritable pantheon of Geek gods.

Geek power is everywhere.

Geeks have made their mark on civilization in varying degrees. Countries differ in their integration of Geeks into the mainstream. In China, overzealous Geeks have turned their country into the world's bank. In Sweden and Finland, Geeks are the new normal. The Third World is brimming with wealthy Geeks who have used their intellectual capital to suction jobs from overseas.

In America though, an anti-Geek movement funded by Folly-wood millionaires called the Glee Party is gaining momentum. It has harnessed the power of the Fighting For Full-Time Fun Fanatics and supporters of the "Don't Task, Don't Spell" policy, and they are threatening Geeks, whom they consider un-American. And so Geeks have begun to go underground in that country. They are treated as a lunatic fringe, despite their vehement protests that they are not a deranged minority, but rather, a minority with great range. Some of them have been seen moving in droves back to the shores of their native lands, marveling at the prosperity of the smirking second cousins they had left behind.

Scholars are still in the process of harvesting material from the past, toppling received paradigms and tracing Geeks to preliterate times. In primitive societies, they observe, the first stirrings of ratiocination were unleashed. Cave paintings have been found depicting an inventive savage initiating cutting-edge technology when fashioning a sharp tool out of stone, while calmly roasting his colleague on a spit. Long before the knowledge business became a flourishing industry, the primal urge to communicate ideas for advantage existed. Shrieks and grunts translated themselves into riveting tracts etched on rock faces and cave walls. Discourse evolved from hair-pulling, spear-impaling and head-butting to musical expression, manipulation and persuasion.

The early Geeks vented their subliminal erudition with feverish intensity, creating colorful narratives, theories and Geek mythology. The first mathematicians, scientists, artists, writers and iconoclasts were all persistent Geeks who wouldn't give up. Some were martyred, others outcast, but, resilience being their hallmark, Geeks have prevailed.

Rishi Mirchandani lives in Pittsburgh, Pennsylvania, where his research on voting theory won first-place awards at statewide science competitions. He has also played piano twice at Carnegie Hall. He sees this piece as an aesthetic tool to express his sentiments about those who are marginalized in social settings.

Testing Theories of Love Using the Scientific Method

Jordan Myers, 18
Thomas Jefferson High School, Alexandria, VA
Jennifer Seavey, Teacher

Abstract

Dating is confusing to those unfamiliar with its rules and regulations. The strange signals that are used by both sides, the inevitable miscommunications that occur and the discouraging awkwardness that permeates the environment all conspire to make this vital component of life so difficult to obtain. It appears that each gender has a dissimilar set of standards and perceptions in which they operate, which only serves to maximize confusion. This article describes the author's attempts to develop a theory to explain the dating process.

After several trials of attempting to successfully navigate the dating scene, the results are inconclusive. There are no observable patterns to love interest; there is no rational process that can describe how love operates; and no logical theory could be deduced. The many variables and lack of honest feedback makes understanding dating behavior nearly impossible. Love refuses to be quantifiable.

Introduction

Love is an odd component of human life. No matter how much one tries to study, rationalize or change its composition, the body still has an innate fear of this desirable emotion. For example, based on the strict logic of behavioral actions, there is very little to lose from asking someone out. Best-case scenario, the suitor lands a date that will lead to a relationship. Worst-case scenario, the suitor feels the minor emotional sting of rejection and moves on. And yet, the fear is still paralyzing.

Through rational theory, it is reasonable to surmise that if a male likes a female and that female reciprocates this feeling, then they will spend more time with each other and a relationship will form out of mutual desire. Oddly, this is not the case in the author's experience. The frequent outcome is: first, the female displays interest, and the author attempts to reciprocate. Second, frustration ensues as each misinterprets the other person's signals. Third, conversation is attempted and ruined because of awkwardness. Fourth, both parties avoid each other to alleviate the discomfort.

The author devised two theories of why high school dating challenges him. (1) The pulchritudinous appearance of the author might intimidate females, resulting in nervous behavior, or perhaps they do not try to pursue the author because they (wrongly) assume that the author knows what he is doing. The assessment of beauty was determined through the following methods: (a) The frequency and duration of female gazes upon the author were noted. The data suggest with a high probability ($p < .01$) that the author is desirable to see. (b) Comments on the author's appearances were inconspicuously collected from unbiased sources to determine relative attractiveness. Statements such as "Wow, look at him. He must be the hottest guy in school" lead to the calculation that the author is in the top 0.1 percentile (there are roughly 1,000 males in the subject high school). (2) Females do not like the author for social reasons. The author admits that he is socially challenged in that he finds it difficult to sustain a long conversation with mere acquaintances. It is difficult to ascertain what females even want in a relationship. By inspection, it appears that sexuality is not the only factor (if it were, the author would not be having these issues). What is the desired balance of romantic and emotional interest? They are not the same thing, as one female was overheard whispering to another after being approached by the author, "He's hot, but I would never date him."

To test the above theories of why dating is challenging, the author conducted a series of experiments. In each dating attempt, the author used the following hypothesis designed to test both theories of dating. If theory 1 is true, then showing interest in the female should alleviate the tension from interacting with someone of high attractiveness. If theory 2 is true, then females who show romantic interest in the author should be willing to hold conversations with him.

Methodology

Dating advice was collected from various sources and compiled into a four-stage plan. Each stage is designed to minimize ambiguity and risk of rejection.

Stage 1, Confirm: The first stage consists of confirming the female's interest in the author. This is broken down into three sub-steps. (1) The classroom is visually scanned to check if the female is staring at the author. If she turns away, this may be due to shyness; the scanning continues until confident the gaze is genuine. (2) Social contact is initiated by talking with her. If she seems friendly, then it is presumed safe to continue. If she is distant or confused, then it is recommended to abort. (3) Her reaction is monitored by eavesdropping on conversations between her friends. For readers who have an ethical objection to this step, please note that this is for assessment purposes only. If she reveals that she is uninterested, then time will be saved for both parties. On a side note, it is amazing what people will say about someone even when that person is within earshot—almost as if they want you to hear it.

Stage 2, Reciprocate: Once the target female's interest is ascertained, the author displays his affection in two steps. (1) Stare back at her in class. A warning to readers: There is a fine line between being mysteriously sexy and undesirably creepy. Staring at her with a side glance fosters the former image. (2) Seduce her by talking to her and conveying your interest. Compliments always help. If theory 1 is correct, then this should reduce the female's fear of approaching the author because she knows the author is interested.

Stage 3, Connect: Establish a personal connection by inquiring about her personal life, such as her hobbies, opinions, etc. By forming a social relationship, it will be much easier to move into a romantic one. If theory 2 is correct, then creating this connection with the female will improve the author's social standing, and thus his romantic desirability as well.

Stage 4, Request: When a reasonable association has been achieved, validate the relationship by asking the female on a date. To reduce pressure, make the request privately and nonchalantly. If accepted, then the relationship is official.

Results and Discussion
The experiment was run multiple times and has achieved different

stages with different subjects. For some trials, the author barely got to stage two before being blown off. On a few accounts, the experiment was shut down at stage four. No attempts have been completed successfully. Because of the ambiguous nature of dating attempts, an exact number of trials are unavailable, but it is estimated to be 12, plus or minus three. The most notable cases have been included below (names have been changed in accordance with psychological study privacy regulations).

Data Point #1
Subject: Samantha

Samantha was the ideal specimen. She was as pretty as she was intelligent—that is, a lot. Prior to taking interest in her, the author enjoyed wonderful conversations with her about several deep topics. Another catalyst is that she was overtly interested. Unlike other infatuated females, Samantha openly stared at the author (she did not turn away when her gaze was returned), and she mentioned him by name when talking to her friends (instead of using an indefinite pronoun). Stage one (confirming her interest) became unnecessary.

The experiment began at stage two. The author scanned the room and rested upon her gazing eyes. Eyes locked and a mutual understanding of affection was secured. After class, the author approached her and began a decent conversation. Unfortunately, this good standing did not remain as stage three was executed. Interestingly, the fact that the interactions were now romantic in nature changed the mood dramatically. What used to be easy conversation turned awkward, and she became noticeably uncomfortable. It seems that the pressure was unbearable; she started avoiding the author 1.5 weeks later.

Even this girl, who once privately proclaimed herself to be obsessed with the author, could not stand him when she got the chance to date him. How discouraging.

Data Point #2
Subject: Sadie

Sadie was a delightfully peculiar subject. Although she was verbally very quiet, she expressed herself in her musical talent and intriguing fashion sense. The author tried to ascertain her attraction, but did not get conclusive results until a certain day.

The class was in a barely supervised study hall during the televised speeches for class officer elections. Naturally, the author was ignoring the speeches and playing card games with friends. Sadie, dressed in a cute skirt that complemented her top, sat in a chair near the corner silently observing. After a particularly impressive game, the author rose up to celebrate his victory. At that moment, Sadie lifted her skirt, revealing her dark-blue panties, while staring directly at the author. He instinctively licked his lips, and blood rushed to his face (and elsewhere) as he tried to regain his composure. She smiled at the reaction and quickly lowered her skirt. The author, thinking that even he could not misinterpret the meaning of Sadie's actions, decided to skip to stage three.

Establishing a personal connection proved difficult. Despite her indiscreet attraction to the author, Sadie was distant during conversation. Is there something the author is doing wrong? Is the author so awkward that it is easier to flash him than hold a conversation with him? This data defies conclusion.

Data Point #3
Subject: Josephine

Josephine was a mysterious target. Her cute face with intelligent eyes often hid behind long, dark flowing hair. She was also bold enough to advance the process herself. During the social contact part of Stage 1, she pulled out the chair next to her, signaling the author to take it. Unfortunately, he was too caught up in the conversation and did not pick up on this cue until later that day. The author recalls thinking to himself, "Why did she pull that chair out? Was she expecting someone to sit there? Oh, wait a minute..." Regardless of this mishap, the female had shown her interest, so it was safe to advance to stage 2. The next day, the author indicated his interest by occupying the chair Josephine had indicated the previous day. Contrary to prediction, this resulted in an awkward moment. Did the author make a mistake? Was there a misinterpretation of her gazes at the author and her worshiping the author to her friends? Why was this so much more uncomfortable than it was just yesterday? Now she seems resistant (perhaps playing hard-to-get?).

It would have been preferable to strengthen the relationship before stage 4, but the impending school dance compelled premature action. The request was made with an obligatory offering of cookies. She declined on the grounds that she "is not going to that dance." When asked why not, she simply said, "I just don't like dances. I'm sorry." Presumably, this was a falsehood to mitigate the feeling of rejection, although ineffective because the intent was obvious.

Against all reason, the author persisted to court her. Evidently, Josephine's volatile affections—she would express interest on some days and exhibit disfavor on others—caused addictive feelings in the author. This was against his better judgment, as a similar situation had occurred before (not discussed in this article) that only resulted in distress. The agonizing cycle with Josephine continued for one month before the author decided to cut his losses.

It seems that the signals used to confirm her interest in stage one were misleading. Josephine still employs her seductive gazes, which elicits a feeling of torture. She was tantalizingly close, but always just out of reach.

Data Point #4
Subject: Wendy

Wendy has a beautiful face and figure and is a fine singer. She is introspective, often seen staring at the distance, but can hold a conversation when she wants to. She resembles the author in that respect. Her audacity is admirable; she has made several advances, which the author did not realize until later. Her reliance on signals will prove to be trouble later on.

Wendy caught the attention of the author when she began seeking conversations with him, which is impressive, because few females converse with the author before establishing friendship. Then one day, she sat in the author's bus seat. The tacit seating chart on the bus made this action highly unusual. It was evident that she held affection for the author but she did not reveal any clues to her behavior. She did not look up, and she left her backpack next to her on the seat. Confused, and taken off guard, the author sat in another seat. There were many components that confused the author: Was she expecting the author to sit next to her? If so, why doesn't she look inviting? Does she want to experience being won over? The probable reason is that she wanted to have deniability in case it doesn't work out. Later that day, the author asked Wendy for her rationale for sitting in my seat. Her response: "What? Oh, no, I just saw that the seat was empty, so I took it." The author concludes that it is inexpedient to address a female's rationale directly.

This confusing signaling system leads to misinterpretations on both sides. The author took a gamble and sat next to Wendy the following day, but the result was undesirable. She barely responded to small talk and seemed downright uncomfortable. After three days of this, she decided to sit at the front of the bus, with the rationale, "Oh, I like sitting at the front of the bus. I would do it all the time if there were room." It seems that displaying interest is not sufficient, nor was the author's interpretation of signals. This is useful information to remember.

Conclusion

Both theories proposed regarding the author's inability to date have been proven false. Theory 1, which states that the author's beauty intimidates females, is unsupported by the data, which indicates that showing interest in the female, which should alleviate that fear, simply causes more fear. Theory 2, which states that females dislike the author for social reasons, is unsupported by the fact that females who have previously shown interest in the author are prone to avoiding the author without explanation.

The results support the following conclusions: (1) A female staring at the author does not make it easy to approach them. (2) A female discussing how attractive the author is does not indicate desire to date him. (3) A female flashing the author does not designate interest. (4) Even when the female makes the first move, pursuing her is futile.

There does not seem to be a theory on how to understand this complex yet critical behavior known as dating. It is unfortunate that the females in this study will not provide honest feedback. Josephine was later overheard telling her friend what she told the author when she rejected him, to which her friend replied, "Wow...that's the biggest lie I've ever heard." Relying on this type of feedback is demoralizing and only exacerbates the problem. Reliable data is critical to any endeavor, and without it, any scientific inquiry becomes guess and check without the checking part.

It is getting harder to keep repeating these trials—most scientists would have given up by now after so many failures. One must ponder if these females know how much their actions affect the male sex and know that every action imprints that feedback as a data point in life. In conclusion, it seems that love is an uncertainty the author, and everyone else, will have to endure.

*Paper is formatted to meet the requirements of standard science article writing.

Jordan Myers is from Alexandria, Virginia, and was inspired to write by his sophomore English teacher, Mr. Miller. He is fascinated by the elusive problem of reproducing human behavior with artificial intelligence. He will study computer science and psychology at DePaul University.

In That Case, I'll Stick to Politics

Szofia Komaromy-Hiller, 16
Notre Dame Academy, Park Hills, KY, **Linda Bricking,** Teacher

Dear Scholastic Art & Writing Awards,

    Enclosed please find my submission entitled *The Declaration of Independence* for your consideration of the Scholastic Art & Writing Awards. My respectable mentor, Mr. Franklin—yes, the one on the one-hundred-dollar bill—is sponsoring my submission, given that my work is written with the highest technical skills. I humbly announce that I am most proud of his endorsement. I would also like to request my composition to be considered for the American Voices Award, as it truly reflects the feelings of my time and the highest ideals of my fellow Americans.

    Sincerely yours,

    Thomas Jefferson

Dear Mr. Jefferson,

    We have received your submission entitled *The Declaration of Independence* for the Scholastic Art & Writing Awards. We are very happy that as a young and aspiring writer you share your talent with us. At the same time, we would like to point out that you must adhere to the outlined submission requirements of the Award Committee. Therefore, we cannot accept your submission in its current, handwritten format. However, we would like to encourage you to resubmit it in double-spaced, typed format. We recommend 12 pt Times New Roman font. The detailed formatting requirements may be found at the following Internet site: www.artandwriting.org. If you submit electronically, it will save trees and will save you postage.

    Best regards,

    The Scholastic Art & Writing Awards

Dear Scholastic Art & Writing Awards,

    I had to ask my dear friend, Mr. Benjamin Franklin, to help me with the formatting requirements. Fortunately, we were able to print my writing in the required format in his printing press in Boston. I cannot imagine all the other Scholastic participants going through the same trouble. I have to admit that writing my composition was much easier and took less time than trying to submit it to you. However, I am proud of my accomplishment and hope that you may find this writing truly exceptional. I was told that my writing contains the best-written sentence in the history of the English language. Additionally, my friends who have read it feel it is truly revolutionary and worthy to be remembered in the annals of history. It is my hope that you at least consider it for one of your publications that features young writers. It fascinates me to think that my work could be part of a traveling exhibit nationwide.

Truly yours,
Thomas Jefferson

Dear Thomas,

It was a delight to read your submission for the Scholastic Art & Writing Awards. While in general it is rather well written, we would like to point out some areas for improvement. Your sentence structure appears to be rather archaic, some of the word usage is outdated, and it seems that the composition contains some run-on sentences. We would like to encourage you to resubmit your composition after the aforementioned editing has been completed. Please discuss these recommendations with Mr. Franklin. Otherwise, we are sad to inform you that the composition docs not meet the standards of the Scholastic Art & Writing Awards.

Cheers,
The Scholastic Art & Writing Awards

P.S. We also need to know in which category you are submitting your composition.

Dear Scholastic Art & Writing Awards,

I have considered your recommendation to improve my writing. While I do respect your highly esteemed opinion, I and the entire Second Continental Congress are satisfied with its current wording and formatting. My close friend, General Washington—yes, the one on the one-dollar bill—personally reviewed and approved it. As such, I do not wish to edit it from its current and final version. In terms of writing category, since the composition reflects my personal feelings and the feelings of my time, I would like to submit it in the Personal Essay/Memoir category.

Best regards,
Thomas Jefferson

Dear Tommy,

One of our grading criteria is the originality of the writing. Your composition does show some technical writing skills, and rather good spelling (by the way, you may want to ask your friend, Mr. Franklin, to use the American, as opposed to the British, spelling), but overall it lacks the originality, the spark that would raise it above the other submissions. The Personal Essay/Memoir category is reserved for works dealing with individual experience and self-revelatory works. Unfortunately, this is not apparent from your writing. Additionally, neither does it appear to be a fictional story that would land it in the Short Story or Flash Fiction categories, and, in fact, the word limit is exceeded for the latter. You may want to consider the Persuasive Writing category, but in that case, your composition truly needs some serious reworking. May we recommend the Humor category?

Cheers,
The Scholastic Art & Writing Awards

Dear Scholastic Art & Writing Awards,

I am truly sorry that my writing, *The Declaration of Independence,* does not qualify for the Persuasive Writing category in its current version. I have to admit that I am rather aghast that you even associated it with laughing matter and jokes, satires, parodies and humorous anecdotes! However, as I am very anxious to submit it for consideration, I would like to submit *The Declaration of Independence* under the Science Fiction/Fantasy category. Please?

Sincerely yours,
Thomas Jefferson

Dear Aspiring Writer,

We sadly inform you that your writing entitled *The Declaration of Independence* did not even make it to Honorable Mention in the

Science Fiction/Fantasy category. Nonetheless, you have shown a bit of talent and most obviously, persistence. We encourage you to continue writing. However, without serious improvement in your personal style, your submissions will not win awards at the Scholastic Art & Writing Awards. Perhaps you may consider writing something simpler, like a constitution, instead.

Take care,
The Scholastic Art & Writing Awards

Szofia Komaromy-Hiller is from Park Hills, Kentucky, speaks three languages and loves learning about the history, art and cuisine of different cultures. She hopes to patent something useful for humanity, illustrate and translate children's books, and never stop visiting new and old places in the world.

The Gone So Sooners

Lylla Younes, 16
Louisiana School for Math, Science & the Arts, Natchitoches, LA,
Clayton Delery, Teacher

I'm running away. There is no particular reason for this rash action. I didn't slam the front door and scream something impassioned and cruel at my mother with theatric finality; didn't run out into the rain, choking on my tears. In fact, the weather is pleasant. It's dusk now, and the sky has this neat orange glow, and the clouds are dark and crusty on the bottom. I'm just following the train tracks because I don't know what else I would do. I like the tracks and what they represent (to me, at least). I feel like I'm walking on freedom.

Maybe it's 1925 again, and I'm about to hop on a train that will take me all the way to New York. And maybe I've never been out of this town, out of Williamson, West Virginia, the coal miner's congregation, the lung doctor's (my father's) pot of gold. I'm going to New York. No, Chicago, because I want to hear Louis Armstrong play me a song, want to see that trumpet bobbing up and down to the beat, and the beads of sweat gathered on his brow like the crowd that followed him there all the way from New Orleans. Then I would dance. Dance and dance until I died. I don't dance now. I'll go to a party every once in a while, but I'll usually just sit on the couch and people-watch because how can it really turn you on when a guy decides that he wants to rub his crotch against your butt or wherever else, while some terrible electronic din bleeps in your ears until your head feels like the Gordian knot and you wish you could resurrect Alexander the Great so that he could take out his mighty sword and solve the problem once and for all?

My friend Meaghan says that "dancing is a sign of confidence," but I know for a fact that I'm more confident than Meaghan. Maybe that's just because I'm indifferent about most things and because she has to reapply her lip pencil every 20 minutes. Whatever it is, I know that if I was in Chicago circa 1925 and Louis Armstrong was playing his trumpet, I would grab a nice-looking fellow and we would kick off our shoes and get down.

But it's not 1925. It's 2011, and I'm a member of Generation Y, the Millennial Generation, the Net Generation, whatever you want to call it is fine. We are technologically innovative, highly developed, just like our computers. I wonder who names the generations, who decided that my grandparents were born in the Silent Generation, because my grandmother's laugh is like a firecracker, starting off with a gentle *pyoww* and then escalating to this earsplitting crackle, and you can almost see gray smoke fogging up the air. And why were the Fitzgeralds, John Dos Passos, and Pablo Picasso members of the Lost Generation? Because they drank too much? I personally think we're all lost. I think we've been lost since we became highly intelligent creatures who pushed past survival instincts to self-actualization. We're lost in the city lights that polish the soft sediment of our irises when we blink and take it all in. Lost in the cables, the servers, and the airwaves. Lost in the surveys and the election polls and the overwhelming statistics. Lost on this tiny oasis in the desert of space.

It's getting chilly now, and the sun is disappearing into the dunes of vapor in the sky. I see the skeleton of an old boxcar a little ways off the track. I walk over and sit inside the part that still has some rusty metal that I can lean against. The tall grass tickles my ankles as I huddle into my oversized jacket. I open my backpack and take out the *National Geographic* inside. I usually don't buy magazines, but this one caught my eye in the bookstore the other day. It's a special edition photography issue. But not the silly photography that the kids at school take with their expensive cameras; pictures of each other dramatically smoking cigarettes and staring out into the distance; pictures of long wavy hair and a girl wearing a vintage dress, drinking some obscure brand of juice.

I like journalistic photography, the Pulitzer Prize photos, the pictures that move the world, or so I think they should. My mother thinks it's silly that I like them because "Sophia, those pictures are so depressing, why do you spend so much time on them?" The thing is, she's right. It is silly. But I can't help it. There's something happy in sadness, something about looking at a photo that stands for a big idea. My favorite picture so far is of two young Palestinian girls, not over age 10, who decided to take a quick dip in the Dead Sea at sunset. They come from a region of chaos—Palestine has not seen peace since 1948. But the way they float in that endless salty pool, with the ripples around them just right, they look infinite, like they'll never die, like if I go to that very place in the West Bank, I'll find them there, still floating by the rocks at sunset.

I hear the train approaching. That exasperated howl, *CHWEEEEEEP*. I wonder where it's is going. Maybe north to Pennsylvania or New York City. That sounds really nice right now, hopping on a train, heading somewhere, anywhere, just like the desperate folks during the Great Depression. The train is getting closer and I think about the movies I've seen where the teenage boy runs beside the train, grabs a rail and hops on, easy. I could do that. I'm not much of an athlete, but I can run. At least for a little while. And here she comes, bellowing. I get really close to the tracks and close my eyes. The train hurdles by and I feel the wind whip across my face and it stings for just a moment and then I'm running— running harder and faster than I have in a long time. But so is the train. She's fast, screaming by, laughing mindlessly at me, the girl who can't seem to keep up, who could never keep up, who has always been lost in her silly books, her big dreams of the past, and her stupid Pulitzer Prize pictures.

My cousins in California can keep up. They study all the time and take practice SAT tests and do science research during the summer and play the viola beautifully. They can keep up because they look forward to the *future*. And I could too, if I wanted to. Anyone could. But the truth is, I'm scared to fall into routine, to work so hard that the hours go by like seconds and time is your worst enemy, because you have a huge test tomorrow and you're taking Adderall to stay up all night. That's what we do in Generation Y. We fight time. Not with swords and tanks and nuclear bombs, but with technology, with drugs, with a crazed consumerist culture and 100-mile-per-hour lives. If it were up to me, we'd be the Time-Fighting Generation. The Clock Crushers. The Gone So Sooners.

I try to grab the rail on the train, but it's damp and my hand slips, slamming into the rusty edge of the next car. The pain is unbearable for a few seconds. My breath gets caught in my throat like a lump of sticky rice. I fall back into the grass and close my eyes for a few minutes; then I look down. It's already starting to swell, a purple bruise beginning to form, and the rusty edge of the rail car bloodied my knuckle a good bit. Flakes of rust are stuck in my skin. I'll probably have to go home to nurse it back to health. I'm sure they're not too worried about me. No big deal. She's probably staring at the stars, being a lunatic, getting moon burned. I forgot to mention that I run away all the time. Maybe twice a month, I pack a backpack of supplies just to *pretend* that I'll never return. Although this is the first time I follow the railroad tracks. I've retired all the other options.

Pretending is fun. It's for those people who never quite grow up inside, who just can't accept that they're even part of a generation at all; just that they're a tiny fold in the endless stretch of time. But if you must give everything a label...the Gone So Sooners. I like that. I'll see you on the other side.

Lylla Younes is from Alexandria, Louisiana, and a lifelong competitive swimmer. In her work, she often ties physical strain to the core of the human condition. She received a scholarship to attend the United World College of America in Montezuma, New Mexico.

A Ticket to Quivira

Janaki Chadha, 16
Governor Livingston High School, Berkeley Heights, NJ, **Doreen Ladinski,** Teacher

I clearly remember the day my mother turned 50, on a murky January evening in the middle of what became a largely forgotten winter. I can still see her aimlessly staring out the kitchen window by the sink, gently scrubbing dishes with an old washcloth, dazedly dreaming. My father and I sat around the kitchen table, eating leftovers from the night before. It was a Tuesday. We liked to think that we would have done something more special on a weekend.

Gazing into the bare, uninviting yard, which the unusual weather of the season had taken its toll on, she remarked softly, "Such an empty, empty country." My father, perpetually withdrawn, did not notice. I glanced up, surprised to see for the first time in my 17 years, her eyes welled up with tears. I pretend that I had not noticed; she excused herself to the bathroom. She came out a few minutes later. I never heard a flush.

It was on that evening, I believe, that my mother realized that she had spent exactly half of her life here. Surrounded by ubiquitous large lawns, houses with bright white doors, clean roads—and emptiness. Years later, I would imagine her sitting in her bedroom that night, pondering her day, her life, her circumstances, perhaps. As if their permanence had not quite settled in until then. I would imagine her eyes, large and sad, a teardrop running down the worn skin of her cheek, a strand of her unkempt hair teasing her face, a fleeting thought of regret passing through her mind. I would imagine nostalgia for a past life, one of crowds, color and a strange, old land. Maybe even a few memories of the beginning, of early dreams and expectations still waiting to be fulfilled.

My parents' dream, at its conception, however, wasn't really a dream at all. Fueled by rumors and whispers that traveled like wildfire in the narrow alleys of the place they would never quite cease to call home, it began as simply a desire, a longing for a different life, a better life. They had heard stories of the unfamiliar land, stories of opportunity, wealth, success. So they decided to chase after the gold, the luck, possibly a story of their own. They joined the mob, along with thousands of others, becoming faceless fractions of the new diaspora.

They arrived on a chilly, wet morning in the month that boasted of bloom. In the airport they would return to dozens of times in the coming decades, they wandered and wandered, suitcases in hand, necks endlessly craned in utter fascination. My mother would later laugh and say, "It was the only other world I had ever seen."

With little luggage and even less money, they slowly made their way to one of the many plain, modest townhouses of Central Jersey. In a time of Michael Jackson, a rising stock market and youthful idealism that had not quite expired, it was easy to approach their new home with a certain level of appreciation. And despite the chipped paint on their walls and the broken dishwasher in the kitchen, my mother would tell me about how refined the air felt during that first month. How she loved the way her saris would sway in the mild May breeze. How when she awoke at 3 a.m. on the day after they came, the complete silence of the night made her think that she had gone deaf.

If anything, it was all very, very promising. I suppose she didn't realize that, in a few weeks, sick of stares full of intrigue and occasional resentment, she would find herself longing for a pair of pants. That, in the coming months, while trying to master her understanding of an American accent, she would only come to realize how strange she sounded herself. That, in 20 years, the people who were once eager to follow her footsteps would quickly retreat back toward home, like a small boy knowing better than to follow his older sibling into the woods.

But as years and decades came to a close, what had once been dubbed as the New World naturally gained an aura of familiarity in her mind. I remember summers in Delhi as a child, many of them. There would be times when she would forget the name of a street or shop and embarrassment would wash over her face in seconds. Or times when she felt overwhelmed by the dense crowds at the market or a train station, and the years she had spent as an immigrant became more and more apparent.

Yet, year after year, as I'd watch my mother pack for the months we'd spend overseas, she would smile to herself. We would fill suitcases with clothes for my aunts and uncles, toys for my cousins. Simple things like cotton T-shirts and Hot Wheels sets. When we got there, they would eagerly ask questions about home, listen carefully with wide eyes and wonder. I can still picture the crowd of them I'd see at the airport on those balmy July nights so many years ago.

But as the new millennium began, our suitcases gradually thinned. Fewer people awaited us at the airport. We were not approached with fascination any longer. Instead, my cousins would laugh at my brother and I when they'd talk about "our country." My uncles would take pride in India's soaring economy, and make playful remarks about how in a few years we'd be looking for jobs in Delhi. They would take us to high-end restaurants and malls that seemed to pop up every other second; places that made my parent's lifestyle seem increasingly modest.

After a while, however, we stopped going so frequently. Instead, we traveled what even my parents admitted was now our country. They were usually only four- or five-day road trips to places like Lake George and Maine, and I was too old to watch my mother pack anyway. The next time we went back to Delhi was after my grandmother died. I sometimes wonder if my parents ever regretted it. I never asked.

I believe that it was during those years that the dream really began. Though more an act of desperation than anything else, in a way, it was what they survived off of. They were the years during which my mother went into depression and her face slowly morphed into a giant question mark of uncertainty. The years during which the loneliness of her world—her new world—got to her. They were the years during which the crease between my father's eyebrows gradually deepened as he went through bill after bill after bill each night when he came home from work, and years during which he was cornered by news of the recession and the economy everywhere he went. They were years of stress, of hardship, of the meltdown of an entire nation.

So they dreamt in the darkness, of the America in the rumors and whispers from the bustling streets of their youth. They dreamt of the America in an old, old promise, one that hadn't been carried out. Yet they still lived their lives as they had before. They went to dinner parties with friends; luckily, over the years, they had mastered the art of pretending. The came to my college graduation, even smiled in the pictures. But they passed their time in waiting, and welcomed middle age in incertitude.

But just as they had come, on that surreal May morning in a strangely chilly spring, they left on a Wednesday night in February. On a Continental direct flight to New Delhi, departing at 11:30. I remember the drive from our old house to the airport that night, with my mother gushing about how great the Delhi weather is in early spring and my father telling me about some Nicholas Kristof article he read in *The New York Times* the other day. They seemed happy.

Of course, there are times when I wonder why they went back. I end up imagining their entire lives here; the lives of two people who searched for success, affluence, prosperity at its highest degree, but ended up with mediocrity instead. I try to imagine their joys, their sorrows, only to realize that I barely knew them at all. I sometimes hope that as my mother got on the plane that night, leaving the country she had given her life to for good, she looked back with at least a smile, acknowledging, perhaps, that nothing is ever really a waste. But a part of me knows that she didn't. That just like the explorers who once scoured the New World for the Seven Cities of Gold, she must have left with at least a few grains of bitterness.

In the end, my parents crossed oceans, borders, cultures. They abandoned parts of themselves in both corners of the world. But though they left, their dream remained. Slowly fading into the faint fields of red, white and blue, it patiently waited for someone else to snatch it, just as they had done all those lives ago.

Janaki Chadha is from Berkeley Heights, New Jersey, where her interest in debate and current affairs kindles the political elements of her work. She hopes to work as a foreign correspondent, as an English teacher or for a non-profit.

Sonata in the Key of Bea; a Eulogy

Marlee Cox, 16
Mehlville High School, St. Louis, MO, **Cheryl Ogolin,** Teacher

> *"Or discendiam qua giù nel cieco mondo,"*
> *cominciò il poeta tutto smorto.*
> *"Io sarò primo, e tu sarai secondo."*
> —Dante's Inferno, Canto IV

I.

I would like to begin by asking you not to listen. My shoes pinch my feet as I walk across the stage, toward my sanctuary, and I remember how we always wore boots, because even at school and at mass and all that, we were just counting the seconds until we could get back into the woods. Back to where the ground tried to trick us and it was too dangerous to learn things by doing them—we had to be smarter than ourselves and anticipate our mistakes.

"Venever you're ready, Mr. Andrasko," says Professor Mendeloff, a Russian man with shiny lips and hair that defies basic laws of gravity. He assesses me sleepily, sacks of skin dropping all around his eyes. I crack my knuckles, preparing to play.

As soon as my hands touch the keys, I feel this: *l'espirit de l'escalier.* French. No English equivalent. The way one feels when a conversation ends, but there is still so much left to say. That's what it's like without you, because there are always more unsaid things than said things. There are always those botched chords or notes you just skip in your eagerness to reach the crux of the movement.

I hate what you've made the music become, especially because I chose it for you. For years, I planned to study superstring theory, but I ditched that dream just like you ditched me, and took a music scholarship to a school just two hours away from Alkali, because you liked who I was when I played the piano.

You haunt every note, your drunken half-smile lingering in every chord. Before you left, I had such concentration. Now, I ignore *legatos* and *decrescendos*, pounding through symphonies on autopilot, too distracted by memories to care when my fingers slip, and a wrong note pierces the auditorium. Plural: auditoria.

II.

We met in our freshman year of high school, after my accident. When I returned, the world was brighter than I remembered it—not that I remembered it very well. In the months after the crash, I had to relearn the words for simple things—*spoon, bracelet, jealousy.* But I still knew who I was. When I woke up, they asked me my name, and I told them without a scrap of hesitation. I didn't forget *Robinson Crusoe* or David Letterman or John 3:16.

Your parents sent an arrangement of Gerber daisies, even though they had met my mom and stepfather only twice, at parties where people discussed the political situation in Nepal and ate bite-size shrimp quiche off crisscrossing trays.

I guess I owe everything good in my life to Ms. Cortez, our biology teacher at Incarnate Heart Day School. She gave you to me, and asked me to teach you about photosynthesis. Instead of tutoring you in the library, though, I had to tutor you in the detention room, under the pious glare of Sister Mary Augustine. You'd broken, like, eight simultaneous dress-code rules or something, and then pissed off the nuns by asking if you'd get your name on the wall for such an impressive feat.

You weren't kidding.

I taught you about autotrophs and pigments. You asked me why your hair was red.

"Because," I began, "our eyes perceive visible light."

And I talked about the atmosphere and Raleigh scattering and the electromagnetic spectrum until you cut me off. "So," you said, "what you're saying to me is that I scatter light? I'm just sitting here, scattering all kinds of light?"

Yes.

III.

Alkali, Ohio, is surrounded by woods on three sides and Lake Erie on the fourth. Somewhere in those woods, a few miles from your house, a wide fissure interrupts the ground, where a strong river once surged through the forest. Spanning that fissure—which we nicknamed the Gash after a while—was a long, flat bridge. The bridge. Backbreak Bridge.

About a month after our first tutoring session, you told me to put on some boots and brought me to the bridge to meet your friends. Apparently, abandoned bridges are the place for rebellious rich kids to hang out, drink wine and discuss literature.

This is exactly what your friends were doing as we approached. A loose semicircle of kids passed around *The Great Gatsby* and a truly sensational merlot. I recognized most of them from school but never would have guessed any of them would be your friends. There was Autumn Schapiro, accompanied as always by her Polaroid camera. Stan Kaikati, who played the clarinet and took AP calculus, even though he was a freshman, like us. Yardley Fisk, a hulking JV linebacker with embarrassed, effeminate hand gestures.

Bethany Garcia. She waved, absolutely trashed.

"This is Daniel," you said. "He knows something about everything. Daniel, say something about bridges."

Taken aback, I grappled for a response. "Of all the bridges in Central Park, no two of them are alike."

The group seemed impressed. I sat down, joining a discussion of whether Gatsby really loved Daisy. The consensus: no, but he thought he did. I played devil's advocate and defended Gatsby.

"Isn't believing you love someone the same thing as actually loving them?" I said, taking a swig of the merlot. "You can't judge someone else's love by your own standards."

That won me some approval.

When the sun went down, the group started wandering home, each taking a different well-worn path. You pulled me to the side, leaning in so close I could smell the drunkenness on your breath. "I know this probably goes without saying," you said, "but don't go running your mouth about this place. We're sort of an exclusive group."

Grinning, I bumped your shoulder with mine as we retraced our steps through the woods. "I've never had a secret before," I whispered.

You looked at me strangely. "Isn't it wonderful?"

IV.

February, junior year—we were in my stepfather's car, going 63 miles an hour, speeding toward that concrete jungle where dreams are made of. I drove. You smoked. Singing "Start Spreading the News" in a ridiculous Billy Joel impression, I tried to make you laugh. But you just slouched, unresponsive, bent toward your cig as if conserving warmth, the tip of your nose red and cold. There was a white flag waving in your eyes, and I wish I had pulled the car over right there and held you until you held me back. I wish I had asked what was wrong, even if you would have told me you didn't know.

Instead, I kept up a one-sided conversation, babbling about Monty Python and Marcel Duchamp. The soundtrack to *A Chorus Line* played in surround-sound, and you sang along to only one line: "We did what we had to do."

"He was an artist," I said, referring to Duchamp. "He took everyday objects, like urinals and snow shovels, and told people they were art. He called them "ready-mades." A lot of people thought it was load of shit. And a lot of other people thought he was trying to see the beauty in unbeautiful things. But he wasn't. He was trying to see the ordinariness in ordinary things."

For reasons unknown, that roused you. "I like that," you said. "If you try to make everything beautiful, you forget that some things actually are."

And then I realized that you were crying. At first, it was just a few tears, lolling down your sharp cheekbones, dripping pathetically onto your shirt. But then you rolled down the window and flicked away your cig, burying your face in your hands. Panicked, I watched your shoulders jerk up and down; I heard the muffled, unabashed sounds of sobbing.

I did pull the car over then, but I didn't touch you, because I stupidly assumed I would have years to touch you and look at you and maybe, one day, tell you I loved you.

I said your name, cautiously, all illusions about you shattered once and for all. You were not the lovely, bubbly freshman girl who scattered light and fought daily with the nuns. Maybe you had never been her. Maybe she was someone you invented, the way James Gatz invented Jay Gatsby, because your life was not what you wanted it to be, and you thought someone else could live it better.

We were all different people in the woods. But what really never occurred to me was that *you*—specifically, personally you—had the capacity to take on a different persona for every occasion. I'd never met someone who could destroy and reinvent herself whenever it struck her fancy.

You could be anything you needed to be. And I thought that was the saddest thing in the world.

"Thank you for letting me wear your coat when it was cold," you said. "Thank you for helping me pass biology and teaching me how to play 'Chopsticks.' Thank you for knowing things about 20th-century Dada and the creation of the universe. Thank you for running away with me without really asking any questions."

Your face was flushed and slack, and I was afraid. A confession: as much as I love you, you scare me to death. You were looking at me, your invincible eyes begging me for something I simultaneously couldn't name and couldn't give. I had nothing to give you, really, and we both knew it. No one had anything to give you. No one could ever make you truly happy.

"Um," I said. "You're welcome. But...why?"

You shook your head, fatigued and bottomlessly sad. "We did a terrible thing, Daniel. But I'm still thankful to have you."

"We ran away. We're going back. It's not a terrible thing."

Your whole body convulsed as you began crying again. "You know what I mean! It was an accident, but we could have done something." You gave a phlegmy cough, and then sighed. "Do you ever dream about it? Do you ever watch her sink...into the water...oh, God! I didn't mean to..."

We sat in that car, on the shoulder of a highway, reeking of smoke. To calm you down, I told you no. I never thought about it. I never dreamed of her dark hair spreading like a Chinese fan around her peaceful face as it met the cold water of Lake Erie. I never grew sick thinking of how the bricks we'd tied to her ankles tugged her down. I never wished I had talked to her one last time—asked her what cartoons she watched as a kid; asked how her parents met; asked what her fucking middle name was, because I didn't even know.

You and I had not killed her. But we could have given her a different ending. You and I.

Plural: we.

"We did what we had to do. Right?"

Right?

V.

Exactly two weeks after Bethany died, it snowed eight inches. School wasn't called off, because school is never called off in northern Ohio, but we skipped. We bundled ourselves up, coiling multiple scarves around our necks and pulling fur-lined boots—always boots—onto our feet. Then, we walked.

The woods looked different during the day: less secretive, less special. Planks of sunlight broke through the trees and lay tranquilly on the shimmering, untouched ground. You walked carefully, trying not to break through all eight inches of the ashy snow, because you didn't want to see the mud underneath.

When we came to the clearing with the bridge, I looked over at you. The cold had beaten a raw flush into your cheeks and drawn tears to the corners of your eyes.

At least, that's what you would have wanted me to think.

"We should go down there," you said, and, before I had time to warn you about ice and erosion and post-traumatic stress disorder, you clambered into the Gash. Mostly because of the magnetic pull between us, I followed.

Faltering occasionally, we picked our way down the rocky slope. You reached the bottom before I did. Our boots sank into the dregs of not-quite-frozen water lingering among the rocks.

Snowy silence cloaked us. We stood on the spot where a girl's life had ended only 14 days previously.

I liked the way your hands looked in your mittens. I liked the way your mittened hand fit perfectly in my gloved one. And when you began to cry, and you wiped the tears away with the back of your hand, I liked the way the salty wetness of them made the yarn smell like first grade.

"Daniel," you said, sniffling. "You were dead once, right?"

Blurry memories of the crash swirled in my mind. I nodded. "For 112 seconds."

A frigid wind ripped through the clearing, rousing the snow on the rocks around us. You asked, "How does it feel?"

Biting my chapped bottom lip, I deliberated for a moment. So many people had asked me, but I wanted to make sure I gave you the right answer. "It feels quiet," I said. "Like this. Like right now. It feels quiet as snow."

"Was there a bright light?" you asked. You weren't kidding.

"Yeah," I said, hardly any sound in my voice. "Yeah, there was a bright light. But it wasn't an actual, literal bright light." I sighed. "It was the way you looked in that white dress last spring—the way the spotlight rushed over you as you came down the stairs on your father's arm...but you shone brighter than it. It was the way you waved when they said your name and shouted, 'Hi, Society!'" You opened your mouth to point out the obvious flaw in this description, but I continued. "And, yeah, I know cotillion was two whole years after I died, but that doesn't matter, because it was also this: It was my grandfather's pocket watch. The face was all cracked, and it couldn't keep time, but he still carried it as, like, a *reminder* of time. That's what it was. Do you remember it? Maybe you do. Because I think you were there. I think you have always been with me, through the assemble and disassemble of it all. Through all the blizzards and the bridges and the balls."

A wistful smile touched your face. "God," you said, "I wish I was in love with you."

You looked so cold, so I unzipped my coat and draped it around your shoulders.

VI.

Our friend Bethany fell from Backbreak Bridge on Halloween night in our junior year of high school. It was nobody's fault. We had all been drinking, and we were all freaked out from playing with your Ouija board.

"Did you know," I said, "that the word 'Ouija' is a combination of the French and German words for 'yes'?"

No one cared. Time fell apart.

...She just slipped. I watched you watch her. Then, we all scattered.

Her scream stabbed through the air around us, cut short with a gurgle and a hideous crunch. Stumbling as our boots struck rocks and roots, we ran, each in our own direction.

Another scream gutted me—Autumn. She was dressed as a nun, which was supposed to be ironic or something, and she had tripped on the hem of her habit and fallen to the ground.

You shouted for us all to stop, and we did. Panting, I dropped to my knees.

I lost track of how long we waited there. After a while, we heard Autumn, praying for Beth in a language we did not know.

"Yit'gadal v'yit'kadash sh'mei raba."

I could see you through the trees. You stood, your chin cocked, still as porcelain. Your expression was that of a chess player contemplating her next move.

"...Y'hei sh'mei raba m'varakh l'alam ul'al'mei al'maya..."

I whispered your name. *"Bea."*

"B'rikh hu."

Blessed is He.

I remembered the silence and the light of death. I remembered the first breath I took as I was reborn into the world, slow and poignant, like the first note in an empty auditorium. And with perfect clarity, I remembered your hand in mine, both in the snowy clearing and in the quiet place where I spent 112 unbeating heartbeats.

You were there, weren't you?

VII.

Exactly two weeks after we graduated from high school, you followed Bethany off the bridge. You left me a note just one line long: *Something good will come from all of this.*

I didn't cry when they put you in the ground, because crying never came naturally to me. Not even when Beth fell. Not even when you insisted we hide the body, to keep us all out of trouble.

Daniel knows something about everything. No. I don't. I know nothing about living in a world you decided wasn't worth the trouble.

But here is what I do know: I know the distance between two points is a line. I know how to play Beethoven and Tchaikovsky and Madonna. I know musicals, the difference between *lie* and *lay*, three inappropriate jokes and how to waltz. I know things about 20th-century Dada and the creation of the universe. I know how to hold my liquor and how to hold you. I know that something good will come from all this, because I have seen that something good comes *after* this. And I know I love you—I love you in the present tense.

Gasping as if coming up from underwater, I stop playing. Professor Mendeloff jumps a little in his seat, in reaction to the sudden silence. Pulse ripping through my veins, I stumble to my feet, knocking over the bench in the process.

"Mr. Andrasko?" Mendeloff calls, clearly shocked. "Are you... finished?"

I turn to face him, nodding. Then, remembering my cotillion training and my basic performance etiquette, I twitch forward in an awkward bow, pry my lips open and say, "Thank you."

Marlee Cox lives in St. Louis, Missouri. She is interested in Judaism, religion and social activism, and her writing often carries spiritual undertones. She would like to study international relations and linguistics.

Riding on Glass Wings

Cary Williams, 18
Milton Academy, Milton, MA, **James Connolly,** Teacher

My dad always told me I could count on him, even though I wasn't sure that was true. When I was little, I ran to his study as soon as the school bus dropped me off at the corner. My mother asked how my day had been—whether I had liked the lunch she packed me, if I had gotten gold stars on all of my homework, but I would go past her toward the soft, musty scent of my father. When he stayed in his office for hours and hours, he began to smell a lot like his old books. His classics came from his father's collection and were yellowed and frayed around the edges. "Still," he chuckled, "they have the same words as your fancy new copy."

When I was 6, he started taking me to the butterfly pavilion a couple of times a year. We went early in the morning, before anyone else got there. I would ask him if we could go in the afternoon, but he always said, "No, Katie, you only get to know the butterflies if you have time with them on your own." I would chase little Summer Azures, which were so pale blue that it was almost as if they were a part of the sky. I wanted to touch them, but I knew that if I did, even with my tiny fingers, I'd smudge away their freedom to fly. I wanted to be like Daddy and watch just one balance on a blade of grass as thin as a strand of my hair and learn his wisdom that sat behind cerulean eyes.

We liked to keep flowers and trees in perfect bloom so the butterflies would find us. My mother was never one for gardening, and when we asked her to help us plant new flowers she would say, "I have to run to my Pilates class," or "We need something for dinner." She was always in a rush.

When we moved into the new house, Daddy loved his library. He sat there for hours, secluded within the mahogany bookshelves, his face masked by the shadow of oak panels. The tight shelves of scientific journals, his investigations and photo albums framed the glass cases in the center of the room. He would come home from a long day and walk straight into the library toward the iridescent wings of his *Morpho Didius*. My mother and I knew when he wanted time alone with the smell of raw wood and the glow of his butterflies, so she stayed out of his way entirely while I sat outside the French doors and quietly watched him think.

My father's voice had a way of sounding a little stuck inside of him, as if he wanted his ideas to stay private once his voice betrayed him. Daddy told me that when he was little, he was the only boy in his class who liked butterflies. His friends told him that butterflies were for girls, but he thought butterflies were so quietly elegant. In kindergarten, he would play with the girls at recess and chase American Painted Ladies around the swings and down the hill of the playground. When his teacher called them inside after recess, Daddy lagged behind, his mind still lingering on the glass wings of a monarch.

That night at dinner, he opened a letter from the university telling him that he had been promoted to an Associate Professor of Biology because of his exemplary work as the institution's leading lepidopterist. I could see my mother's mind working as she weighed whether the house should be repainted before the kitchen was remodeled.

"That's great, honey. Things are looking up for us!" she said, the insincere smile that he couldn't read clear across her face.

"Katie, I'll take you on that ski trip out west you always wanted to go on."

"Sure, Dad, or we could just stay home for spring break. Whatever you want."

"We'll go. I want to get away for a little."

That night, when I got into bed and curled under the covers, I could hear the printer spitting out his latest manuscript as he paced around the thin glass cases. I waited up for a little while, but finally let my eyes flutter closed when I realized he wouldn't remember to come up to my room to kiss me goodnight.

My father started going to Mexico for the month of December to observe monarch migrations when I was in high school. I called him almost every night during winter break, and I could hear him smile through the phone as we talked about our days apart. The

Christmas tree my mother bought looked slightly off-balance because it was shorter than the towering ones of my childhood, but I didn't tell him that. We needed my father to bear the weight of the heavier ones, so my mother and I had to settle for one we could manage.

"Dad?" I started, unsure of how to start a real conversation with him, "I was wondering if I could visit you after Christmas."

There was a silence between us that was long enough to let me know that it wasn't just the poor connection. He stammered and stuttered as he would when he got nervous in front of me, "I would love that."

"Mom already said she would be fine with me visiting you."

"I'll talk to your mother, and it's a done deal. You can come see my lab and I'll take you sightseeing and—well, we'll figure out what to do."

"Dad, I already have my plane ticket. I knew you'd say yes," I blurted, a little embarrassed.

"I'm not surprised."

Packing felt like the days before I left home for summer camp. My mother and I gathered up my closet, examining my room for any detail I could have missed or forgotten, folding it neatly into a 26" suitcase whose lock had been hacked off by the TSA. She had always excelled in geometry and could meticulously fold anything so it would fit. Her latest Costco run produced every possible size of Ziploc bag so everything could be sorted into its proper bag, as she thought it should be.

"Two weeks is longer than I expected," she started, as she gathered my hair to begin a French braid.

"I need to go, Mom."

"I know you do. It's just that—"

"You could have come. You never even asked."

"I'll miss you. That's all."

I looked at my mother's reflection in the dusty mirror she asked me to clean off weeks ago. Her face didn't glow like it used to. It was severe and unlike the dewy complexion I saw in the wedding pictures on the living room mantle. People change, I thought to myself, as she wrapped an elastic around the end of my braid and tucked a couple of loose strands on the underside. She sighed, exasperated, and tore her fingers through my hair to start over.

"Mom! Stop it. That hurts."

She took a long breath, and I felt the exhale on the back of my neck. "Sorry. Just let me try again."

I sat at the foot of my bed and looked into the mirror, watching her reflection gather my chestnut layers in a silent rhythm.

On the third day of my vacation with my father, I got a scar that ran across the right side of my face. He chartered a fishing boat for the day that belonged to a guide with a thick accent. I had never been one for fishing, but it reminded me of our days in the Long Island Sound when we dug for earthworms by the shore when the bait shop was closed. The water brought out a different side of him. I sat on the banks with the worms and watched him cast. *Flick and dip, flick and dip,* he thought, the fly-fisherman's creed from *Gone Fishin',* the movie he always had on his computer, tucked away for long plane rides to conferences. That day the waves weren't high, but a storm had just passed through, leaving the waters unsettled. The boat pounded the surface, but my father knew how to keep his balance and cast in a perfect arch. He stood at the bow looking regal and in control.

"I've got a bite!" he said, and started to reel in.

Our guide, following in my father's excitement, turned the boat to the right in pursuit of the mackerel.

"Katie! Katie! Bring it in!" he said, just knowing I'd be at his side to take over the rod and claim the prize as my catch.

I didn't answer.

He turned toward the stern and saw me flailing not too far away, but the waves looked taller and stronger at eye level.

"You're a lifeguard," he yelled, as he hurried to place his rod in the rod-holder.

"Daddy, I can't! I'm not that strong."

He dove in after me, arcing like an animal that was born for the sea. I had one of the oldest fathers in my class, but he swam like a college boy that afternoon. I heard his heavy breathing over the sound of the waves and I tried not to scream. When he got to me, I felt him take all my weight on his back like a dolphin, and his warmth settled the goosebumps on my arms. When he lifted me onto the white bench of the boat, that's when we both noticed the blood trailing down my cheek.

My father moved his careful hands over my face and looked at me in the same way I remembered him studying the nearly translucent veins of his specimens. I had wondered what it was like to be inside one of his glass cases, to be watched constantly by his patient, vigilant stare. I felt him telling himself to be confident, but there was something inside of him that betrayed him, and I saw in his eyes the breaking of a stoic, calmly vulnerable man.

He held a piece of gauze against my cheek, and I felt the cotton stick to the open wound as he tried to pull it away. The first-aid kit on the boat wasn't much, but it would do until we got back to land. Using the tiny scissors on his Swiss Army knife, he fashioned a bandage that would stop the bleeding for long enough. I laid on the bench in the stern of the boat with my head in his lap for the ride home, my right cheek covered by his hand that exerted the pressure to begin to heal it.

I only went to the university hospital when I really needed to—for an X-ray when I hurt my collarbone, flu shots every fall, one night during the summer when my cousin had to get her stomach pumped. Walking into the revolving door made me feel trapped. There were color-coded signs everywhere that told you exactly where to go, signs that never left room to wander about. My father shuffled a few steps ahead of me, his body shifted on the slightest angle. His sweater drooped off his side as though his body lost the sense of what was center, the axis thrown as the spine curved out of alignment.

"Stage four," Dr. Bronson told me.

"It's getting serious. What will it do to him now?" I asked, fidgeting in the imitation-leather chair.

"His memory will continue to weaken. He'll need your help and—"

"But he'll still know me? Won't my mother and I be the last ones he'll remember?"

"Yes," the doctor nodded, "that's how it usually works. But with Alzheimer's you can never be sure."

"Is there anything I can do? I read that some families make scrapbooks or videos or signs in the house or—"

"Love him. Be patient and love him." Dr. Bronson smiled, and I felt him take my hand in his before he walked out of the room to see the next family surviving on its last leg.

My father's house felt big and unfamiliar when I moved back. The summer before I went to law school, he got sicker, and I couldn't leave him alone. He and my mother got divorced while I was in college, and they stopped speaking. My childhood room looked the same from when I had left it: Cutouts of teenage celebrities covered the wall around my desk, favorite quotes were tacked to a corkboard above my bed, and pictures of my friends and me were in frames we had decorated together when we found out we were going to schools time zones apart. I slipped into the sheets that had the scent of my mother's favorite laundry detergent baked into them, and tried to fall asleep in the detached familiarity of home.

The crash was loud. I thought I was dreaming that something shattered, but I felt my feet slide into my slippers as I got out of bed and walked down the stairs toward the sound of broken glass. The soft glow of the lamps in my father's office radiated out of the room, and I couldn't walk any closer to him when I reached the threshold of the door. His back was to me, and he had a large case in his hands, suspended over his head. His forearms were bleeding. I wanted to say something, but I just watched in awe as he smashed another case to the hardwood floor. The petrified butterflies crumpled under his force. They, more fragile than the shards around him, fractured along the veins of their wings. Antennae snapped off while still airborne, the fall alone strong enough to break them before impact.

"Dad!" I yelled, "Dad! Why are you doing this?"

He turned around. He heard my voice, but not what I had said to him. "Heather," he said, controlled, with an edge of threat riding on his pronunciation of my mother's name. "Stay out of this."

"No, Dad. It's me, Katie," I said, taking a step into his office, a piece of glass sinking into the sole of my slipper.

"Heather, I know it's you. Get out!"

"Mom is gone," I said. "It's just us now."

He reached into a case and crushed a monarch with his left hand.

"Trust me." My voice was measured. I could feel his eyes looking for proof that I was an impostor.

He ripped his research papers out of the files on the bookshelves surrounding us, and started shredding them in his bloody hands. "I know you want to be Katie, Heather." He stopped shredding the papers. "I want to be alone."

We were stuck. I wrapped his injured fist in my hands and held him, hoping that holding hands would trigger something in his memory and let him know that I was who I said I was. Behind me, he saw a picture of us from our trip to Mexico. We were on the beach, smiling in front of the Gulf. It was nearly sunset after a day of fishing from land because we both had had enough of boats. My father still held his rod in his hand, eager to get back to the water to make one last cast while he had a bit of light. My face was turned toward him the littlest bit, and the scab over my cut was noticeable.

"I remember that." He sounded unsure.

"What?"

"I remember when Katie got that cut. You have a scar in the same place," he wavered.

"Because I am Katie," I said, my tone even and patient.

I felt him trying to piece it together.

Once Dr. Bronson told me that appealing to different senses could spark a memory. "Touch it, Dad."

He rubbed the soft back of his hand against my face. He didn't want to use his palm that was still bleeding.

"It's all right," I said, "I'll clean it up."

He opened his fist and turned his hand over on my face. He traced over the scar as he searched my eyes for a sign of the girl I had been.

I broke away from the eye contact for a second and noticed the butterfly that had fallen from his grip onto my slipper. The monarch's wings were distorted and covered in his blood. He picked it up and held it between us, his eyes moving from the dark edge around its wings to the hyperpigmented mark down my face. I watched as he tried to flatten out its wings before placing it in an open case that was still intact in the middle of the room.

I rested a hand on his shoulder. "Daddy—"

He reached behind him, bringing my other hand to his back, and guided my fingers together so I gently clasped his neck. He said, "I remember holding you like this when you thought you were going to drown." I could see him smile in the mirror over the mantle before his face turned anxious. "Don't go, Katie. Just stay with me a little longer."

I turned him around so we faced each other. He took me back into his arms and asked, "Why is it such a mess in here?" His bleeding hands startled him as he tried to figure out what had happened. I felt my fingers ache as I collected the pieces of glass around the room before he drifted to his desk and sifted through a drawer for a pair of gloves. He watched as I cleaned the office well into the night. When a draft passed through the window of our old house, the imperfect monarch shook, its broken gold and black wings quivering until finally settling in the same position it had been in before, as though nothing had disturbed its unassuming elegance at all. *It was,* I thought to myself, *too fragile to be anymore ruined.*

Cary Williams is from Milton, Massachusetts, and is grateful to her grandmother, who taught her the power of writing as a means of reshaping African-American identity. This piece was inspired by her father's strength of character and her grandfather's struggle with Alzheimer's. She will attend Harvard University.

Green

Emily Frech, 16
Norman High School, Norman, OK, **Elizabeth Ballard,** Teacher

Silent Night

The man did not ask for her name. Sarah didn't give it to him, either. Sarah Irijah Phillips. Her mother chose Sarah, which is Hebrew for "princess," and her father chose Irijah, a boy's name, Hebrew for "God sees me." Her mother tried to go for a more reasonable Rebecca or Esther, but Irijah it was. When their daughter was five, Sarah's parents enrolled her in the local kindergarten; that is when Sarah went through the mischievous stage that little children often experience. After week three of kindergarten, Mr. and Mrs. Phillips came home to quite a sight. Sarah had poorly slathered her nails with her mother's OPI "Teal We Meet Again," which her mother saved for just two occasions a year: her wedding anniversary and Valentine's Day. As they scrubbed the blue-green smears off the beige carpet, curtains, and Sarah's petite fingernails, they told the blubbering child what they always did during these sorts of circumstances. You have to be a good girl now, Sarah. God sees you, her mother and father told her. God sees you. Blaming her impish albeit normal behavior on the toxic environment of public school kindergarten, her parents withdrew her from the public school system and her mother began homeschooling the girl. Mrs. Phillips quite enjoyed crafting together a curriculum, complete with arithmetic, science experiments in the kitchen, fun Bible stories, and many trips to the library for reading lessons. When they drove by the elementary school, Sarah sometimes stared at the gaggles of children bundled in a rainbow of Lands End parkas as they wrestled over deflated kickballs and the four swings on the playground. However, Sarah enjoyed school at home. Who wouldn't enjoy trips to the zoo for science class and their mom cooking grilled cheese and quesadillas for lunch every day, she thought. On the rainy afternoons, Sarah and her mother would curl up on the squishy couch in the living room and read Sarah's favorite stories. Sarah usually wanted to read the story about Joseph and his pretty coat. Sometimes, if timed just right, as they would read the part of the story where Joseph tries on his coat again after he returns to his father and brothers, the rain would stop, and a faint rainbow would crest the sky. Look, Sarah! Her mother would gush. It's your own coat of many colors!

However, Sarah's mischievous habits died down after the supermarket incident, at age six. After Sarah and her mother returned from the grocery store one afternoon, Sarah's mother found her in her room, cherubic face smeared with milk chocolate and peanut-butter filling, devouring a Reese's peanut butter cup. Eyes watering, Sarah pled. I borrowed it, Mommy, I promise! One letter to the store later (with the 87-cent-cost of the candy attached), Sarah's father administered what was to be the last lecture of its type. Sarah, you know that God sees you. You can't take things like that. That makes you a bad girl. God knows that you are a good girl, Sarah. But you make Him sad when you are bad. Sarah? Are we going to be a good girl from now on? Bursting into tears, Sarah whimpered out a "yes." And why, he continued, will you be good? Through the trademark snot-and-tears of a child caught with her hand in the cookie jar, Sarah managed to whisper, "Because God sees me."

But if God could see Sarah on that February night years later, God did little. Sarah showed up at the church, expecting to find the youth group. Living in a town nearly three times that of her childhood home from which her family had just moved, Sarah hoped to find solace from unfamiliar faces and strange streets. Her parents walked her to the new church. Sarah sat on the faded red couch in the youth room and traced her fingernail, shakily adorned with clear nail polish (only clear, as stated by her father), along the snaking cracks in the leather. No one showed up. The minutes blinked by on her purple Timex watch, and after seventy-two blinks, she finally began the three blocks walk home.

She walked slowly, two steps per square of sidewalk, until she just began to pass by the park. Two loafer-clad feet stood in her next sidewalk square. Sarah looked up into a startlingly green pair of eyes. She jumped. The man did not ask for her name. Sarah did not give it to him either. He greeted her cordially, and Sarah muttered a "Hello, excuse me" and tried to step around him. But then he wanted to know why such a pretty girl was in such a rush. And then he wanted to know if she would like to go get some coffee with him. And then he was upon her. Sarah's soaring soprano voice was locked up tight in her pale throat as the wood chips ground into the small of her back. God sees you, Sarah Irijah's parents had told her. Be a good girl now, Sarah. God sees you. The green-eyed man continued, and Sarah prayed, screamed, cried within her racing mind. Sarah's trembling lips silently mouthed a prayer. "But the Lord stood by me and strengthened me, so that through me the message might be fully proclaimed and all the Gentiles might hear it-" The man struck her across the mouth. She squeezed her eyes and waited for the iron taste to come. Scarlet oozed through the cracks in her chapped lips. She stared up at the underside of the gaudy plastic yellow slide, spattered with dirt and stuck-on bits of woodchips and waited. Silent tears whispered down Sarah's face on that silent night. "And so I was rescued from the lion's mouth," the man sneered, finishing Sarah's prayer. And then, emerald eyes and all, he was gone.

Holy Night

Hours later, Sarah lay in the starchy hospital bed. Swabbed and interrogated, she listened to her father arguing with the mousy doctor. He pleaded for Mr. Phillips to step aside, but the burly man stood between him and the hospital bed. "Mr. Phillips, I simply want to insure that Ms. Phillips will not experience any...physical repercussions after this incident." Reddening profusely, Mr. Phillips exploded. "My daughter," he sputtered, "is not with child." The doctor nervously clasped and unclasped his sweaty hands. "Mr. Phillips, we don't know that for a fact. I simply want to insure that she will not become so as a result of what occurred earlier this evening." The doctor took the paper cup with the three pills in it and set it down on the gleaming surgical table. Mr. Phillips roared, "Even so, even so, size is not a determinant of a human!" The doctor removed his glasses and wiped them on the corner of his dingy white coat. "I don't want to argue with you, Mr. Phillips, or your religion, but-". Mr. Phillips visibly relaxed and calmly took the doctor by the forearms. "Doctor, my daughter has provided the complete physical evidence and undergone a full inter-rogation, in addition to enduring the events of earlier this evening. Please let us leave. I, and my wife, need to be with my daughter." The doctor sighed. "Very well, Mr. Phillips. The receptionist will be on your left." Mr. Phillips strode out of the room. The doctor approached Sarah's bedside. "Ms. Phillips, you have the right to accept...this medical treatment without parental consent," he urged softly. He held the paper cup in his calloused palm. Sarah shook her head silently. "As you wish, Ms. Phillips. But should anything happen, Sarah, you can call—" Sarah interrupted him with a definite "No." At that moment, Mr. Phillips returned to the room for his daughter, and the family left.

All Is Calm

Sarah's life did not return to normal, as her parents assured her it would. Their smiles were uncertain, their hugs rigid. Their over-reaching kindness nauseatingly permeated every aspect of her life. Her mother made her favorite food for seemingly every meal, and her father enthusiastically sat down in his study with her every night to have a devotional. They even studied her favorite childhood stories: Noah's Ark, Jonah and the whale, David and the lions' den, Joseph and his rainbow coat. Sarah's parents sent her to a therapist once a week, although Sarah detested both the therapist and her office. Doctor Maureen asked few questions and twirled her chemically-dehydrated blonde hair around her fingernail with sea-foam green nail polish. Sarah counted the blinks on her watch until the moment when she could bolt out of the office with the Diet Coke-stained carpet and escape home, which wasn't much better. Too-cheery parents and night after night of spaghetti and pot roast and red velvet cake. But it was a peaceful monotony, and Sarah grew accustomed to it. Yet she could not shake away the gnawing pain, the terribly unique pain only known by victims of such terrible things. A violating, searing pain, which surged with every door slam, every doorbell ring, every sudden voice from the television or street. It was a cold bolt of panic that blistered from her toes to the top of her mousy-brown head.

All Is Bright

One March morning, Sarah sat cross-legged on the tile floor, watching her breakfast disappear into the tall white bowl for the third time that week. It was then that Sarah realized that something was wrong. She was aware of a cycle missed somewhere, or two, but that happens to women all the time, she had read on the computer in the library. The next week, she grabbed a handful of coins from the Smuckers jam jar in her father's study and took the bus to the hospital. She wandered through the halls until she found the mousy doctor. "Ms. Phillips!" he exclaimed. He wiped his sweaty hands on his olive corduroys. "What can I do for you?" Sarah explained and his greasy, bushy eyebrows knitted together. After the blood sample, Sarah waited patiently in the chrome-coated examination room on the table with the crinkly white strip of paper, kicking her feet back and forth. Crunch, crunch, crunch. The bright fluorescent lights gleamed off the tiles. When the mousy doctor returned, Sarah closed her eyes. She already knew his answer. "Ms. Phillips," he stated after revealing the results, "you have options. You are only six weeks along." Just as before though, Sarah's answer was a definite "No."

Round Yon Virgin

Sarah handed her parents the doctor's paper with the test results. Her father closed his eyes and sank into his study chair. Both assured her that this was not her fault. The three of them sat in silence for a few minutes. Sarah slipped out of the study and trudged up the stairs. Just as she sat down on her bed, her father knocked and entered. "You know I love you, Sarah." Sarah looked up dutifully. "But Sarah Irijah Phillips, you are having that baby." She frowned. "I had never planned otherwise." she managed. "Before I formed you in the womb I knew you, before you were born-" he began. "I set you apart," Sarah finished. "I appointed you as a prophet to the nations." He nodded his head and closed the door behind him. Sarah sank into the fuschia duvet, drowning among Jeremiah 1:5 and her own tears.

Church was the worst. The powdered ladies in their Chico's dresses and pink lipstick could not keep their made-up eyes from traveling toward her rounder middle. They had seen the articles about the attack in the newspaper: they understood. But their eyes gleamed with that hunger of the average middle-age woman when she recognizes that lump. Baby. Sarah could almost see the word floating through the air with their scorchingly-floral perfume. Yes, baby! She wanted to scream. Baby! It's there all right! The pastor had taken her aside and told her that the job of the church was to love mother and child, and was there anything he could do? Although she politely declined, the church ladies brought dinners by the house. Sympathy casseroles. Pity pot pies.

Sarah thanked goodness for homeschooling and began the long wait. At first, besides the inevitable weight gain, nothing really changed. A vitamin every morning. More fruits and vegetables. But a few weeks later, something moved inside her. *Something moved.* She stumbled into the bathroom and gagged until tears streamed down her face. There was someone, something inside her. As the weeks progressed, each kick took her back to February. "A baby's kick is a wonderful reminder of the love between you and your partner," she read in a gestation manual she had checked out from the library. "Treasure each one." But each blow against her ribs and abdomen did not make her feel loved. Each kick provoked a memory. Kick. Woodchips. Kick. Green eyes. Kick. Yellow slide. Just as she had been beaten black and blue from the outside in on that February night, now she was beaten black and blue from the inside out.

Mother and Child

Barraged by kicks from the child and blinks from the Timex, Sarah could only wait. At her first ultrasound, the technician found the tiny feet and hands. The heartbeat. "Oh, Sarah. Look! Listen!" Her mother gushed. Sarah rolled her head away from the wall and toward the screen. A monstrous looking thing, with an oversized head and scrawny feet and hands, radiated from the computer. At the next ultrasound, the technician asked if she would like to know the sex of the child. Sarah simply shook her head. By the seventh month, the manuals said, she should have a name picked out for the baby. She and her partner should feel a strong connection to the child and be attending labor classes. Sarah, however, could not ignore the feeling inside her. It was not love. It was not excitement. It was loathing. Much to her parents' dismay, there were no baby showers, no crib-shopping expeditions as the months passed. Sarah's mother began to convert the guest bedroom into a nursery. "Sarah Irijah, this is your child. You need to engage," her mother insisted as she slathered the walls with a neutral butter yellow. But Sarah wanted nothing more than to forget about this all. How do you begin to heal when your pain grows every day, grinds against your ribs, kicks you during your nightmares of a single night, a single man, a single act so seemingly long ago? The December due date came and went, and Sarah could stand it no longer. So Sarah's parents and Sarah drove to the hospital to have Sarah induced. And on a cold December night, Sarah gave birth to a seven pound baby boy.

Sleep In Heavenly Peace

After those long hours of pain, Sarah held out her arms to hold her child. Her mother and father stood beaming at her bedside. Sarah melted. Wrapped in a cerulean blanket, the boy's eyes were scrunched tightly shut. The beautiful child sleepily waved a tiny fist and wrapped his miniscule fingers around her pointer finger. He relaxed against her weary body. His face, crinkly and pink, smoothed out and the boy deepened into sleep. So much pain, for so much perfection. She gently traced her finger along his smooth pink cheek and counted his perfectly small toes. He stirred and she held that blue-blanketed bundle, the healing she had waited so long for, closer.

Sleep In Heavenly Peace

Sarah awoke to the boy screeching horrendously. She held him closer to hush him, and suddenly, for the first time, their eyes locked together. Plain brown on searing green. An undeniable, horrible, severing green. Sarah Irijah Phillips opened her mouth to scream, but just like nine months ago, nothing came out.

Emily Frech is a rising senior from Norman, OK who writes well in many genres. When a proposed state tax cut threatened the budget for her high school, Emily employed her persuasive writing skills to craft a much-reposted protest letter to the local paper. In it she addressed Oklahoma Governor Mary Fallin directly, "My school is not just good, Gov. Fallin, it is excellent. Please start treating it as such."

Papi

Audrey Bransfield, 15
Buckingham Browne & Nichols School, Cambridge, MA,
Rob Leith, Teacher

It takes a few minutes after opening my eyes to remember that my father is gone. Once the few blissful moments before I am fully awake have fled, the events of the past day crash down on me like a wave hitting the shore. My father is in jail, and the Immigration and Customs Enforcement (ICE) agency is going to send him back to Guatemala.

I stand up and begin to make my squeaky twin-size bed. As I lift the pillow and pull up the sheets, my hand brushes the wet spot from the tears I cried last night. I had buried my face in the pillow so my little brother Mike would not hear my sobs. If today was a normal day, our father would come home in a few hours, exhausted from the night shift at the Greenwood Iowa Dairy plant, where most of the workers are illegal immigrants, like him.

My mother opens the door to the room and peeks her head inside. I notice the dark circles under her eyes. She probably slept less than I did.

"Is Miguel awake?" she whispers. My little brother's name is Miguel, but only my parents call him that. Everyone else calls him Mike, the American version of his name.

"No, still sleeping. Are you going to work today?" My mother works for a woman down the street, cleaning her house and watching her children. One of the woman's daughters sits two desks to the right of me in math.

"I wish I could stay home, but I already took the day off when I was sick last week, and I can't take another. You should go to school Marcella, I don't want you staying home alone on a day like this."

I sigh, but I know my mother is right. I need to get out of this house, where everything reminds me of my father.

I wander into the bathroom we all share and look in the mirror. The same reflection as always meets my eyes; plain brown eyes, plain brown hair to just below my shoulders, slightly crooked teeth that my parents say are straight enough to go without braces. My appearance is simply average. I wish that one day I could look into the mirror and see someone beautiful, unusual. Until then, I suppose I will have to be satisfied with average.

In the kitchen, I see my older sister Gabrielle and my mother bent over a pile of envelopes on the table, whispering urgently. I only catch a snippet of their conversation, but I hear enough to know what they are talking about.

"Water, electricity..."

"Not enough money..."

As I approach them, Gabby tucks the envelopes into her bag. My mother falls silent. I know that they are trying to protect me by hiding our problems, but I am 12 years old now, and more aware than they think.

A plate of steaming hot eggs sits on the kitchen table. Yesterday, my father had placed the same breakfast in front of me, as he had every morning before this one. As I gaze down at the pale pink plate, I know something is wrong—Gabby sees it too. I can tell from the way her left eyebrow is just a little lower than the right, the way it always is when she is worried. I remember when Gabby lost her job as a waitress last year, that eyebrow was pulled down for weeks.

Over many years of breaking and replacing them, my family has acquired a mismatched collection of plates. Each of us has a favorite. Mike has a blue plate with a painting of a sailboat in a harbor. The one I like is green with a chain of flowers around the edge. My father has a deep red plate with a gold pattern, and my mother's is white with various fruits painted on it. Gabby's plate is the pink one in front of me now. I know that my mother must have forgotten, but I can't tear my eyes away from the red plate sitting in the kitchen cabinet. I glance at Gabby, whose gaze is fixed on the plate as well. I know we are both wondering the same thing: if that beautiful red plate will ever be used again.

The sound of footsteps outside jolts me back to reality. My mother opens the door, and I hear her inviting the visitors inside. The owners of the two-family house we share step into the kitchen. They are from Guatemala like us, but they have been here much longer. Long enough for all of them to get papers, I mean.

Seven people is a few too many for our tiny kitchen, but we

all manage to squeeze in. Marisol, Roberto and their two children crowd around our kitchen table as I push the eggs around on Gabby's plate. They taste awful. My dad used to make them with a Guatemalan sauce that his mother, my grandma, taught him to make. He never told us what was in it, but promised he would when we were older. I guess now we will never know.

One of the children, Graciela, is in my grade at school and walks with me every morning. She has been my best friend for as long as both of us can remember. She pushes through the crowded room and stands next to me, leaning on the table.

"Hello, Grace," I mumble.

She throws her arms around me, whispering, "I'm so sorry Marcie, so sorry."

I try to hold it in, but a dry sob escapes. We sit there for a while, Grace squeezing me as hard as she can, but I do not cry. It seems I have run out of tears.

The adults all sit down in the living room, and talk about my father in the way that adults do: without noticing that the children are listening. Grace and I can hear them from the kitchen, so as kids do, we listen.

"This must be so hard for you, Eva." Marisol and Roberto try to comfort my mother. "If there is anything we can do for you..."

My mother breaks down into tears. "We were so close! The kids and I have our papers, we thought he could get them too. But then—then they denied his applications for residency, they said he wasn't eligible..." she pauses, and we hear the sound of her blowing her nose. "We thought it would be ok, we would try again, but then they came and took him. I don't even know where he *is!*"

"All we can do now is pray," Marisol says.

I hear a soft cough from the corner of the kitchen, and look over to see Mike standing in the doorway.

"Mike," I sigh. "You woke up."

As he steps out of the shadows, I see the fear in his eyes.

"The men last night. They took Papi away. Are they going to give him back? Where did they take him?" Mike whispers.

His eyes, just like my father's, search my face for answers, but I have none to give. "I'm sorry, Mike," I say.

Grace looks at the clock and gasps. "Marcie, we're late for school. We have to go!"

I grab my backpack and run out the door. Grace and I walk as fast as we can, but still we arrive late for the first class. Slowly, I creak open the door to my math room and peek inside. The entire class turns, their eyes fixed on me. I feel the heat rise to my cheeks as I open the door a little more and step inside. My teacher, Mrs. Clark, turns to face me with an icy glare.

"Well, Marcie, I am so glad that you decided to join us for our *test*." Her voice drips with sarcasm as she thrusts a piece of paper in my face. "Sit down and please do not disturb the class any further."

Shocked, I take my seat. Mrs. Clark is my favorite teacher, and is known to be one of the nicest in the school. I have no idea why she would speak to me so harshly. I take a pencil out of my backpack and look down at the test. As I scan the problems, I slowly realize that I don't know the answers to any of them. After what happened yesterday, I never even thought about doing my homework. The rest of the period, I try to guess for as many answers as I can.

When the bell rings, I stay in my seat and flip through the test, embarrassed by how poorly I know I have done. I am an A student. I earn my superior marks because I work harder than everyone else. I know if I don't, I will end up working in the dairy plant just like my father, or taking care of someone else's children like my mother, or always between jobs like Gabby. I want to go to college and become a doctor or lawyer or work in a big office with my name on the door. I want to get out of Greenwood.

The sound of Mrs. Clark tapping her foot brings me back to the present. I look up and realize that the class is over, and the room is empty. Mrs. Clark stands over my desk with her hands on her hips, making a face similar to the one Gabby makes when it's her turn to take out the garbage.

"Marcie, don't you have somewhere else to be? Or have you decided to be late for all of your classes today?" she sneers.

"I'm sorry, Mrs. Clark, I was waiting to talk to you. Can I retake the test? I didn't get a chance to study last night."

Mrs. Clark raises her eyebrows. "Why was that?"

"ICE came and took my father." I whisper, unable to meet her eyes.

"You can't retake the test." She turns around and walks briskly towards her desk.

I sit in disbelief. What happened? Just last week, Mrs. Clark had told me that I was one of her best students.

"Listen, Marcie. Your father was arrested because he is a criminal; he broke the law. The faster you accept that, the easier it will be. Now I have a class to teach, but in the future, come to class prepared." She opens the door and motions for me to leave.

My face turns red, as my hands ball into fists and I feel tears spring to my eyes. I look into that woman's eyes, and I feel the anger simmer and stir deep inside of me. I want to slam the door and scream until she understands that my father is a good man whose hard work would ensure that his children could have a better life than he did in Guatemala. He isn't a criminal; I refuse to believe it.

My rage recedes as a tear slides down my cheek. I open my mouth to speak, but no words come out. I just turn around and walk out the door.

I pass the rest of the day in a fog. I wander down hallways, in and out of classes, mumbling excuses about why I don't have my homework. After school I meet Grace by her locker, and we walk home.

"How are you doing?" She asks.

"Mrs. Clark says my father is a criminal."

"You can't believe her, she doesn't know what she's talking about."

"I associate criminals with violence, but my father is so kind."

The front door of my house creaks, as it always does, when it opens. I take off my shoes, put my backpack in the corner, and walk into my room. I lie down on top of my bed and close my eyes.

Yesterday, I opened the front door to see my father chasing Mike around the kitchen. As I walked inside, he picked me up and spun around in circles.

"Marcella, you're getting too old for me to pick up!" He exclaimed, after placing me back on the ground.

Gabby walked into the kitchen, laughing. "Maybe it's you who is getting older."

"Me? No I'm still 25 at heart, *hija*." He laughed. "Now how about a movie before dinner? I think it is Miguel's turn to pick."

Laughing, we all squeezed onto our old lumpy dark-green couch. Mike sat on the floor, shuffling through a pile of DVDs, as Gabby's cell phone vibrated softly on the table next to me. One new text message, it said. Gabby looked over but ignored it, knowing that dad would just tell her to put it away, as he always did when we were all together. *"I never had a phone in Guatemala. I just talked to my family and friends face-to-face."* He would say. Gabby often rolled her eyes, but she never argued.

"Eva, are you coming?" my father yelled.

"Oh, José, I haven't even looked at today's mail, and the bills aren't going to pay themselves."

"Come on, Mommy, please?" Mike begged.

She sighed, but we all saw the smile on her face as she walked into the living room. "Fine, what are we watching?"

"Loony Toons!" Mike yelled. "My favorite!"

The flickering of the TV lit up the faded brown wallpaper that my mother insisted we keep up, saying it reminded her of her abuela's house. The first cartoon had just started when we heard the telephone ring from the kitchen. My mother eased herself up from the couch and walked into the kitchen. A few seconds later we heard her call to my father, her voice shaking.

"José, come here."

My father picked up Mike and placed him down on the couch next to Gabby.

"I'll be right back, little man."

Gabby turned to me. "Marcie, hand me my cell phone."

I gave it to her and turned back to the TV as she opened the text. I heard her take a sharp breath, and when I turned to see what surprised her, I noticed that her left eyebrow was tugged down further than I had ever seen it before.

"What's wrong, Gabby?" I whispered.

Silently, she handed me her phone. It was from one of her friends whose father also works at the dairy plant. *"Gabby,"* it read, *"immigration raid at the plant. They took my dad and have a list of names. Your dad is on it. They are coming to your house."*

Gabby jumped up from the couch and ran into the kitchen. I followed, little Mike trailing behind me. My mother was leaning against the counter with the phone to her ear and an anxious look on her face.

"How many names do they have?" she asked. "Three *hundred?* Ok, *gracias. Adios.*" She hung up the phone and turned to my father. "What do we do now?"

Before he could answer, there was a sharp knock at the door.

"It's too late," my father said, his face expressionless. "I'll get the door."

Frozen, we all watched as he reached out his hand to turn the doorknob. Outside stood three men. Each wore a shirt with ICE printed in yellow, but the first thing my eyes were drawn to was the gun strapped to each of their waists.

"We're looking for a José Alvarez," one of the men said.

"That's me." My father stepped forward.

"We have a warrant for your arrest." He held out an official-looking piece of paper.

My father took the paper and read it carefully. "I see," he said.

"Mr. Alvarez, you're going to have to come with us." The man held up a pair of handcuffs.

From behind me, I heard my mother cry. "Please don't take him. You don't understand, you can't..." She trailed off, unable to continue.

I felt something brush my leg and looked down to see Mike moving toward the men.

"What are you doing? Where are you taking my Papi?" he asked, a concerned look on his face.

My father reached down and picked up little Mike. "It's okay, Miguel, I have to go with these men. I love you so much," he said as he set him down.

The man in the doorway jingled the handcuffs impatiently. Mike looked up at them, confused.

"Why do you have those? Those are for bad people." He looked at my father and back at the man. "My Papi is a good man. He doesn't need those."

My father put out his hands so the man could apply the handcuffs. As I heard the click of them snapping closed, I saw a tear slide down my father's cheek, like a single drop of water gliding down a windowpane.

It was the only time I had ever seen him cry.

As the men guided him out the door, he called back to us one last time. "I love you."

As I lay in my bed going over yesterday's events, I still can't believe that my father is gone. I hear my mother calling me from the kitchen.

"Marcella, there was a letter in yesterday's mail for you," she says, excited. "It's from that summer program at Yale you applied to."

In the events of the past 24 hours, I had completely forgotten that the letter from Yale was supposed to arrive. I tear the envelope open, and yank out the enclosed letter.

Dear Marcella Alvarez,
Congratulations, you have been accepted to the Ulysses S. Grant Foundation summer program at Yale University for talented and motivated young students. Your tuition, room and board will be covered by a financial aid grant. We hope that you will choose to attend this summer.

I thrust the letter toward my mother, a huge smile on my face. I only wish that my father could be here to read it too.

Audrey Bransfield *hails from Cambridge, Massachusetts, and spends every summer backpacking through the wilderness. In "Papi," she hoped to explore the personal and social implications for the children of deported parents, a perspective she felt is overlooked in debates on immigration.*

The Footage of Yangon

Yi-Ling Liu, 16
Chinese International School, Hong Kong, China, **Brian Kern,** Teacher

The early September morning in Yangon smelled of late-summer humidity and drooping honeysuckle, of salted fish and *ngapi* lying on the market stalls, of sweat and euphoria. Never had the people been so awake—workmen stood diligently by the construction site, hawkers by their stock. Mothers clutching wary-eyed babies watched the streets outside the window. The betel-chewing men, usually squatted by the road, were standing still, upright and expectant. Yesterday, the monks marched in a flurry of saffron robes and banners and bare feet. Today, Burma eagerly waited for their return, and the world waited for Maung to wake up.

* * *

He woke up to the discord of Monday morning outside the window and a thin stream of sunlight that crept through the blinds. Over the past two months, this had been his routine—seven hours straight of sleep until the street outside became noisy. He sat up, eyes darting quickly from his sandals propped on the carpet to the cardboard box at the corner of the room, heaped with an mélange of cords, tangled wires, battery packs and two tired video cameras, bearing scratches and faded SONY logos.

He dressed, strolled swiftly to the kitchen counter and poured himself a cup of chocolate milk. Usually he had water in the mornings, more water in the afternoon and some beer at six o'clock. But today was a big day—the monks had come out, the people had marched to Aung San Suu Kyi's house, and he needed to stay vigilant. Then, he opened the cupboard, taking a pill out of the primeval bottle of iron and vitamin C supplements his mother found at the Western market at Mrauk U. She was always looking ahead, his mother. She was always a pragmatist. If he was going to march and wave flags and chant *"reconciliation now!"* she said, he might as well keep his hemoglobin and immune system working and healthy.

His mother was a light sleeper, so Maung learned to be silent in the mornings. His feet knew which floorboards creaked and which could not be treaded on. If he did wake her up, she would methodically slip on her felt slippers and patter to the kitchen. She would sigh with wet, creased eyes, fix his collar and tell him to be careful and to come home by 10. He cherished his mother's love and constant admonishment. But when he scoured through Yangon, video camera in hand, under the menacing scrutiny of the junta, her love bridled him, restrained him and saddened him. He could not deal with that.

He grabbed a video camera from the cardboard box, placed it in his bag, a modest, pedestrian thing of unraveling straw that always accompanied him throughout the day, and then walked out of the house. His home was in the center of Yangon, Mandalay, and a line of robed monks and restless students were already scattered throughout the street. He stepped onto the uneven concrete of the road and joined the line, his leather sandals in sync with the callused soles of the monk in front of him.

"Min-ga-la-ba," Maung greeted him.

The monk, a man with a short, thickset build, an egg-shaped head and robes that hung too loosely on his shoulders, turned around and replied with a curt nod. "Morning."

His eyes darted nervously. His cheeks were still ruddy, smooth and unshaven like Maung's own. It was an innocent face, a face unfamiliar with adulthood.

"How many people today?" Maung said.

"I'd say there was a hundred of us coming over from the village and 200 more have joined. Definitely more than yesterday," the monk replied, "and there are more coming."

"And nothing from Than Shwe?"

"That bastard, raising our prices to buy fancy ammunition and big, thick tanks." The monk smiled. "No, nothing yet. More than 300 of us in Mandalay and the junta is silent."

Maung nodded and then carefully reached into his satchel and pulled out his video camera. "My work," he explained, "DVB."

The monk's smile dropped. His pace quickened as they reached the middle section of the road, where it forked two separate ways, to the exodus of banners and dissonance at the park, and the small meandering street to the U Wiwara Market.

"You want to be careful with that," he muttered, "the junta are everywhere." The monk cocked his head subtly toward two military men donned in the telltale dress of the Burmese police—camouflage shirt, felt hat, shotgun—who were purveying the crowds.

Maung thanked the monk and crept away from the line toward U Wiwara. But he did not want to put the camera away, so he turned it on and began to record. One of the military men saw him and began walking in his direction. They saw the camera. He covered the lens quickly, shoved the camera into his jacket pocket and strolled briskly into the market street, diving into the throng of people. During the lunch hour, he would have to stay low and quiet. He had to film later, in the afternoon when the crowd thickened. Be patient, Maung, his mother always said. Don't be too greedy.

* * *

His father was too greedy. He would go to work in the morning with his pudgy Nikon camera hanging lopsided by his waist, its lens, meticulously wiped every morning with a piece of cloth, perpetually shining. The streets of Yangon were covered in his footprints—he captured anything he pleased: interviews of the workers, all of Aung San Suu Kyi's speeches, snippets of junta men interrogating another DVB undercover reporter like himself. He was greedy for footage —he wanted the world to see Burma. He went to all the rallies and the protests, and the people were already accustomed to the rasp of his voice, familiar with the tawny, incandescent flash of his camera. Let the world see the oppression of Burma, boy, he used to drill into Maung every day, let the world see.

He remembered his mother's face when his uncle knocked on the door that night seven-and-a-half years ago to tell her that her husband was dead. Her face was unresponsive and stony-eyed—almost indifferent. Her jaw was rigid and her lips held taut against her skin. Maung was surprised at her callousness, how reserved she was. But she was the woman who stifled her tears. She was the wife who incessantly told her husband to relax, to be patient, to be a father. And now here was Uncle telling her that her husband was shot while trying to sneak into the government building with a camera in one hand. Two bullets, he said, one in the right temple and one in the stomach.

* * *

It was 3 o'clock. Maung grew restless from sitting in a convenience store accompanied by a cooler of drinks. He stepped onto the street and made his way to the park. The protests had blossomed—people were pouring in from all sides like a steady, rapid stream. The smell of the collective sweat of the protesters and the faded dye of the monks' robes lingered stagnant in the air. People were leaning from their windows, pacing the streets, squatting on the sidewalk. A line of students were leaning against the new building erected last year, an awkwardly placed slab of concrete in the middle of Mandalay's most colorful, tumultuous area. Flags and placards adorned its white-washed walls, each embellished with "Killer Than Shwe's!" and "Free Aung San Suu Kyi!"'

Maung inched his way through the crowd to find a good spot to film but there were none. There was another old building opposite the park, with a low, flat rooftop that he could film from. He knew the entrance was locked from the inside, so he decided to climb the misshapen fire escape that twisted to the roof of the building. He ran up the stairs, one hand sliding against the rusted metal of the escape, one tightly gripping the camera. He was nervous, the peeling record button on the surface of the camera quivered under his fingertips. He heaved his body over the end of the staircase onto the roof. It was hot and humid. He wiped the sweat on his forehead with the back of his sleeve and looked down.

It took his breath away. From above, the ground was a mosaic of crimson robes and raised fists and scarlet hues of the banners. The sun slanted in from the right, directly onto where the monks stood, so that the tops of their heads glistened. Wide-eyed children peeked out of the windows of the apartment buildings, clapping so hard that the palms of their hands were pink and raw. A cluster of women stood by the pavement, handing out plastic cups of water and popsicles. "Our cause! Our cause!" Their voices, the soft tenor of the monks and the throaty holler of the students, rang through the park, melding into one chorus—the voice of the frustrated, the voice of Burma. Maung watched, entranced, listening to the soundtrack of his own frantic heartbeat.

* * *

The camera stayed in his hand. It stayed in his hands even when he saw trucks of the junta making their way like a funeral procession from the road to the park. It stayed in his hand even when he saw the young soldiers clamber out of the trucks, stayed in his hand when the loudspeaker announced that anyone who remained in the park in five minutes would be shot. The people didn't move and the guns were loaded. But the camera stayed in his hand, even as he heard the shots and listened to the cacophony of cries and semiautomatics.

He knew he had to hide, sprint down the fire escape and run home, but he didn't. The camera was welded to his fingers. So he stood on the rooftop and filmed the people slowly disappear, filmed the broken bullets on the ground. *Let the world see, Maung.* He filmed, watching the little screen flicker, feeling a gush of awe and pride, mingled with guilt.

He stood on the rooftop and filmed. When it was too dark to see, he climbed down the fire escape and walked home thinking of excuses to tell his mother.

* * *

It was an early September evening in Rangoon. The footage was uploaded and swiftly on its way, from camera, via firewire, to the rest of the world.

Yi-Ling Liu is from Hong Kong. A self-described "exercise junkie," she loves cycling in cities where traffic laws are ignored or nonexistent because this provides the adrenaline necessary to battle writer's block.

A Teacher's Guide to *The Best Teen Writing of 2012*

Inspire your students to write poignant, original works. You can use the award-winning works of teen writers to get your students excited about their own.

1. Short Story—Discussion—15 minutes
Choose a piece from BTW to have the class read and discuss. Ask students the following:
- What is your favorite aspect of the piece as a whole? (i.e. the opening, humor, dialogue, tone, style, character, theme)
- Mark your three favorite lines.
- Help each student articulate opinions by helping identify what it is that makes the piece powerful as a whole and what makes specific lines engaging or poetic.

2. Short Story—Exercise—35 minutes
Ask students if a BTW story inspired any characters or storylines in their minds. Ask them to write the following in the same style as the BTW story, with their own characters and storylines:
- an opening scene
- a dialogue-driven scene
- an ending
- Writers may read their opening scenes aloud

3. Poetry—Discussion—45 Minutes
Review the use of rhythm and rhyme in poetry, both when you read to yourself and read aloud.
- Have students choose two poems from BTW to read silently, and then aloud.
- Ask: Did the poet use rhythm or rhyme to move the poem along? How does it help with the message and feeling? Is it easier to perceive when the poem is read aloud?

4. Poetry—Exercise—45 minutes

Ask students to write two poems, inspired by the unique tone/style of the two BTW poems read in class.

- Create a safe space for writers to read aloud.
- Discuss how sharing personal or creative writing can make a writer feel vulnerable.
- Encourage poets to read their work and offer positive feedback.

5. Memoir/Personal Essay Discussion and Exercise—45 minutes and Homework

a) Read a memoir/personal essay from BTW aloud.

- Ask students to write a 6-word memoir interpretation of the piece (such as Hemingway's famous 6-word memoir, "For Sale: Baby Shoes, Never Worn.").
- Students should read aloud the 6-word memoirs.

b) Ask students to write original six-word memoirs about their own lives.

- After sharing these with the class, students can expand them into full memoirs in class or at home. If writers have diffculty getting started, encourage them to mirror the format of the BTW memoir.

6. Genre-Shifting Exercise—45 minutes (Possible homework)

Ask students to choose a BTW piece and transform it into another genre (poem to play, play to short story, etc.).

- Alternatively, students can use music, performance art, or visual art to express their understanding of the piece.

7. Letter to the Author—45 minutes (Possible homework)

Ask students to write a letter to a BTW author of their choice.

- Students should include positive feedback for the BTW writer and ask questions about the work. (i.e. Is this based on something real? How did you come up with this idea? Who are your favorite writers?). Mail to: AYAW, 557 Broadway, New York, NY 10012, Attn: BTW Author Letters

8. Discussion and Exercise on Theme—45 minutes and Homework
Ask students to choose a work with a provocative or unique theme.
- Do students agree with the author's message? Disagree?
- For homework, students should write a "counter" work or a work expressing the same theme in a different way (i.e. with a different plot, character, genre, style).

9. Researching for a Work—Exercise—45 minutes (Possible homework)
Ask students to choose a nonfiction piece (i.e., personal essay, journalism) with an interesting topic. Did the author seem to do any background research for the work (historical/cultural, scientific, etc.)?
- Ask students to do their own research on the same topic in order to write their own piece in any genre, such as poetry or flash fiction: but it must be grounded in fact.
- For extra credit, encourage students to meet with teachers in other departments. (i.e. If writing a poem about astronomy, a student can meet with a science teacher.)

10. Blog—Exercise—30 minutes and Homework
Ask students to write a blog post expressing thoughts about a specific piece or BTW in general. Posts will be sent to the Alliance and may be included on its blog.
- Students should express their opinions, offering positive fee back or constructive criticism, and discuss a specific work or BTW as a whole. Posts may be emailed to ctan@artandwriting.org.
- For homework, students may comment on another post by visiting blog.artandwriting.org, sharing their ideas or reactions.

Encourage students to continue working on their pieces throughout the year. These exercises and discussions may inspire one of next year's Best Teen Writing pieces!

With thanks to Writopia Lab's New York City Team:
Rebecca Wallace-Segall, Founder and Executive Director
Danielle Sheeler and Yael Schick, Instructors

Acknowledgements

The Alliance gratefully acknowledges the thousands of teachers who annually encourage students to submit their works to the Scholastic Art & Writing Awards and the remarkable students who have the courage to put their art and writing before panels of renowned jurors. Our mission is greatly furthered through special partnerships with the National Art Education Association and the Association of Independent Colleges of Art and Design. In addition, we would like to especially recognize the National Writing Project for its continued commitment to our program and for its far-reaching effects in the writing community. Our ability to honor creative teens is also made possible through the generosity of our supporters: Scholastic Inc., the Maurice R. Robinson Foundation, Command Web Offset, the Jack Kent Cooke Foundation, *The New York Times,* Ovation, Amazon.com, Dick Blick Co. and the AMD Foundation.

Regional Affiliate Organizations

The Alliance would like to thank the regional affiliates listed for coordinating the Scholastic Art & Writing Awards.

NORTHEAST
CONNECTICUT
Connecticut Art Region
Affiliate: Connecticut Art Education Association

DELAWARE
Delaware Art Region
Affiliate: Delaware State University

MAINE
Southern Maine Writing Region
Affiliate: Southern Maine Writing Project

MASSACHUSETTS
Massachusetts Art & Writing Region
Affiliate: New England Art Education Conference, Inc.,
  and The Boston Globe

NEW HAMPSHIRE
New Hampshire Art Region
Affiliate: The New Hampshire Art Educators' Association

New Hampshire Writing Region
Affiliate: Plymouth Writing Project

NEW JERSEY
Northeast New Jersey Art Region
Affiliate: Montclair Art Museum

NEW YORK
Central New York Art Region
Affiliate: CNY Art Council, Inc.

Hudson Valley Art Region
Affiliate: Hudson Valley Art Awards

New York City Art & Writing Region
Affiliate: Casita Maria Center for Arts and Education

Twin Tiers Art Region
Affiliate: Arnot Art Museum
  (serving parts of New York and Pennsylvania)

PENNSYLVANIA
Berks, Carbon, Lehigh and Northampton Art Region
Affiliate: East Central PA Scholastic Art Awards

Lancaster County Art Region
Affiliate: Lancaster Museum of Art

Lancaster County Writing Region
Affiliate: Lancaster Public Library

Northwestern Pennsylvania Art Region
Affiliate: The Times-Tribune

Philadelphia Art Region
*Affiliate: Philadelphia Arts in Education Partnership at
 the University of the Arts*

Philadelphia Writing Region
Affiliate: Philadelphia Writing Project

Pittsburgh Art Region
Affiliate: La Roche College

Pittsburgh Writing Region
Affiliate: Western PA Writing Project

South Central Pennsylvania Art & Writing Region
Affiliate: Commonwealth Connections Academy

Southwestern Pennsylvania Art & Writing Region
Affiliate: California University of Pennsylvania

RHODE ISLAND
Rhode Island Art Region
Affiliate: Rhode Island Art Education Association

VERMONT
Vermont Art & Writing Region
Affiliate: Brattleboro Museum & Art Center

SOUTHEAST
DISTRICT OF COLUMBIA
DC Metro Writing Region
Affiliate: Writopia Lab

DELAWARE
Delaware Writing Region
Affiliate: National League of American Pen Women, Diamond State Branch

FLORIDA
Broward Art Region
Affiliate: American Learning Systems

Central Florida Writing Region
Affiliate: The English Teacher's Friend

Miami-Dade Art Region
Affiliate: Miami-Dade County Public Schools

Miami-Dade Writing Region
Affiliate: Miami Writes

Northeast Florida Art Region
Affiliate: Duval Art Teachers' Association

Palm Beach Art Region
Affiliate: Educational Gallery Group (Eg2)

Palm Beach Writing Region
Affiliate: Blue Planets Writer's Room

Pinellas Art Region
Affiliate: Pinellas County Schools

Sarasota Art Region
Affiliate: Sarasota County Schools

GEORGIA
Georgia Art Region
Affiliate: Georgia State University Ernest G. Welch School of Art & Design

KENTUCKY
Northern Kentucky Writing Region
Affiliate: Northern Kentucky Writing Region

Louisville Metropolitan Area Art Region
Affiliate: Jefferson County Public Schools

MISSISSIPPI
Mississippi Art Region
Affiliate: Mississippi Museum of Art

Mississippi Writing Region
Affiliate: The Eudora Welty Foundation

NORTH CAROLINA
Eastern/Central North Carolina Art Region
Affiliate: Barton College

Mid-Carolina Art & Writing Region
Affiliate: Charlotte-Mecklenburg Schools

Western North Carolina Art Region
Affiliate: Asheville Art Museum

SOUTH CAROLINA
South Carolina Art Region
Affiliate: Lander University

TENNESSEE
East Tennessee Art Region
Affiliate: Maryville College

Middle Tennessee Art Region
Affiliate: Cheekwood Botanical Garden & Museum of Art

Mid-South Art Region
Affiliate: Memphis Brooks Museum of Art

VIRGINIA
Arlington County Art Region
Affiliate: Arlington Public Schools

Fairfax County Art Region
Affiliate: Fairfax County Public Schools

Richmond County Art Region
Affiliate: Virginia Museum of Fine Arts

Southwest Virginia Art Region
Affiliate: The Fine Arts Center for the New River Valley

WEST
ALASKA
Alaska Art Region
Affiliate: MTS Gallery/Alaska Art Education Association

Alaska Writing Region
Affiliate: F Magazine

CALIFORNIA
California Art Region
Affiliate: The California Arts Project

California Writing Region
Affiliate: California Writing Project

Los Angeles Art Region
Affiliate: Armory Center for the Arts

COLORADO
Colorado Art Region
Affiliate: Colorado Art Education Association

HAWAII
Hawaii Art Region
Affiliate: Hawaii State Department of Education

IDAHO
Idaho Art & Writing Region
Affiliate: Boise State Writing Project

NEVADA
Northern Nevada Art Region
Affiliate: The Nevada Museum of Art

Northern Nevada Writing Region
Affiliate: Nevada Alliance for Arts Education

Southern Nevada Art & Writing Region
Affiliate: Springs Preserve

OREGON
Oregon Art Region—Central Oregon Area
Affiliate: The Oregon Art Education Association

Oregon Art Region—Portland Metro Area
Affiliate: The Oregon Art Education Association

Oregon Art Region—Willamette Valley Art Region
Affiliate: Benton County Historical Society

WASHINGTON
Snohomish County Art Region
Affiliate: Schack Art Center

MIDWEST
IOWA
Iowa Art & Writing Region
Affiliate: The Connie Belin & Jacqueline N. Blank International Center for Gifted Education and Talent Development

ILLINOIS
Chicago Writing Region
Affiliate: Chicago Area Writing Project

Mid-Central Illinois Art Region
Affiliate: The Regional Scholastic Art Awards Council

Suburban Chicago Art Region
Affiliate: Downers Grove North and South High Schools

Southern Illinois Art Region
Affiliate: John R. and Eleanor R. Mitchell Foundation/Cedarhurst Center for the Arts

INDIANA
Central/Southern Indiana Art Region
Affiliate: Clowes Memorial Hall of Butler University

Central/Southern Indiana Writing Region
Affiliate: Clowes Memorial Hall of Butler University and Hoosier Writing Project at IUPUI

Northeast Indiana and Northwest Ohio Art & Writing Region
Affiliate: Fort Wayne Museum of Art

KANSAS
Eastern Kansas Art Region
Affiliate: The Wichita Center for the Arts

Western Kansas Art Region
Affiliate: The Western Kansas Scholastic Art Awards

MICHIGAN
Macomb St. Clair & Lapeer Art Region
Affiliate: College for Creative Studies

Southeastern Michigan Art Region
Affiliate: College for Creative Studies

West Central Michigan Art Region
Affiliate: Kendall College of Art and Design of Ferris State University

MINNESOTA
Minnesota Art Region
Affiliate: Minneapolis College of Art and Design

MISSOURI
Missouri Writing Region
Affiliate: Prairie Lands Writing Project at Missouri Western State University

NEBRASKA
Nebraska Art Region
Affiliate: Omaha Public Schools Art Department

OHIO
Central Ohio Art Region
Affiliate: Columbus College of Art and Design

Cuyahoga County Art & Writing Region
Affiliate: The Cleveland Institute of Art

Lorain County Art Region
Affiliate: Lorain County Regional Scholastic Arts Committee

Northeast Central Ohio Art Region
Affiliate: Kent State University, Stark Campus

Northeastern Ohio Art Region
Affiliate: Art Outreach Gallery

Northeastern Ohio Writing Region
Affiliate: Writing Project at Kent State University

Southern Ohio, Northern Kentucky and Southeastern Indiana
  Art Region
Affiliate: Art Machine, Inc.

WISCONSIN
Kenosha Writing Region
Affiliate: Harborside Academy

Milwaukee Writing Region
Affiliate: Still Waters Collective

Wisconsin Art Region
Affiliate: The Milwaukee Art Museum

SOUTHWEST
ARIZONA
Arizona Writing Region
Affiliate: Arizona English Teachers Association

LOUISIANA
North-Central Louisiana Writing Region
Affiliate: Northwestern State University Writing Project

Southeast Louisiana Writing Region
Affiliate: Greater New Orleans Writing Project

OKLAHOMA
Oklahoma Art Region
Affiliate: Tulsa Community College Liberal Arts Department

Oklahoma Writing Region
Affiliate: Daniel and Kristen Marangoni

TEXAS
Harris County Art & Writing Region
Affiliate: Harris County Department of Education

San Antonio Art Region
Affiliate: SAY Si (San Antonio Youth Yes)

Travis County Art Region
Affiliate: St. Stephen's School

West Texas Art Region
Affiliate: Wayland Baptist University, Department of Art

Support the
Scholastic Art & Writing Awards

The Best Teen Writing is made possible through the generous support of our donors.

Over 200,000 works were submitted and judged for the 2012 Awards, and nearly 60,000 middle and high school artists and writers were recognized for their talents. Of the top national winners in the Awards' eleven writing categories, over 70 works are highlighted in this publication.

The Alliance for Young Artists & Writers, which presents the Awards, is a nonprofit 501(c)(3) organization, and is supported entirely by charitable contributions from institutional partners and individuals like you. Donations underwrite the production of the Awards at the national and local levels; exhibitions, readings and workshops; publications; and award and scholarship opportunities for creative young artists and writers in grades 7—12 across the country.

Help us continue to celebrate our nation's most creative teens in both writing and art. Please make your tax-deductible contribution today.

To give online: Visit www.artandwriting.org
To give by check: Mail check, made payable to Alliance for Young Artists & Writers, to:

Alliance for Young Artists & Writers
Attention: Development/External Relations
557 Broadway
New York, NY 10012

To make a special gift or to discuss other ways to provide your financial support, please contact Jonathan Ettinger, Director, Development & External Relations, by phone at 212-343-7773 or by email at jettinger@artandwriting.org.